Public Health and Population Change

PUBLIC HEALTH AND POPULATION CHANGE

Current Research Issues

EDITED BY

MINDEL C. SHEPS AND

JEANNE CLARE RIDLEY

University of Pittsburgh Press

FOREWORD

This book is the product of a Symposium on Research Issues in Public Health and Population Change sponsored by the Graduate School of Public Health at the University of Pittsburgh, Pittsburgh, Pennsylvania in June, 1964. The conference was made possible by a grant from the A. W. Mellon Educational and Charitable Trust.

The purposes of the conference were:

(1) to review the present state of knowledge and research with respect to population change, with special reference to natality;

(2) to identify future research needs in the areas of natality and population growth;

(3) to promote understanding and communication among workers in the fields of public health, medicine, biology, demography, and the social sciences regarding their mutual interests in the determinants and consequences of population growth;

(4) to further the development of teaching and research programs in problems of health and population change; and

(5) to provide material for a publication useful to persons interested in these matters, particularly to those with public health interests.

The relevance of the dynamics of population change to the concerns of public health workers is receiving increasing attention. The existence of an organic, complex interconnection between the demographic characteristics of an area and its health status and programs is universally recognized. In the pursuit of its traditional objective of optimum health for all, public health may have to adapt its methods and goals to the changing problems engendered by unprecedentedly rapid growth of populations. The problems are particularly challenging for nations that aspire to move from a preindustrial to an advanced technological economy. To deal with the health problems of such nations and to plan their health programs, an understanding of population dynamics is essential. Moreover, public health is becoming increasingly involved in efforts to reduce the rate of population growth. Such efforts require a knowledge of the biological and social factors that influence population trends and an ability to appraise the likely effects on them of programs of social change. As the papers in this volume reveal, we now stand only at the threshold of an understanding of these factors; practically, as well as intellectually, there is a great need for deepened understanding that can come only from increased scientific investigation.

These considerations led to the decision to arrange the Symposium by the Graduate School of Public Health. The identification of natality as a major focus of the Symposium reflects the widely held view that the future course of natality is crucial to future population trends. Undoubtedly, the omission of mortality and migration from the topics included, as well as the neglect of the relationships of demographic factors and population growth rates to economic development, prevent a complete assessment of population dynamics or of the "population problem" as it is posed today. It was, however, felt that since an effort to be comprehensive would probably prohibit detailed and critical discussion of any issues, concentration on a more limited range of topics was preferable. Consequently, it was concluded that consideration of current knowledge about the social and biological determinants of natality would fulfill an important function both by defining the present situation and by identifying questions that are in need of further investigation.

For the published presentation, the papers originally prepared for the Symposium were revised by the authors. The editors have changed the order of presentation from that followed at the conference to what seems a more suitable arrangement for the book. The presentation is made in seven parts.

The papers in Part I examine historical data, attempting to identify the factors responsible for increased rates of population growth as well as those responsible for reduced natality in Western countries. Possible policies and strategies for slowing down current rates of population growth are examined in the light of historical data and of current research on human motivation. Part II is concerned with current natality patterns and programs for effecting change. As such, the papers consider a number of questions ranging from the determinants of human reproduction to the organization of programs intended to change natality behavior. The papers in Part III discuss valid, suitable, and sensitive methods for the measurement of natality and its components and for the evaluation of programs aimed at reducing natality. Part IV deals with biological aspects of human reproduction and its control. Part V presents material drawn from the panel discussion on methods of controlling reproduction, in the form of three presentations made at the panel discussion, and an article summarizing its highlights. In Part VI, we attempt to identify the important research issues that emerged from the extensive discussions held at the Symposium. Finally, in Part VII, an address on the implications of the population problem for public health, given at the closing of the Symposium by James A. Crabtree, Dean of the Pittsburgh Graduate School of Public Health, is presented.

The Graduate School of Public Health is indebted to the authors of the papers and the other invited participants in the Symposium for their many contributions to the success of the meeting. The cooperation of the authors in preparing their papers well in advance of the Symposium and thus allowing for their prior distribution was an important factor in stimulating fruitful discussion. Their prompt revision of their papers for publication is greatly appreciated, as was the tolerance they exercised toward editorial suggestions.

The success of the Symposium was further insured by the able chairmanship of the several sessions. The Graduate School of Public Health acknowledges the significant role of the chairmen: Antonio Ciocco, Leslie Corsa, Jr., James A. Crabtree, Nicholson J. Eastman, Louis Lasagna, and Irene B. Taeuber.

Like all such undertakings, the Symposium and this volume represent the joint efforts of a large number of individuals. In addition to those already mentioned, other contributors must be acknowledged. A committee composed of members of the University of Pittsburgh faculty formulated the original plans for the Symposium. Members of the committee, who gave considerable time, energy, and thought to this planning, were: Joseph W. Eaton of the School of Social Work, Ernst Knobil of the Medical School, Jiri Nehnevajsa of the Department of Sociology, and Antonio Ciocco, Conrad Seipp, and Samuel M. Wishik of the Graduate School of Public Health. The editors, Mindel C. Sheps and Jeanne Clare Ridley, served on the committee as chairman and executive secretary, respectively.

In addition, a number of outstanding men and women from outside Pittsburgh served on an Advisory Committee for the Symposium. It is doubtful that the Symposium would have achieved its purposes without their help. The members of this committee were: Marshall C. Balfour, The Population Council; Margaret Bright, School of Hygiene and Public Health of The Johns Hopkins University; LaMont C. Cole, Cornell University; Kingsley Davis, University of California, Berkeley; Nicholson J. Eastman, Ford Foundation; Martha M. Eliot, Professor Emeritus, Harvard University School of Public Health; Philip M. Hauser, University of Chicago; Warren O. Nelson,* Albany Medical College of Union University; John Rock, Rock Reproductive Clinic; Joseph J. Spengler, Duke University; and Irene B. Taeuber, Princeton University.

The efficiency of Marcia G. Arnold, who was responsible for travel and hotel arrangements for the participants and the numerous other details for the conference was exemplary. In

* Deceased

addition, we wish to acknowledge her invaluable editorial work in the preparation of the material for this volume. Mrs. Arnold was ably assisted by Edith Diamond, Joan Lingner, and Ann Martin. A number of staff members of the Graduate School of Public Health helped in numerous ways in the preparation for the Symposium and of the volume. Especially we are indebted to the expert secretarial work of Arlene Crossan, Shirley Ginsburg, Catherine Karwoski, Rose Ann Ranft, and Bonita Smyczek.

It is hoped that this volume will be of interest to persons from the many disciplines concerned with population change and to students in these disciplines. To increase its accessibility to individuals from different disciplines we have appended a glossary of technical terms used in the papers. A special note on terminology by the editors relating to natality and fertility follows this foreword.

MINDEL C. SHEPS
JEANNE CLARE RIDLEY

NOTE ON TERMINOLOGY

Since this book, like the meeting out of which it grew, is the product of demographers, social and behavioral scientists, biologists, physicians, statisticians, and public health workers, and is intended for scholars from these different fields, the ability to communicate across these fields is paramount. As is well known, semantic barriers to interdisciplinary communication may be formidable. One man's precision is another man's jargon. Good-will alone may help the reader to tolerate the idiosyncrasies that are alien to him. With the hope of making the task of understanding easier, we append a glossary of specialized terms, defined as they are used in papers in this volume.

Special mention must, however, be made of the word *fertility* and related terms. Demographers have felt a need to differentiate between reproductive capacity and reproductive performance, as well as to define a variety of measures of each. In this effort, English-speaking demographers use the word *fecundity* to denote the capacity to reproduce, and the term *fertility* to denote the production of children. The latter term is used generally as a measure of reproductive performance. It is also used more specifically. For example, a general fertility rate is the number of live births occurring in a defined period of time in a specified geographic area, divided by the average number of women aged 15–50 living in that area during the time specified.

Unfortunately, this usage is in conflict with that of biologists (and as a rule of physicians also) who use the term *fertility* to mean the capacity to reproduce, and do not normally need a term for statistical measures of actual reproduction. An *infertile* woman denotes, to a demographer, a woman who has had no live born children; to a biologist this phrase describes a woman who cannot conceive.

The situation is further complicated by the fact that in French, Italian, and Spanish, demographic usage is the reverse of English demographic usage. The words related to *fertile* denote the capacity to reproduce; those related to *fecund* denote production of live births. Thus arose the term *fecundability* which was adopted directly into English from Italian to denote the monthly probability of conception. ''Fertilizability'' would have been more consistent with English demographic usage though even less euphonic.

Disagreement exists also in the specification of *parity* number. For a physician the parity of a woman is determined by the number of pregnancies she has had that lasted sufficiently long for the fetus to become viable (about 28 weeks). A stillbirth adds one to her parity; a multiple birth also adds one. Parity as defined by demographers, however, refers to the number of live born infants. Thus a stillbirth adds none; the birth of twins adds two.

We consider the current situation deplorable, and strongly agree with the participants at the Symposium who urged that a strenuous effort be made to alter it. Thus, Irene Taeuber pointed out that since the interdisciplinary dialogue is increasing and will undoubtedly continue to do so, it is mandatory to remove the terminological confusion. She recommended that this be done by an international interdisciplinary body.

In what we have written in this volume, we have modified our own terminology to avoid the word fertility as far as possible. As editors, however, we did not think it feasible to impose an arbitrary change in terminology of our choosing on the authors of the papers presented here, and to commit violence from without on their several well-entrenched habits. Consequently, the reader is warned that different papers in this volume use different definitions. The relevant terms are defined in the glossary, both biologic and demographic meanings being given where applicable.

CONTENTS

PART I

Demographic History and
Population Policy

D. V. Glass

POPULATION GROWTH
AND POPULATION POLICY

INTRODUCTION

Although the title of this paper is comprehensive enough to cover all types of population policy bearing upon any demographic situation, there is no doubt that the major concern among demographers today is with specific policies for a particular situation. Discussion has become focused primarily upon policies to reduce fertility in developing societies. During the last few years, concern has spilled over to developed societies in which rates of natural increase are also quite high. But the bases of such concern are less grossly economic and so far there has been no widespread demand for action programs in countries like Canada or the United States—certainly nothing comparable to the demand for programs in India, Pakistan, or Puerto Rico. It is in respect of the latter type of country that there is now much more general agreement on broad policy aims. Indeed, one of the most important results of the improvement of demographic statistics and of the many national, regional, and international meetings in recent years has been to narrow to almost manageable proportions the disagreements still sharply visible a decade ago. That rapid population growth acts as a brake upon economic development and upon raising the very low levels of living which obtain among some two thirds of mankind is now widely accepted. Religious differences—they have been primarily differences in Western religion—have become more or less restricted to questions of technique and formal morality. Political differences, too, have been blunted as socialist societies have come to accept—though on a different ideological basis—the validity of birth prevention. It would, of course, be unrealistic to assume that major differences of approach are likely to disappear. Nevertheless, the "development decade" has brought with it a greater measure of consensus than ever before on the relevance of population policy as part of general policy for economic and social development. Even if the international agencies continue to meet difficulties in responding to requests for direct assistance, other agencies will be available and we may expect to see a marked increase in "action programs" designed to encourage the spread of birth control and the development of lower family-size "targets." Equally, we may expect to see demographic considerations taken more explicitly into account in general social policy in developing societies. How far can we, as demographers or more generally as social scientists, offer pertinent suggestions about the kinds of action which may help to produce the desired changes in the rate of population growth?

Let me say at once that I do not intend to attempt any systematic answer to this question; indeed, I am not in a position to do so. Instead, I propose to draw attention to a few of the difficulties inherent in the question itself and then to consider some possible implications for population research and policy. Two difficulties in particular are worth stressing. First, that although history displays many examples of population policies, there is no unequivocal evidence of the success of any set of measures aimed directly at influencing population growth. And second, that we ourselves are far from having an adequate theory of demographic change.

POPULATION POLICIES IN THE WEST

As to the first point, most historical population policies have been pronatalist, designed primarily to increase marital fertility and often also to encourage more and earlier marriage. Sometimes the policies included measures to stimulate immigration and to discourage emigration. The actual policy provisions might favor particular groups in the population—such as the attempts of Augustus to encourage the senatorial class to reproduce itself, or the concern of Colbert with the nobility and the bourgeoisie; or they might be comprehensive, as in the case with recent French and Swedish profamily legislation. Only once in the past was there a major attempt to reduce population growth, namely in a number of German states in the mid-nineteenth century. The influence of Malthus, coupled with a fear of rising costs of poor relief, persuaded some of the states to restrict permission to marry to those couples who could be assumed to be able to support a family.[1]

Of the earliest efforts to influence population growth, we naturally know very little. In some cases we do not know which measures were actually implemented or—if we know as much as that—how far the positive provisions were actually taken up by those for whom they were supposed to be available. In other cases we can be reasonably certain, even without factual evidence, that the objectives could not have been achieved to any substantial degree and were not in general practical possibilities. Colbert, for example, prescribed pensions for families with 10 or more living legitimate children. But, given the probable level of mortality at the time, Montesquieu was certainly justified in saying that such provisions were aimed at encouraging "prodigies."

Even of the more recent and extensive policies, it is not

---

1. The most recent general survey of current population policies is that of H. T. Eldridge, *Population Policies* (Washington, D.C.: International Population Union, 1954). On postwar profamily policies in France, see C. Watson, "Birth Control and Abortion in France Since 1939," *Population Studies*, V (March, 1952), pp. 261–286; C. Watson, "Recent Development in French Immigration Policy," *Population Studies*, VI (July, 1952), pp. 3–38; C. Watson, "Housing Policy and Population Problems in France," *Population Studies*, VII (July, 1953), pp. 14–45; C. Watson, "Population Policy in France: Family Allowances and Other Benefits—II," *Population Studies*, VIII (July, 1954), pp. 46–73; as well as "Haut comité consultatif de la population et de la famille," *La population française*, Vol. 1 (Paris, 1955). For policies in Sweden, see H. Gille, *Population Studies*, II (June and Sept., 1948). On Colbert's population policy there is no full study, but see L. Schöne, *Histoire de la population française* (Paris, 1893), Chap. 9, and E. Esmonin, *La taille en Normandie au temps de Colbert* (Paris, 1913), pp. 260–262. On Malthusian policies in Germany, see D. V. Glass (ed.), *Introduction to Malthus* (London, 1953), Chap. 2.

possible to speak of "effectiveness" in any definite or precise way. The measures were too often inconsistent and unrealistic. In France, for example, interwar legislation attempted to restrict the spread of birth control but (and this is still the position) excluded the condom from the restrictions.[2] In any case, coitus interruptus, which was widely practiced, could scarcely be brought under the control of the law. On the positive side, too, there was a lack of realism. Propaganda emphasized the cost of bringing up large families, but the family allowances offered prior to 1939 met only a small fraction of that cost. In Italy, there was a still greater reliance upon exhortation and even less in the way of positive inducements. And in no country was there an adequate attempt to assess the effectiveness of the measures applied. Perhaps the nearest approach to assessment was in Nazi Germany. But the rise in current fertility, attributed largely to the "psychic rebirth" of the nation, was—as Hajnal has shown—compatible with a stationary family size.[3] And though that may still leave something to be explained, the explanation is one which may not be unique to Nazi Germany or attributable to its population policy, for postwar studies have shown a much wider tendency in Western societies for family size to become stable with the marriage cohorts of the 1930's. Nor, since World War II, has there been much more in the way of assessment in those countries which still have comprehensive population policies—France, Belgium, and Sweden. It is true that there has been a very great improvement in many Western countries in the provision and analysis of fertility statistics in general. But the most evident developments in the combined demographic and sociological investigation of fertility trends and patterns have taken place in the United States, which has no explicit population policy (leaving aside immigration), rather than in France, which has the most explicit profamily policy. Europe has certainly seen some interesting attempts to assess

2. The douche and the sponge were also available and there was reported to be a substantial clandestine sale of reputedly prohibited contraceptives. In Belgium, with similar legal restrictions, the situation was even more confused in that, according to a decision of the Supreme Court of Appeal in 1931, only those dealers engaging in propaganda or display, and only those propagandists who had mercenary intentions, appeared to come within the scope of the law. See D. V. Glass, *Population Policies and Movements in Europe* (London: Oxford University Press, 1940), Chap. 4.

3. J. Hajnal, "The Analysis of Birth Statistics in the Light of the Recent International Recovery of the Birth-Rate," *Population Studies,* I (Sept., 1947).

the results of particular measures affecting population growth. But perhaps the most interesting so far are the studies of abortion and birth control undertaken in Czechoslovakia and Hungary, where abortion legislation has been liberalized; there have been no comparable studies in France and Belgium, where the aim has been to suppress abortion.[4]

The above comments on France and Belgium are not intended —and I hope they will not be considered—as "attacks" on the countries, their policy makers, or their demographers. Similar comments would be equally applicable to all Western countries in respect of a wide range of policies. Thus in the field of health, we now know a good deal about the efficacy of particular forms of treatment for particular diseases. But we know far less about the effectiveness of particular health policies or about the reasons why they have not been fully effective in achieving their declared aims. This is so, to cite one example, of policies aimed at reducing infant mortality; for we have not devoted sufficient study to the question of why there are still substantial differences between the rates for the different social classes.[5] In the field of education, too, it is only in recent years that the serious

4. The most useful collection of general reports on abortion in Europe is to be found in K-H. Mehlan (ed.), *Internationale Abortsituation, Abortbekämpfung, Antikonzeption* (Leipzig, 1961). References to the special studies in Czechoslovakia and Hungary are given in C. Tietze, "Induced Abortion and Sterilization as Methods of Fertility Control," this volume, and in D. V. Glass, "Family Limitation in Europe: A Survey of Recent Studies," *Research in Family Planning*, ed. C. V. Kiser (Princeton: Princeton University Press, 1962).

5. In Britain, for example, after a magnificent beginning with social class analysis of infant mortality undertaken by the Registrars General, far too little attention was given to the specific components accounting for continuing social class differences. Since World War II, there has been a considerable extension of research, some jointly with the Registrar General of England and Wales. See, for example, the series of papers by J. N. Morris *et al.*, *The Lancet*, CCLXVIII (1955), and in *Archives of Disease in Childhood*, 1958; also J. A. Heady and M. A. Heasman, *Social and Biological Factors in Infant Mortality* (London, 1959) and some by nongovernmental research groups. Under the latter heading see in particular F. Grundy and E. Lewis-Faning, *Morbidity and Mortality in the First Year of Life* (London, 1957); J. W. B. Douglas and J. M. Blomfield, *Children Under Five* (London, 1958); R. Illsley, "Social Class Selection and Differences in Relation to Stillbirths and Infant Deaths," *British Medical Journal*, II (Dec. 24, 1955), pp. 1520–1524; N. R. Butler and D. G. Bonham, *Perinatal Mortality* (Edinburgh, 1963). But in spite of this newer work, there is still much to be done and, in particular, a need for experimental action as part of applied research. An example of such applied research in France (though, unfortunately, not a controlled experiment) may be seen in M. Croze, "La mortalité infantile en France suivant le milieu social," *Études statistiques* (July–Sept., 1963); and A. Girard, L. Henry, and R. Nistri, *Facteurs sociaux et culturels de la mortalité infantile* (Paris: I.N.E.D., 1960).

study of differential opportunity and differential performance of various groups of pupils and students has been initiated, and this in spite of the fact that there has been a vast and growing public expenditure upon education in most Western societies. Population policy may be a specially unexplored field from the point of view of assessing the results of policy—it probably is. Hence, even when we have had—or have—policies in that field, we cannot say much that is significant about their consequences. Nor is the position made clearer by the actual record of demographic change. For in the West, the countries in which the rate of population growth fell first were not those with antinatalist policies; while the increases in fertility since the 1930's have not been greatest in countries with the most explicit or comprehensive profamily or pronatalist policies.

THE DEMOGRAPHIC TRANSITION IN THE WEST

At the same time we do not have an adequate knowledge of our own "demographic transition." Our data on historical change are poor—to a considerable extent irremediably so, though considerable progress is now being made in reconstructing the evidence and very much more could undoubtedly be done. It is not surprising, therefore, that discussions—mainly by historians—of industrialization and population growth in the West should have moved from one controversy to another.[6] As Kuczynski once wrote, "An explanation does not necessarily look less plausible if the event which is explained has not occurred;"[7] and the fewer the "hard facts," the greater is likely to be the number of plausible explanations. In addition, our search for facts and our ability to utilize those we have are limited by the lack of an adequate theoretical framework—or rather, since it would be giving excessive dignity to what I mean by calling it "theoretical"—by lack of an adequate framework of study. Such a framework would need to give as much emphasis to the substantiation and meaning of the "facts" or

6. This is especially the case in respect of population growth in Britain before the nineteenth century. Falling mortality, rising nuptiality and rising fertility have all been suggested at various times—separately or in combination—as explanations. But until quite recently there were few attempts to establish the facts of the demographic situation.

7. R. R. Kuczynski, *Colonial Population* (London, 1937), p. xiii.

"trends" we are trying to explain as to the categorization of possible "explanatory variables." A few examples may help to show that this requirement is not quite as obvious or as simple as it may first appear to be.

The question of changing marriage patterns and propensities has long been discussed as a possible explanation of the increased rate of population growth during Western industrialization, and the discussion could only have flourished because of the lack of conclusive evidence. But it is becoming increasingly clear that the available data do not provide much support for the hypothesis of more and earlier marriage during the eighteenth century. Of far greater consequence, too, as Hajnal has shown recently, is the fact that the basic change in Western European marriage patterns was of the reverse order and that it occurred well before the eighteenth century. For some 300 years or more, Western Europe displayed marriage patterns markedly different from those of Eastern Europe or, as far as one can judge, from those of underdeveloped societies. In these latter regions, marriage appeared to be more "natural" in character—in the sense that it took place early (not too long after physiological maturation) and was almost universal. This seems also to have been the case in Western Europe in the Middle Ages. But by the seventeenth century the new and "artificial" pattern was becoming established.[8] Hollingsworth's study of the complete British peerage shows the process of development of the pattern among the cohorts born at the end of the sixteenth and the beginning of the seventeenth centuries.[9] Thus the "facts" are different from those which are widely assumed to have obtained and the problem of "explanation" is correspondingly different.

The history and nature of mortality change provide another illustration of the relationship between "facts" and the problem of explanation. Here, again, controversy has flourished in the absence of firm evidence. Not so long ago it was customary to stress the importance of improvements in medicine and of the

8. J. Hajnal, "European Marriage Patterns in Perspective," *Population in History*, ed. D. V. Glass and D. Eversley (London, 1965).
9. T. H. Hollingsworth, "The Demography of the British Peerage," *Population Studies*, Supplement, XVIII (Nov., 1964), pp. 3–108.

establishment of hospitals in contributing to the decline in death rates during the eighteenth and early nineteenth centuries —and this before there were many solid data on the course or extent of that decline. More recently, a survey of the field by McKeown and Brown has paid particular attention to the role of medicine and of hospitals and has concluded emphatically that they could not have made any significant contribution, save in respect of vaccination.[10] Attention has now been directed once more to the possible effect of variolation in reducing smallpox mortality before the advent of vaccination. This was a question which was debated during the eighteenth century itself and spurred Bernoulli in his attempt to estimate the effect upon mortality of the elimination of smallpox. The question has been opened up again, partly in response to Miller's account of the adoption of variolation in England,[11] and a new study has shown a two-phase spread of the practice, first among the upper classes and later among the general population.[12] But these various

10. T. McKeown and R. G. Brown, ''Medical Evidence Related to English Population Changes in the Eighteenth Century,'' *Population Studies,* IX (Nov., 1955), pp. 119–141.

11. G. Miller, *The Adoption of Inoculation for Smallpox in England and France,* (Philadelphia, 1957).

12. This study, by P. Razzell, will appear in the *Economic History Review,* and is an interesting attempt to document the spread of inoculation. It is much more comprehensive in that respect than Miller's earlier study, though it is difficult to assess how far eighteenth century reports of the adoption of the practice can be regarded as reliable. Nevertheless, there is little doubt that the degree of personal involvement (and perhaps also public involvement) in this form of preventive medicine was unusually high as compared with earlier periods. The possible effect of the practice on mortality in general, or on smallpox mortality in particular is, of course, a very different matter. The difficulty here is well illustrated by the city of Carlisle, for which there are the exceptionally good Bills of mortality of John Heysham. In one Bill (for 1781) Heysham stated that ''within these six or seven years, some thousands have been inoculated in the town and neighbourhood of Carlisle. . . .'' In a later Bill (for 1783) he claimed that, following an outbreak of smallpox, ''great numbers were inoculated not only by the Surgeon to the Dispensary but also by most of the other Surgeons in the Town.'' Still later (Bill for 1784) he reported a further 200 inoculations. But these claims do not seem to agree with the numbers reported (in the same Bills) as being inoculated at the Dispensary. And in any case, for the period 1780–87 (excluding the especially heavy smallpox year of 1779) smallpox accounted for almost 10 per cent of all deaths. (Heysham's Bills are summarized in H. Lonsdale, *The Life of John Heysham, M.D.* (London, 1870). For details of inoculations and discussions of smallpox deaths it is necessary to consult the original yearly Bills. Unfortunately, the only collection I have come across—in the Carlisle Public Library—is incomplete, lacking the Bills for 1779, 1780 and 1784.)

findings and hypotheses need to be reviewed together in relation to the actual decline in the death rates—as shown, for example, by Hollingsworth's data for the British peerage. The data indicate that child mortality—deaths under five years of age—fell substantially in about the period during which inoculation became fairly widely adopted by the aristocracy for their children. But the fall in child mortality contributed only a part of the increase in life expectation; this could scarcely have been otherwise with expectation of life at birth being already above 35 years for the cohorts born before the new practice was accepted.[13] Moreover, death rates fell at all ages, while the different age-specific mortality rates began their systematic fall at different times—some in the seventeenth century and others in the eighteenth century. Taking expectation of life at birth as a summary indicator, it is from the cohort born in 1675–99 that a systematic rise is displayed—increasing, for example, from 33.5 years for that cohort to 47.9 years for the cohort born in 1775–99. We therefore have to look for more general factors, and for those beginning to exert their influence earlier, in trying to account for the fall in mortality. And if the factors involved in the fall of mortality are reflections of, or components in, improved levels of living, they might also help to explain the

---

13. Technically, the effect upon expectation of life at birth of reductions in smallpox mortality would depend upon the proportionate contribution of smallpox to total mortality. But that in turn would depend upon the age-incidence of smallpox deaths. Calculations based upon U.N. model life tables (I am indebted to Norman Carrier for those calculations) show how this works out. Thus, if smallpox deaths fall on the 0–9 years group (as was the case in the eighteenth century urban communities persistently exposed to infection and hence with relative immunity at the higher ages), this itself limits the possible contribution of smallpox to total mortality—it could account for 10 per cent, but not for as much as 15 per cent with an expectation of life at birth of about 34.4 years. With a life expectation of about 24.8 years, however, the contribution could in theory be as high as 20 per cent. A reduction of 50 per cent in smallpox mortality would raise the expectation of life at birth to about 28.4 years in the latter case; but in the former, with smallpox accounting for 10 per cent of all deaths, life expectation would rise to 36.6 years. However, we know far too little about the actual age-incidence of smallpox in small towns or rural districts, or about the actual contribution of smallpox to total mortality in the eighteenth century. In addition, there is the problem of the type of smallpox in different areas at different times and the relative immunity of different sections of the population. Hence, even if we had reliable estimates of the spread of inoculation—and the estimates can hardly be reliable—we should still be unable to assess with precision the effect of inoculation.

increased interest in medicine (including interest in personal health) and in the establishment of hospitals in eighteenth century England.[14]

A third example relates to the study of fertility trends, to the kinds of indicators used in different contexts and to the movements they are likely to exhibit. It is unnecessary to recount the changes which have taken place since the 1930's in the measurement of fertility or to stress the disenchantment with indices based upon reproductive behavior displayed in calendar periods. There is now general agreement on the importance of cohort measures—whether of birth or marriage cohorts—and the use of such indices has facilitated a much closer link between formal and sociological demography. But cohort indicators are not always available, either now or historically, and in any case there are questions for which the study of calendar changes in fertility levels is relevant. The translation of one type of index into another is thus of considerable importance—or rather, the assessment of the way in which (and the extent to which) changes in the components in one type of index will affect the appearance of the other. Hajnal drew attention to this in examining the compatibility of relatively stable family size with sharp increases in duration-specific marital fertility rates in Nazi Germany, and a similar compatibility was confirmed for interwar movements in fertility in Britain.[15] Analyses of this kind are no less essential to our understanding of what happened in the period of industrialization in the West. At the most elementary level, for example, it is necessary to see how far

14. An indication of the increased interest in health is the sale of manuals written by physicians for the "intelligent layman." One such manual, *Domestic Medicine*, by William Buchan, M.D., first published in 1769, is said to have had 19 editions in the author's lifetime and to have sold more than 100,000 copies. (See J. H. F. Brotherston, *Observations on the Early Public Health Movement in Scotland* [London, 1952], pp. 19–22). Buchan intended his book for the educated "opinion leaders" who could follow his recommendations—many of which were very sensible— and who could help the poor. Brotherston's view of eighteenth-century developments in Scotland is that "It is reasonable to suppose that there was a better standard of treatment of the sick in general, as the people were gradually relieved of the constant fear of starvation. As the standard of life was raised people must have become less preoccupied with the struggle for mere existence, and some attention could be devoted to the sick and impotent. Medical teaching became more rational, and a public grew which was more fitted to learn." (Brotherston, *op. cit.*, p. 19.)

15. J. Hajnal, *Population Studies*, Sept., I (1947); D. V. Glass and E. Grebenik, *The Trend and Pattern of Fertility in Britain*, Vol. 1 (London, 1954), pp. 238–240.

changes in mortality are likely to have affected the numbers of first and subsequent marriages and the probability of a marriage surviving intact through the childbearing period.[16] Mean family size may thereby be affected as it comes increasingly to represent the average fertility of first marriages. Marriage rates themselves may be modified as, with an increasing curve of annual births, there is a possibly growing disproportion between the numbers of girls and men available for mating according to the given social "rules" concerning the relative ages of husband and wife. Reductions in fertility may produce changes in death rates in childhood by altering the ages at which exposure to infection occurs. Direct analysis of these questions, coupled with the development of models—as, for example, in the work of Ryder [17]—are required if we are to know what is explicable as forming part of a "demographic process" and what requires explanation by recourse to other disciplines.

CHANGES IN REPRODUCTIVE BEHAVIOR: THEORETICAL APPROACHES

Assuming that we know—or come to know—what it is that we have to explain in terms outside of formal demography, what kinds of explanatory framework are likely to help us, at least in the sense of indicating the range and nature of the questions which have to be answered? I am concerned here in particular with the "transition" models and concepts which have been developed during the past 30 years and which—unlike much of the "grand theory" in our field—are fairly explicit and specific and capable of being tested and modified. This has in fact been the case since Landry enunciated his thesis on the "demographic revolution." [18] Beginning with hypotheses regarding the

16. T. H. Hollingsworth, "A Demographic Study of the British Ducal Families," *Population Studies*, XI (July, 1957), pp. 4–26, shows that as mortality fell during the eighteenth century, the proportion of marriages of completed fertility (of marriages remaining intact until the wives had passed through the childbearing period) rose from 35 per cent for the 1680–1729 birth cohort to 60 per cent for that of 1730–1779 and 74 per cent for that of 1780–1829 (dukes' sons; the change is similar for dukes' daughters).

17. See N. B. Ryder, "The Influence of Declining Mortality on Swedish Reproductivity," *Current Research in Human Fertility* (New York: Milbank Memorial Fund, 1955); and N. B. Ryder, "Problems of Trend Determination During a Transition in Fertility," *Milbank Memorial Fund Quarterly*, XXXIV (Jan., 1956), pp. 5–21.

18. A. Landry, *La révolution démographique* (Paris, 1934), especially pp. 44–55.

extent to which, historically, reproduction came to be controlled by means of marriage as such, or within marriage, or by both means, the element of the staggered phasing of mortality and fertility decline was introduced by Carr-Saunders.[19] The concept was generalized and extended by Notestein [20] and Blacker [21] and has subsequently also been used—by Ryder,[22] for instance—to exemplify broad categories of socio-demographic relationships in contemporary societies. The most recent development is by Kingsley Davis in his theory of the "multiphasic response."[23] In the Davis version, the analysis is both more comprehensive and sophisticated. It attempts to include what was formerly regarded as a "deviant" case—that of Ireland; Japan, with its relatively well-documented transition, is taken as a starting point for the analysis, rather than preindustrial European countries with their inadequate data; and the staggered reaction of fertility to mortality decline is not viewed as a reaction to rising poverty, but as one occurring because the maintenance of the earlier patterns of reproductive behavior would have meant that, as a result of falling mortality, the populations concerned would have handicapped themselves in "their effort to take advantage of the opportunities being provided by the emerging economy." Leaving aside the designation "multiphasic response"—which is a high-powered term for a simple meaning—this modified transition approach is undoubtedly attractive, and not least in that it tries to substitute for conventional and rather mechanical responses to falling mortality some substantive sociological analysis. But does it fit the facts and does it take us much further in our inquiry into the nature of population change?

There are some facts which clearly do not fit. In particular, the beginnings of fertility decline among the British peerage antedate any systematic fall in mortality,[24] and the European

19. A. M. Carr-Saunders, *World Population* (London: Oxford University Press, 1936), pp. 60–66.

20. F. W. Notestein, "Population—The Long View," *Food for the World,* ed. T. W. Schultz (Chicago, 1945), especially pp. 39–52.

21. C. P. Blacker, "Stages in Population Growth," *Eugenics Review* (Oct., 1947).

22. N. B. Ryder, "Fertility," *The Study of Population,* ed. P. M. Hauser and O. D. Duncan (Chicago, 1959).

23. K. Davis, "The Theory of Change and Response in Modern Demographic History," *Population Index,* XXIX (Oct., 1963), pp. 345–366.

24. Hollingsworth's study of the complete British peerage suggests that the

nobility had also shown a reduction in family size before expectation of life at birth had reached modern levels.[25] Equally, for the *ducs et pairs* in France, among whom mortality appears to have been high and to have shown little improvement in the eighteenth century, family size had fallen sharply by the beginning of the eighteenth century, while male celibacy was high.[26] Moreover, the data for the British nobility suggest that, during the first stages of the systematic fall in mortality, fertility may actually have increased—though we do not know whether a reduction in stillbirths may have played any part in this rise.

In addition, in his understandable aim to "generalize," Davis minimizes the particularity of certain developments, and thereby loses explanatory power. Thus, although it is true that later marriage and higher celibacy in Ireland may be treated merely as extreme forms of the Western European marriage pattern, there are special circumstances, too. It is a mistake to assume— as Davis implies—that the formal attitude of the Roman Catholic church towards marriage is reflected with uniform intensity by the priesthood in all Catholic societies, or that the population at large reacts in the same degree to the priests in each society. It has been suggested, for example, that the reimposition of religious conformity in France after the sixteenth century helped to provoke the reaction of a diminished obedience to the rules of the church and that by the end of the eighteenth century married couples refused to accept those rules so far as birth control practice was concerned.[27] By contrast, it has been reported that the Irish priesthood has been so concerned with dangers to chastity as to interfere with courtship practices which, while no doubt constituting a danger, are elsewhere regarded as being bearable and as a customary stage before marriage.[28] There is, further, the question of whether the

---

fertility of completed marriages was lower among the late seventeenth and early eighteenth century cohorts than among those of earlier or later periods.

25. S. Peller, in the revised version of his earlier papers—"Births and Deaths Among Europe's Ruling Families Since 1500," Glass and Eversley, *op. cit.*— suggests a peak number of births per married man for the marriage cohort of 1600–49 (higher than in earlier cohorts), followed by a persistent decline.

26. C. Lévy and L. Henry, "Ducs et pairs sous l'Ancien Régime," *Population*, XV (Oct.–Dec., 1960), pp. 807–830.

27. See A. Sauvy, "Essai d'une vue d'ensemble," pp. 389–390, and L. Henry, "L'apport des témoignages et de la statistique," pp. 365–368; *La prévention des naissances dans la famille*, ed. H. Bergues *et al.* (Paris: I.N.E.D., 1960).

28. R. C. Geary (*Weekly Bulletin of the Department of External Affairs*, Eire,

extreme features of Irish demographic development may not also be in part attributable to the relative lack of an early nineteenth-century native middle class which, as in many other countries, might have introduced an element of rationality, whether or not the religion was Roman Catholic. And though low rates of economic development and of urbanization may be a general explanation for the responses of migration and lowered marriage rates, in Ireland there is the added feature that in such circumstances, and more than in some other Roman Catholic societies, the present urban middle class will contain a larger fraction of professionally religious priests, nuns, and teachers, firmly opposed to birth control as an alternative. The nature of the response in other countries needs equally to be looked at not only as coming under the heading of "multiphasic" but also with reference to particular historico-social contexts. The present resort to abortion in Japan is not simply an extension of a practice which occured in many societies, but should be considered in terms of its traditional role in the society; and there are parallels in France, too.[29]

March 29, 1954) has rightly criticized some of the arguments in *The Vanishing Irish*, ed. J. A. O'Brien (London, 1954). Nevertheless the points made by several of the contributors are worth further investigation—notably the reluctance of parents to give responsibility to their sons; and the role of the church in respect of "courtship" relations. The points are by no means new. Indeed, one of the clearest expressions of the first view is given in R. Lynd, *Home Life in Ireland* (London, 1909). Unfortunately—even taking the work of Arensberg and Kimball into account —(*Family and Community in Ireland* [Cambridge: Harvard University Press, 1940])—far too little has been done to investigate the factors affecting Irish marriage patterns. These include the relevant teachings of the church, the selection and training of Irish priests since the early nineteenth century, and the nature and attitudes of the Irish middle class. See also R. C. Geary, "Some Reflections on Irish Population Questions," *Studies* (Summer, 1954).

29. Although it is true that abortion is practiced in all developed societies—and, since World War II, especially in East European countries—there appear to have been wide variations in the intensity of practice in the past. The literary evidence— obviously such evidence is far from conclusive—does not, for example, suggest that abortion was very widespread in the seventeenth or eighteenth century in England. In France, on the other hand, the contrary is suggested by such indications as the attempts (from the sixteenth century onwards) to compel women to register their pregnancies; the inclusion among the prisoners in the Bastille of professional abortionists; and growing debate on criminal abortion in the nineteenth century. There is, indeed, considerable continuity in French history—from the sixteenth century to the present day—in respect of the persistent efforts to suppress abortion. On abortion in seventeenth and eighteenth century France, see J. Mathorez, *Les étrangers en France sous l'Ancien Régime*, Vol. I (Paris, 1919), pp. 30–31; A. Corre and P. Aubry, *Documents de criminologie rétrospective* (Lyons and Paris, 1895),

Finally—and this is a rather different matter—there is the question of whether, in throwing out some of the earlier, mechanistic generalizations on response, Davis has gone far enough in one respect. Is it either necessary or appropriate to take as the starting point in "transition analysis" the establishment of a downward trend in mortality? Before dismissing this question as mere heresy, it is worth considering a few points which may be cited against the old orthodoxy. There is, to begin with, the evidence of the nobility in Britain and in continental Europe and possibly also of the shift to a new marriage pattern in Western Europe prior to a systematic fall in mortality. Equally there are the anomalies of the United States and of France; in the latter country overall fertility had almost certainly began to fall by the end of the eighteenth century.[30] The differential rate of decline in fertility in different European countries in which the initial fall occurred at different times requires no less to be taken into account. Perhaps at least as relevant is the possible explanation of the fall in mortality itself. For if the explanation of that fall lies chiefly in improvements in levels of living, it may be that it is these improvements as such, rather than their reflection in mortality, which were important in helping to bring about a change in reproductive behavior. And it should be remembered that orthodox "transition" analysis began largely as a result of the simple observation that, in a number of countries, there was a lag between mortality and

---

Chap. 11; E. Locard, *Le XVII° siècle médico judiciaire* (Lyons and Paris, 1902), Chap. 16. For the original act of Henri II, 1556, "contre les femmes qui cèlent leur grossesse," see [P.] Le Ridant, *Code Matrimonial* (Paris, 1766), pp. 9–15. For not untypical views of the high incidence of abortions in the nineteenth and early twentieth centuries, see S. Du Mouriez, *L'Avortement* (Paris, 1912), (which stresses the effect of Pasteur's work, in that the application of antiseptic techniques had greatly reduced the danger of abortion and had resulted in a marked increase in frequency); Balthazard and E. Prévost, *Une plaie sociale* (Paris, 1912); P. Brouardel, *L'Avortement* (Paris, 1901); C. Floquet, *Avortement et dépopulation* (Paris, 1892); H. Berthélemy, *De la répression de l'avortement criminel* (Paris, 1917).

30. On the decline in fertility in France, see J. Bourgeois-Pichat, "Évolution générale de la population française depuis le XVIII° siècle," *Population*, VI (Oct.–Dec. 1951), pp. 635–662; and E. Gautier and L. Henry, *La population de Crulai: Paroisse normande* (Paris: I.N.E.D., 1958). On the decline in the United States see Y. Yasuba, *Birth Rates of the White Population in the United States, 1800–1860* (Baltimore, 1962), Chap. 1; and A. J. Coale and M. Zelnik, *New Estimates of Fertility and Population in the United States* (Princeton, 1963), Chap. 4.

fertility decline and without regard to what might be implied in the relationship between the two factors in the population balance.

If, for the moment, we abandon the fall in mortality as the necessary starting point for analysis, we may look at the problem in somewhat different terms. We may assume—as an aid in analysis—that the deliberate and persistent control of reproductive behavior (including control of the marriage variable) involves a conflict between levels of living and aspirations, to an extent which is sufficient to make it socially visible and in some degree "institutionalized." (This latter condition is specified not simply to avoid psychologism but also because without institutionalization the conflict is unlikely to influence a group, and without group support an individual or family is less likely to break away from earlier patterns of behavior.) The conflict may take place at various levels of living—though it is unlikely to produce a persistent response at the lowest levels, since at such levels the population would be occupied only too fully with the facts of crude hunger and premature death. The aspirations need not be purely material or focused exclusively on one's self. But they would have to be of a kind accepted as valid by one's reference group. And the conflict must appear to be more easily capable of resolution by individual action affecting demographic variables than by other types of action: hence the opportunities for such action must be visible. The response or responses would then need to be of a character in keeping with the *mores* of the reference group or the *mores* themselves would have to be capable of being changed without undue difficulty to accommodate those responses which appear to be most relevant and practicable.

There is no reason to believe that, in the very rudimentary form in which they have been listed, these categories are likely to replace the more customary analysis. For one thing it would be necessary to redefine and elaborate the categories operationally for purposes of investigation. For another, they would in any case be far less convenient and "neat" in their application; it is difficult enough, for example, to search for a starting point in the decline in mortality, and how much more difficult to search for conflict between levels and aspirations. But convenience and "neatness" are not the overriding requirements, and on the side of formal demography we have been forced to abandon them in moving away from the conventional reproduction rate as a measure of replacement. This is not the place for an extended discussion of the ways in which such a modification of approach might become of use in demographic study. But at least a few positive points might be noted. Apparently deviant cases are less likely to be deviant if looked at in this way. The case of the seventeenth-century French nobility can certainly be accommodated in terms of the pressures from the Court for conspicuous consumption. So can that of Ireland, if it is remembered that the Great Famine not only provided "trigger action" of a catastrophic kind (two modern equivalents would be the defeat of Germany in World War I and that of Japan in World War II) but also—because of massive emigration and mortality —the opportunity to consolidate land holdings.[31] Tenant eviction had failed, but the post-Faminine years saw the rapid elimination of the smallest holdings; delaying marriage fitted in with the accepted practices and might have come to be regarded as not too heavy a price to pay for avoiding the fragmentation of a farm; while those who would not accept the delay still had the opportunity to emigrate, their costs being, in large part, financed by remittances from earlier emigrants. The change of approach would also avoid the problem of mechanistic explanation (and of the search for rationalizations which this sometimes implies), while leaving the pressures on reproductive behavior firmly imbedded in the social structure. And they have certainly been so imbedded in the industrialized West and in Japan.

If this has been the case, there is little reason to believe that pressures on reproduction will emerge automatically in developing societies simply as a result of mortality decline. Davis states that "whenever and wherever mortality declined on a sustained basis, there the continuation of old demographic patterns brought a train of disadvantages." But he is also emphatic that, "obviously, the demographic response of the Japanese is not to

31. On the change in the size of farms, see K. H. Connell, "Peasant Marriage in Ireland After the Great Famine," *Past and Present* (Nov., 1957), especially pp. 77–78; M. J. Bonn, *Modern Ireland and Her Agrarian Problem* (Dublin and London, 1906), p. 46; A. Schrier, *Ireland and the American Emigration, 1850–1900* (Minneapolis, 1958), pp. 67 *et seq.*

be explained in terms of spreading poverty or diminishing resources."[32] If both statements are correct—and I believe they are—this is because, until recent decades, the persistent fall in mortality was the result of rising levels of living; because those raised levels became incorporated in the social structure and pressed people to behave in such ways as might prevent the levels from being lowered; and because the institutionalization of higher levels of living provided a springboard for raising aspirations. But with the new techniques for reducing mortality, a rise in levels of living is not essential—at least, not in the short run. And, on the other hand, with present levels as low as they are, and especially in societies with systems of "shared poverty," increased population growth, if it were to press upon the circumstances of living, might not provoke a counter-control of fertility. Developing societies cannot afford to count upon a spontaneous adjustment of fertility. In any case, they cannot afford to wait for one. There is not the margin of play which Western societies or Japan had during their stages of industrialization. Relatively speaking, those societies were already more advanced in terms of technology and conditions of life; their rates of natural increase were considerably lower; the limited ability to control mortality with the techniques available at the time meant that the rate of population growth could not rise to the point which it has already reached in developing societies today,[33] and preindustrial changes in marriage patterns had in many countries already provided some built-in control of reproduction.

POPULATION POLICY AND PROGRAMS IN DEVELOPING SOCIETIES

Of course, many developing societies today are neither waiting for nor counting upon a spontaneous readjustment of fertility to declining mortality. They are striving to push up the

32. Davis, *op. cit.*, pp. 352 and 350.

33. On the differences between mortality control in underdeveloped societies and the nineteenth century industrializing West, see G. J. Stolnitz, "Comparison Between Some Recent Mortality Trends in Underdeveloped Areas and Historical Trends in the West," *Trends and Differentials in Mortality* (New York: Milbank Memorial Fund, 1955), and D. V. Glass, "Population Growth, Fertility and Population Policy," *The Advancement of Science* (Nov., 1960). In addition, of course, the nineteenth century West had vastly greater opportunities for emigration and was not faced by the contrast of higher levels of living in other societies.

rate of economic development and some of them are adopting, or have already adopted, programs for promoting the spread of birth control and of sterilization. What can be done to increase the effectiveness of efforts to produce by conscious action the kinds of changes which took place more or less spontaneously in industrialized societies?

On the side of birth control, the next few years are likely to see an increasing number of ''action programs'' and these will certainly be very necessary. But even in advance of such programs, other action may be helpful. Thus there are still many underdeveloped societies which have high rates of population growth but in which the ratio of population to resources is by no means as acute at present as, say, in India. It is obviously desirable that these countries should not delay the initiation of birth control programs; their chances of success may be considerably greater now than later. Every opportunity should therefore be taken to assist such countries to appreciate the nature and urgency of the problem—by helping to organize national seminars, by providing courses for individuals who may be able to influence opinion, by giving opportunities to some of those individuals to see relevant programs in other countries. Equally, assuming that programs will come to be adopted, it would be useful to consider what kinds of communication, distribution, and reinforcement are most feasible in the different societies, having regard to their institutions and resources, and especially to their actual or probable cadres of trained personnel. This will also have a bearing upon the kinds of birth control techniques which can be made available. Techniques as such are likely to show substantial improvements in acceptability and use-effectiveness, now that research into contraception is ''respectable'' and is being given greater support. But so far as the next 10 to 20 years are concerned, the perfection of the newer intrauterine devices and the development of a relatively simple form of reversible sterilization may be of far greater importance than research into biological or chemical contraceptives. The relevance of legalized abortion should also be considered, at least as an interim measure, not least in that if action programs result in a sizable increase in the proportion of couples practicing birth control, contraceptive failures in the

early stages may give rise to strong demands for the termination of accidental pregnancies.[34]

As for the action programs themselves, Berelson is undoubtedly right in emphasizing the need, given the time-scale of
urgency, for applied rather than fundamental research, as well
as in focusing more upon expertise in communication than on
communication research.[35] But this does not obviate the importance of substantial and comprehensive applied research. The
fact that many surveys have shown the existence of an apparent
interest in controlling family size does not mean that the mere
distribution of contraceptives will be sufficient; it has not been,
and it is rarely likely to be so. In such circumstances, to rush
into the establishment of a large-scale program of family
planning centers or similar units might well be a waste of
resources. The failure of such a program might also have
serious repercussions on the possible success of later action;
and in any case, in many underdeveloped societies it would not
even be possible to assess failure or success without a great deal
of preparatory work.[36] What is much more practicable and
desirable in the initial stages is a series of trial programs so
designed that they provide their own tests of effectiveness (and
this would mean including periodic surveys of fertility levels
and patterns, since the official statistics are generally neither
comprehensive nor reliable) and their own evaluation of the
success or failure of the major components in the programs. The
application of experimental design may sometimes be feasible.
More important, however, is the provision of reasonable controls; the use of sufficiently probing interviews to follow the
path of reaction—whether positive or negative—of couples
exposed to the program and to examine the socio-cultural

34. And this in turn may lead to an increased resort to clandestine abortion and
also to a reduction in the effectiveness of a birth control campaign. There is a great
deal of ambivalence towards induced abortion, not always for strictly medical reasons
and not solely in countries in which (except on very restricted grounds) it is
illegal.

35. B. Berelson, ''Communication, Communication Research, and Family Planning,'' *Emerging Techniques in Population Research* (New York: Milbank Memorial
Fund, 1963).

36. I have discussed some of these points in greater detail in a paper (''Notes on
the Establishment of a Family Planning Programme'') prepared for the seminar
convened by the Government of Thailand, held in March, 1963. (National Research
Council, *Academic Seminar on Population of Thailand*, March, 1963).

characteristics of groups with different types of response; and the location of reference groups through whom educational and motivational action might be taken. Equally, there is the question of selecting test areas and groups. Since underdeveloped areas are heavily agricultural, test programs must certainly be tried out in rural areas. But societies also need successful demonstration projects to serve as models and to incite emulation. Hence programs should also be attempted in urban communities and among such middle class or other groups as may have begun to show breaks with traditionalism or at least to have become subject to the kinds of pressure which have operated in industrial societies. Whatever is done, it should be remembered that the programs will be aiming at influencing behavior which is the resultant of a network of individual and social pressures. As yet we have very little in the way of successful experience in this field.[37] There is thus all the more reason to test action at each stage.

Direct programs for spreading the use of birth control are, however, only a small part of the action in which developing societies will require to engage. The largest part will have to consist of planned economic and social development—and development at a considerably higher rate than appears to have been evident so far. This will be needed because, without an improvement in levels of living, birth control programs may well be empty frameworks. And development will have to be at a pace sufficient to ensure higher levels of living while at the same time meeting the further population growth which is a function of present age-structure and which, short of catastrophe, is therefore bound to take place even if fertility falls sharply. The estimates of the appropriate scale of national investment and of

37. The most successful "experiments" so far are those in Taiwan, South Korea, one area in Ceylon, and Singur (India). On Taiwan, see R. Freedman, J. Y. Peng, Y. Takeshita and T. H. Sun, "Fertility Trends in Taiwan: Tradition and Change," *Population Studies*, XVI (March, 1963), pp. 219–236; and R. Freedman and J. Takeshita, "Studies of Fertility and Family Limitation in Taiwan," this volume. On South Korea, see J. M. Yang, S. Bang, M. H. Kim and M. G. Lee, "Fertility and Family Planning in Korea," *Population Studies*, XVIII (March, 1965), pp. 237–250. Brief accounts of the Singur and Ceylon projects are given in *Studies in Family Planning*, 1 and 2 (New York: The Population Council, July, 1963 and Dec., 1963), and more extensive preliminary reports in contributions by K. K. Mathen and A. Kinch, *Research in Family Planning*, ed. C. V. Kiser (Princeton: Princeton University Press, 1962).

international aid must take account of this double requirement and must also allow for the fact that desirable social change (defined in the present context as being favorable both to economic development and to the emergence of new reproductive patterns) may involve additional expenditure beyond that justifiable for purely economic considerations. Expenditure on education is a case in point; the social requirements would go far beyond the supply of technically or scientifically trained manpower to be used for short-run industrial expansion or for the improvement of agricultural technology.[38] Many of the developing societies themselves could and should do much more to mobilize and use their own resources, and especially their human resources. Economic and social development must be shown to have meaning for, and impact upon, the population in general. Social legislation could be adapted to provide incentives for later marriage and for smaller families and to offer the kind of support which might help to lessen dependence upon kin.[39] Greater recourse to progressive taxation and the guarantee of more effective equality of opportunity in access to education, housing, and employment might help to convince the ordinary man that he will really profit from the new circumstances and that to aim at a small family size is not just a negative form of conduct but a positive contribution to the present and future welfare of his children. These areas of policy, too, require study and evaluation. But they also demand decisive and visible action if societies are to become fully identified with the process of change.

38. This is especially so if formal education is to be used as one of the major ways of breaking down traditionalist attitudes. But even looked at from the strictly economic point of view, the calculus is often far too narrow. On the economic relevance of education (and research) for agriculture, see T. W. Schultz, *Transforming Traditional Agriculture* (New Haven and London, 1964), Chap. 12.

39. See, as an example, R. Titmuss and B. Abel-Smith, *Social Policies and Population Growth in Mauritius* (London, 1961), Chap. 12. In general, far too little attention has been given to the possible role of social legislation or of the assistance which might be given by emphasizing specific aspects of economic and social development programs. All this, of course, involves not merely enacting legislation but ensuring that it is actually implemented. Really implementing, for example, a "compulsory" primary school program is likely to have much greater effect than erecting on paper an elaborate scheme covering secondary and technical education, while allowing large proportions of children to escape the primary school net.

Thomas McKeown

MEDICINE AND WORLD POPULATION

INTRODUCTION

An acceptable interpretation of the influences responsible for the rise of population in the West is badly needed. Without it we are handicapped in evaluating the possibilities of control of population growth, and in planning services, particularly for developing countries where the lack of resources makes it imperative to have a correct assessment of priorities. There are several reasons for the lack of a convincing interpretation.

(1) *Uncertainty about the contribution of birth rate and death rate.* In countries such as England and Wales the modern rise of population began before national statistics were available to put the behavior of the two rates beyond dispute. Hence there are differences of opinion on the relative contribution of a rise of the birth rate or a decline of the death rate to the first phase of population growth.

(2) *Exaggeration of the effectiveness of medical measures.* It has been widely believed that the rise of population in England and Wales during the late eighteenth century was due to a decline of mortality caused by the work of doctors.[1] This

1. G. T. Griffith, *Population Problems of the Age of Malthus* (Cambridge, 1926).

conclusion rested on exiguous evidence but until recently it was not seriously challenged.

(3) *Confusion between different features of environmental change.* The environmental improvements attributable to the Industrial Revolution have often been confused with those introduced by the sanitary reformers. It is admittedly not always easy to separate these influences, but it is essential to do so.

(4) *Failure to distinguish between different kinds of medical improvements.* Many discussions of the contribution of medicine to the decline of mortality fail to distinguish between specific therapy applied to the individual, and hygienic improvements in the environment.

Our task in interpreting population growth in a developed country is twofold: first, to assess the relative importance of birth rate and death rate; and second, to account for the significant features of the behavior of the two rates.

Before tackling this task we should recognize its difficulties. There are no data which put the issues beyond dispute, nor are they likely to become available. It is true that many countries are awaiting both the industrial and the sanitary revolutions with the accompanying improvement in standard of living, literacy, and health. But we shall not see a repetition of the unique set of circumstances which existed in Western Europe between the late eighteenth century and the beginning of the twentieth. Both the time and manner in which the changes occur must be profoundly altered by the increased knowledge of the past hundred years, and by the existence of other countries at a more advanced stage of development. The choice, therefore, is not between a correct and an incorrect answer; it is between the best answer that can be given and none at all. This being so, many natural scientists will no doubt prefer to leave historical research of this kind to others with a greater tolerance of uncertainty.

THE RELATIVE IMPORTANCE OF BIRTH RATE AND DEATH RATE

Figure 1 shows in simplified form the levels of birth rate, death rate, and population in England and Wales (a) as we believe them to have been before registration (in 1838), and (b)

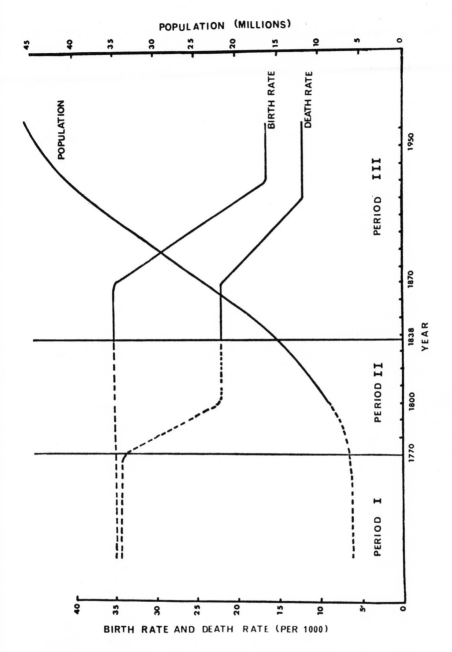

Fig. 1. Diagramatic representation of birth rate, death rate, and population in England and Wales since the eighteenth century.

27

as we know them to have been after registration. In assessing the contribution of birth rate and death rate to growth of population it is best to consider separately three periods in which the issues are different: before 1770, 1770–1838, and after 1838. For different reasons the relative importance of the birth rate and death rate are not in doubt in the first and third intervals and the uncertainities—to which a considerable literature is devoted—are chiefly in respect of the middle period.

Period I: Before 1770

From the Norman Conquest until the eighteenth century the population of England and Wales increased very slowly. Hence in spite of sharp fluctuations from year to year, over any considerable period the margin of births over deaths must have been very small. There is also no doubt that in general both rates were high, and that the chief cause of death was infectious disease.

Period II: 1770–1838

From 1770 the population increased rapidly and it is evident that a considerable excess of births over deaths had been established. The lack of reliable numerical evidence accounts for the differences of opinion about whether the rise of population was due initially to a decline of the death rate or to an increase of the birth rate.

Until recently it was widely believed that the most important influence was a decline of mortality, attributable to medical advances during the eighteenth century.[2] There are no grounds for this view, and the relative importance of birth rate or death rate must again be regarded as an open question.[3]

Those who believe that the birth rate was the more important influence are impressed with the effect of economic conditions on it. They recognize that the frequency of marriage appears not to have changed much in the second half of the eighteenth century,[4] but draw attention to the high correlation between marriage

2. *Ibid.*
3. H. J. Habakkuk, ''English Population in the Eighteenth Century,'' *Economic History Review*, Second Series, VI (1953), pp. 117–133; T. McKeown and R. G. Brown, ''Medical Evidence Related to English Population Changes in the Eighteenth Century,'' *Population Studies*, IX (1955), pp. 119–141.
4. Griffith, *op. cit.*; T. H. Marshall, ''The Population Problem During the Industrial Revolution,'' *Economic Journal* (1929), p. 444.

rates and economic conditions (as indicated by real wages).[5] It is suggested that men postpone age of marriage when economic conditions are bad and advance it when they are good; hence an increase in the birth rate in the eighteenth century is attributed to a reduction of age of marriage encouraged by the opportunities for employment offered by the Industrial Revolution. This interpretation is believed to be supported by experience in certain preindustrial societies such as late eighteenth-century France, colonial America and Ireland in the late eighteenth and early nineteenth centuries.[6]

Those who believe that a decline of the death rate was a more important influence on the size of population in the eighteenth century start from a somewhat different viewpoint. In the first place they find it hard to believe that a reduction of age of marriage could have had a substantial effect on population growth in a period when the birth rate was already high. There are several grounds for reservation.

(1) *The difference between age of husband and age of wife at marriage increases as husband's age advances.* This is merely a complicated if more precise way of saying that when men postpone marriage they tend to marry women younger than themselves. The effect of postponement or advancement on fertility, which depends mainly on the wife's age, is therefore reduced.

(2) *The reduction of fertility of women with increasing age is less marked than it is commonly thought to be.*[7] This is because our observations on the trend of fertility with age are almost exclusively from a period when the relationship has been obscured by the practice of contraception.

(3) *Since the late nineteenth century, when age at marriage was first recorded nationally, it has not changed very much.*[8]

(4) *In the eighteenth century, when mortality was high because a substantial proportion of children died soon after birth, an increase in the birth rate would have had relatively*

5. D. V. Glass, ''Marriage Frequency and Economic Fluctuations in England and Wales, 1851 to 1934,'' *Political Arithmetic*, ed. L. Hogben (London, 1938), p. 266.

6. Habakkuk, *op. cit.*

7. D. V. Glass and E. Grebenik, *The Trend and Pattern of Fertility in Great Britain*, Part I (London, 1954), p. 271.

8. 74th Annual Report of the Registrar-General (London, 1911), Table VII, p. xvii; General Register Office, *Statistical Review, Tables, Part II, Civil,* 1951 (London, 1953), Table 1, p. 71.

little effect on population growth if mortality remained un-changed. A less obvious, but not less important consideration is that mortality from infectious diseases increases sharply with increasing family size.[9] Marriage rates were high in the eighteenth century and an increase in the birth rate would have been due chiefly to addition of children to existing families, rather than to an increase in the number of one-child families. Hence any increase in the birth rate would have been offset largely by an increase in postnatal mortality.

Our own view is that a decline of mortality was the more important influence.[10] Behind the controversy concerning birth rate and death rate, however, lies what is in some respects a more fundamental question: What was the reason for the disturbance of either rate? We shall return to this question in the next section.

Period III: After 1838

From 1838 national statistics put the position of the two rates beyond dispute. A considerable excess of births over deaths had been established before 1838 and has continued until the present time. The birth rate remained high until about 1870 when it began to fall. Mortality also remained fairly constant until the eighth decade of the nineteenth century when it too began to fall.

THE DECLINE OF MORTALITY

We have concluded that a decline of mortality is the more plausible explanation of the initial rise of population in the late eighteenth century, and certainly accounts for the continued increase after 1870 in the face of a declining birth rate.

Hitherto the causes of the decline of mortality have been considered separately by the economic historian and by the biologist. From the point of view of the economic historian the crucial issue is the interpretation of the relationship between population growth and the Industrial Revolution. He asks: Did the Industrial Revolution create its own labor force?—a pithy

9. J. R. Gibson and T. McKeown, ''Observations on All Births (23,970) in Birmingham, 1947, VII. The Effect of Changing Family Size on Infant Mortality,'' *British Journal of Social Medicine*, VI (1952), pp. 183–187.
10. McKeown and Brown, *op. cit.*

way of inquiring whether it resulted in improved economic conditions which led to an expansion of population. Or was the growth of population which assisted the Industrial Revolution due to some other cause essentially independent of it? As we have seen, the traditional answer attributed the rise of population to a decline of mortality caused by medical measures.[11] This conclusion rested on little evidence, but so long as it was accepted it seemed unnecessary to look further for an explanation of the trend of mortality.

The approach of biologists to the same issues has been quite different. They have been interested particularly in the behavior of individual infectious diseases and a considerable literature has been devoted to discussion of possible reasons for the decline of mortality from tuberculosis, smallpox, typhus, scarlet fever, typhoid, and other infections. The biologist has not had the incentive of the economic historian to explain the behavior of mortality as a whole, and while by remaining silent he may seem to have endorsed Griffith's explanation,[12] he has really ignored it. Medical achievement has not been a theme of medical history in the way that population growth has been a theme of economic history.

If pressed to give reasons why consideration of the behavior of infectious disease is not carried further, many biologists would probably feel that the difficulties are too great. Attempts have been made to determine which diseases contributed to the decline of mortality, but they have stopped short of an assessment of the relative importance of influences which affected the trend of mortality as a whole. The subject is admittedly complex, requiring evaluation of such different influences as genetic selection, preventive and curative measures, sanitary science, and a rising standard of living. But it has been made unnecessarily difficult by exaggeration of the contribution of therapy, by the grouping together as "medical advances" of such different elements as specific therapy and sanitary measures and by failure to consider separately trends in the nineteenth and twentieth centuries. In the discussion which follows we shall consider first the period since registration when information

11. Griffith, *op. cit.*
12. *Ibid.*

about cause of death is available from national sources. Within this period we shall be concerned mainly with interpretation in the nineteenth century [13] before venturing an opinion about the twentieth. Finally we shall comment on possible reasons for the decline of mortality before 1838, against the background of our conclusions about the later period.

Mortality since 1838

Five diseases or groups of diseases accounted for the decline of mortality in the nineteenth century after 1838: tuberculosis for a little less than a half; typhus, typhoid and continued fever for about a fifth; scarlet fever for a fifth; cholera, dysentery and diarrhea for nearly a tenth; and smallpox for a twentieth (Table 1). Our conclusions about the reasons for the reduction of mortality from each of these diseases are as follows.

TABLE 1

Mean Annual Mortality Rates per 1,000,000 [a] Due to Certain Communicable Diseases in Decennia 1851–60 and 1891–1900

Cause	1851–60 (a)	1891–1900 (b)	Difference (a)–(b)	Difference per cent of total difference (a–b) 100 / 3,085
Tuberculosis—respiratory	2,772	1,418	1,354	43.9 ⎫ 47.2
Tuberculosis—other forms	706	603	103	3.3 ⎭
Typhus, enteric fever, simple continued fever	891	184	707	22.9
Scarlet fever	779	152	627	20.3
Diarrhea, dysentery, cholera	990	715	275	8.9
Smallpox	202	13	189	6.1
Whooping cough	433	363	70	2.3
Measles	357	398	−41	−1.3
Diphtheria	99	254	−155	−5.0
Other causes	13,980	14,024	−44	−1.4
Total	21,209	18,124	3,085	100

[a] Standardized to age and sex distribution of 1901 population.

13. T. McKeown and R. G. Record, "Reasons for the Decline of Mortality in England and Wales during the Nineteenth Century," *Population Studies*, XVI (1962), pp. 94–122.

Tuberculosis. Mortality from tuberculosis began to fall in the fifth decade, at least 30 years earlier than in the case of the other major infections. Experience of the preregistration period is less certain, although there is no serious doubt that mortality from the disease was very high during the previous three centuries.

It is quite certain that specific therapy, preventive or curative, made no contribution to the course of tuberculosis before the twentieth century. In the case of an infectious disease it is never possible to be confident that there has been no change in the balance between the virulence of the organism and the resistance of the host. But there is reason to believe that there has been no significant variation in the tubercle bacillus. Man's resistance to it is a more difficult issue. The fact that the population has been heavily exposed to the infection for several centuries makes it unlikely that genetic selection could explain the favorable trend in the nineteenth century, unless it resulted from contact with the disease for the first time by a large part of the rural population which had not been exposed previously. The movement into the towns was too late to be consistent with this possibility, which in any case could not have been expected to have so profound and prolonged an effect on the death rate.

Having excluded therapy confidently and genetic selection with reservations (we have concluded only that it is very unlikely to have been the main influence), we are left with changes in the environment as the most acceptable reason for the trend of mortality from tuberculosis. There are four features of the environment to be considered—conditions of exposure to the disease, diet, and physical and mental stress—and in the circumstances of the nineteenth century only the first two of them need be considered seriously. Exposure to infection is determined mainly by crowding at home or at work; it must have increased in the first half of the nineteenth century and was not significantly reduced before its close.

The evidence in respect of diet is highly suggestive. The increase in tuberculosis mortality in both world wars is most plausibly attributed to a deterioration of nutrition. And in the nineteenth century, the time at which we can be fairly confident that mortality began to decline rapidly—the fifth decade—is also the time when we can be reasonably certain that the standard of living began to improve. But although a better diet is not the only consequence of a higher standard of living, it is probably the one which is relevant in this context, as there was no significant reduction in crowding at home or at work. We conclude that improvement in diet was probably the main cause of the decline of mortality from tuberculosis during the nineteenth century.

Typhus, enteric, and simple continued fever. Because they were not separated in national statistics before 1871, these ill-assorted diseases are grouped together. But the data are given separately for the last three decades, and in this period mortality from enteric fever was reduced by about half and the other two causes of death almost disappeared.

Interpretation of the behavior of typhus is complicated by the fact that its prevalence varied greatly at different periods, and it is impossible to say to what extent this was attributable to environmental or genetic change. Nevertheless, it is generally agreed that the disappearance of the disease from the British Isles, many years before identification of the body louse as the vector, was due largely to an improved standard of living. But although a good deal is now known about the nature of the disease and the way in which it is spread, it is still difficult to assess the relative importance of various features of the environment affected by the standard of living. It seems probable, however, that the two main influences were: (a) improved hygienic standards—particularly an improved water supply and better personal cleanliness—which prevented infection by reducing contact with the louse; and (b) better diet, which affected the response to infection. The first of these influences would have begun to operate in the eighth decade, and the second somewhat earlier.

There is little difficulty in interpretation of the behavior of typhoid fever. The spread of the disease is due to defective sanitary arrangements, and the rapid reduction of mortality during the last third of the nineteenth century can be attributed confidently to the specific measures—particularly the improved water supply—introduced at that time.

Continued fever still appears in the international classification, where it refers to pyrexias of unknown origin. In the nineteenth century they must have comprised a very mixed group, including undiagnosed respiratory infections such as tuberculosis, as well as other fevers in which a rash was either absent or unrecognized. In view of the fact that they were not shown separately before 1871 we can only guess about their earlier behavior. But since the whole group (typhus, enteric, and continued fever) began to decline sharply in the eighth decade, perhaps the most reasonable guess is that the trend was due to the specific hygienic measures which were also responsible for the reduction of mortality from typhus and enteric fever.

Scarlet fever.   Views concerning interpretation of the trend of mortality from scarlet fever are perhaps more consistent than in the case of any other infectious disease. No specific measures of prevention of treatment were available in the nineteenth century, and the only possibilities are environmental improvement or a change in the nature of the disease.

Scarlet fever has exhibited at least four cycles of severity followed by remission.[14] These changes appear to have been largely independent of environmental changes and there is no reason to differ from the general opinion that they resulted from a modification of the nature of the disease. This was probably due mainly to variation in the virulence of the hemolytic streptococcus rather than to a change in man's response to it.

Cholera, dysentery, and diarrhea.   Although the bowel infections were grouped in national statistics before 1871, cholera must be distinguished from the endemic diseases referred to as diarrhea and dysentery. Cholera was not endemic in the British Isles, and was introduced from the continent of Europe at least five times during the nineteenth century, but apparently not before. It is therefore not possible to speak of the reasons for its disappearance with quite the same confidence as in the case of the other causes of death.

But with this reservation there is little doubt about the main reasons for the rapid reduction of mortality from the bowel infections in the late nineteenth century. These diseases are spread mainly by infected water and food, and their decline

14. H. S. Banks, *The Common Infectious Diseases* (London, 1949), p. 52.

began in the eighth decade when substantial improvement in hygienic conditions also began. There are no grounds for thinking that either therapy or (with a possible reservation in the case of cholera) modification of the nature of the disease made any impact. We conclude that the reduction of mortality attributable to the decline of bowel infection resulted from the specific measures introduced under the sanitary revolution.

Smallpox. Since the contribution of smallpox to the reduction of mortality was small, the reasons for it are of secondary importance in interpretation of the causes of the total decline. This is the one disease in which a specific measure—vaccination —appears to have made a substantial contribution and the only difficulty is to decide how large it was. The fact that the disease, present for several centuries, virtually disappeared from the time when vaccination became compulsory suggests that this was the main reason for its decline.

To sum up: In order of their relative importance the influences responsible for the decline of mortality in the second half of the nineteenth century were: (a) a rising standard of living, of which the most significant feature was improved diet (responsible mainly for the decline of tuberculosis and less certainly, and to a lesser extent, of typhus); (b) the hygienic changes introduced by the sanitary reformers (responsible for the decline of the typhus-typhoid and cholera groups); and (c) a favorable trend in the relationship between infectious agent and the human host (which accounted for the decline of mortality from scarlet fever and may have contributed to that from tuberculosis, typhus, and cholera). The effect of therapy was restricted to smallpox and hence had only a trivial effect on the total reduction of the death rate.

Evaluation of the reasons for the decline of the death rate becomes much more difficult after 1900. The most striking feature of the trend since that time has been the decline of infant mortality (that is, mortality of live born children within the first year of life). It is a remarkable feature of the improvement in mortality during the nineteenth century that it appears not to have affected this age group,[15] and at the turn of the century about 150 of every 1,000 children born in England and Wales

15. McKeown and Record, *op. cit.*

still died within a year of birth. By the midcentury the deaths were reduced to 30 and in the last available records (for 1962) there were only 21. The reduction of mortality in other age periods, and particularly in middle and late life, has been much less impressive.

Assessment of reasons for the decline of infant mortality, and still more of mortality at all ages, would require a close investigation of different causes of death which has not yet been attempted. Several developments in the twentieth century have made this task more complicated than it was in the nineteenth. In the first place there has been an extension, amounting almost to a remaking, of medical and related social services. The personal medical services concerned with school health and maternity and child welfare were developed progressively from 1806. The relative importance of the varied measures—cheap food, routine inspection of children, advice about health and treatment—embraced by these services is still uncertain, but there can be little doubt that together they contributed significantly to the amelioration of health. In the same period the standard of living continued to rise and was supported by improvement in the social services. Further advances were made in the control of the physical environment which had been launched so effectively in the second half of the nineteenth century. And finally specific measures of preventing and treating disease in the individual began to fulfil the much heralded but long delayed promise of clinical medicine.

There is indeed considerable justification for the view that without a much more careful investigation—and some might feel even with it—it is impossible to express any worthwhile opinion about the relative importance of the influences that have contributed to the improvement in health during the twentieth century. But the problem is more tractable if we consider the period since 1838 as a whole. A substantial part of the total reduction of mortality occurred during the nineteenth century, and we are on firm ground in attributing it almost exclusively to the rising standard of living and the control of the physical environment. Both have continued to advance since 1900, and unquestionably they have contributed powerfully to the improvement of health since that time. Without denying the value of the personal health services, or of the specific therapy which has been a notable achievement of the past 40 years, it seems right to conclude that in order of relative importance the main influences responsible for the decline of mortality—our best index of improved health—since deaths were first registered in 1838 have been: a rising standard of living, sanitary measures, and specific preventive and curative therapy.

Mortality before 1838

Finally we must inquire whether our conclusions about events since registration help us to understand what happened in the earlier period for which national records of births and deaths are not available. Since we are satisfied that therapy made no significant contribution there are two possibilities to be considered: modification of the character of infectious diseases and changes in the environment.

There is no reason to doubt that some infections may have declined during the eighteenth century, as scarlet fever has been observed to do more than once since then, as a consequence of a change in the organism or of man's genetically-determined resistance to it. But it hardly seems credible that a change of this kind, occurring at the same time in a number of major infectious diseases, could alone account for the remarkable increase of population between 1700 and 1851. Moreover we should have to believe that both the coincidence of this increase with the Industrial Revolution, and its continuity with the growth of population after 1850 when the rising standard of living is not in doubt) were purely fortuitous. It is more reasonable to accept the view of those economic historians who believe that the standard of living improved at an earlier date.[16]

It seems natural to assume that the change in the environment —the second possibility to which we are led by exclusion of the

16. J. H. Clapham, *An Economic History of Modern Britain—I. The Early Railway Age 1820–1850* (Cambridge, 1926), pp. 128, 561; T. S. Ashton, "The Standard of Life of the Workers in England, 1790–1830," *Capitalism and the Historians*, ed. F. A. Hayek (London, 1954), pp. 127–159; T. S. Ashton, "Changes in Standards of Comfort in Eighteenth Century England," *Proceedings of the British Academy*, XLI (1955), pp. 171–187; R. M. Hartwell, "The Rising Standard of Living in England 1800–1850," *The Economic History Review*, Second Series XIII (1961), pp. 397–416; A. J. Taylor, "Progress and Poverty in Britain, 1780–1850," *Essays in Economic History*, ed. E. M. Carus-Wilson, III (London, 1962), pp. 380–393.

first—must have been an improvement. Yet it is sometimes proposed that, on the contrary, health got better because the environment got worse. The suggestion is that the deteriorated hygienic conditions which resulted from the Industrial Revolution led to death of individuals susceptible to infection, and hence to survival of a fitter population. (We should note that this change in the organism/host relationship is not identical to the one already discussed, since it is attributed to environmental influence rather than to spontaneous change. The distinction is, of course, one only of degree, since the relationship is always influenced by the environment in which it exists, and is therefore only in a restricted sense spontaneous.) If we accept this suggestion we should have to believe that we owe the tremendous advance in health between 1700 and 1851 to unhygienic conditions, and that to achieve a similar advance in underdeveloped countries today it is only necessary to make conditions worse than they already are.

The question remains whether and in what way the environment improved. Undoubtedly the physical environment of the industrial town deteriorated, and the most plausible answer is that it offered better opportunities for employment and hence an improved diet. There are some who find even this difficult to accept. Was it not always possible to lift a cabbage or chicken in rural England when one was hungry as a former colleague assures me is now possible in rural Wales? If so why did people leave Goldsmith's deserted village for Engel's industrial town? Wordsworth's poem "The Reverie of Poor Susan" provides a touching reminder that they were not attracted by the glamor of town life.

We conclude that the advance in health since the eighteenth century has been due to a rising standard of living from about 1770, sanitary measures from 1878, and therapy from the second quarter of the twentieth century.

THE CONTROL OF POPULATION GROWTH

Finally we must inquire whether our explanation of the rise of population in a developed country throws any light on the contemporary problem of control of population growth. In England and Wales a rising standard of living was the earliest and most powerful influence on size of population. (This is true whether it was exerted mainly on mortality, as we believe, or on the birth rate, as some economic historians suggest.) After about a century it was reinforced by sanitary measures; but their effect on growth of population was offset by a coincident decline of the birth rate. The improved standard of living was both the most important cause of the increase of population and, indirectly, the means of bringing it under control.

In developing countries this order of events is being changed. With present knowledge it is quicker and cheaper to apply sanitary measures than to raise living standards. But sanitary measures do not lead to reduction of the birth rate; hence the urgent need to find some other means of restricting family size in illiterate populations. There are two possibilities which can be explored singly or in combination: to raise the level of literacy, or to devise techniques of birth control suitable for use by the illiterate.

Because time and money are needed to raise the level of literacy, the emphasis so far has been on refinements of techniques, such as chemical contraceptives. But all methods of lowering the birth rate require individual action (unlike methods of lowering the death rate, which can be applied by public action). In developed countries a reduction of the birth rate has occurred when a certain stage of literacy has been reached and nowhere has a reduction preceded it. Moreover the reduction did not depend mainly on improved contraceptive methods, but on the use of traditional methods which were applied once the desirability of restricting family size had been recognized. Similarly in developing countries, experience has suggested that if illiterate women are to control their reproduction by counting beads they must first learn to count.

It is possible therefore that the main requirement for control of population growth in developing countries today is not improved methods of contraception which can be used by the illiterate. It is a general recognition of the need for reduction of family size. When this need is recognized the birth rate will be lowered without improved techniques; until it is recognized it is unlikely that improved techniques will be effective. If this interpretation is correct the problem must be solved, not in the laboratory, but in the native village.

Judith Blake

DEMOGRAPHIC SCIENCE AND THE
REDIRECTION OF POPULATION POLICY

In recent years informed laymen as well as demographers have become increasingly convinced that poor but densely settled countries must achieve a successful demographic revolution and a rapid one. Although consensus on this goal is nearing unanimity, persons equally committed to it frequently disagree about how it is to be achieved. In fact, policy aimed at reducing rates of population growth in developing countries has become bipolarized. One group tends to say that decreases in family size will occur only as an end-product of advanced economic and social development which, in due time, will lead to a desire for fewer children. The other group is inclined to bypass the institutional setting of reproduction entirely and assume that education and communication respecting birth control will eventually reduce births to a level consonant with low mortality. Yet these approaches do not appear to be adequate in fact or in theory when taken alone, or even in some combination. Consequently additional strategies designed to solve the dilemma of population growth are needed. This can be seen by examining each position and the objections to it.

The development school of thought emphasizes that motives for a transition from high to low birth rates such as occurred in presently industrial countries were contingent not only on declines in mortality, but also on changes in the social and economic organization that previously had led individuals to desire numerous births. Without such changes (and in spite of mortality declines) individuals would have continued to attach independent importance to institutionalized roles, activities, and goals that directly or indirectly provided the motivational underpinning for many offspring. Hence, it is claimed, changes similar to the industrial and urban revolutions of the Western world must occur in developing countries if their family structures are to alter and a wish for drastically curtailed reproduction is to evolve. Policy must therefore be directed at accelerating overall social and economic development which, in turn, will indirectly affect the family and reproduction. The most that can be expected by way of directly reducing family size is to spread birth control knowledge and means among crucial groups (such as educated urban elites) where desires for smaller families may already exist.

This position is clearly open to objections of both a scientific and practical nature. For instance, it can be argued that social structures are far less tightly integrated than the theory just outlined presupposes. Since all societies have visible lines of cleavage, strain, and vulnerability, important social changes can occur without a complete socioeconomic revolution. Particular sectors of the population such as the young, the females, the peasants, or the outcastes may be so chronically dissatisfied that they are eager to experiment if the opportunity arises. In actual fact, many developing countries have undergone enormous, if piecemeal, changes in recent years. These changes have typically been accelerated by the importation of technical knowledge and assistance, the rapidity and influence of which should not be underestimated.[1] We therefore hesitate, on purely empirical grounds, to assume that these societies do not have their own internal sources of motivation for change, and that these cannot

1. For a discussion of the multiphasic theory of demographic change, see K. Davis, "The Theory of Change and Response in Modern Demographic History," *Population Index*, XXIX (Oct., 1963), pp. 345–366.

be stimulated to an unprecedented degree by close contact and cooperation with more modern societies.[2] From a practical standpoint, the objections to exclusive reliance on the ''development approach'' center on the appalling dilemma it poses. If birth rates will not decline markedly prior to industrialization and modernization, what will happen if the latter are effectively slowed down, as seem to be the case, by the very malady they are supposed to cure—population growth itself? A shift back to higher levels of mortality is, of course, the answer, and it is one that few people are willing to accept without a struggle.

Many thoughtful persons have, therefore, been induced to advocate demographic strategies more directly geared to affecting reproduction. Unfortunately, so little systematic thought and analysis have been devoted to the presuppositions involved and the possible alternatives available that this more direct population policy has fallen into what appears to be an intuitively ''obvious'' course of action. The assumption is made that high birth rates in developing countries are today primarily a result of unwanted births. On this assumption, population policy has recently taken the form of an intensive planned parenthood campaign for contraceptive education and distribution. Such policy seems to have gone beyond a modification of the sociological and economic assumptions of the ''development'' approach to the pole of ignoring them altogether. It is hardly surprising that this extreme course of action is not leading to marked reductions in birth rates and rates of population growth among the illiterate, rural masses that predominate in developing countries.[3] In fact, because family size desires are so substantial in these countries, primary reliance on inhibiting the births in excess of these desires may have little effect on birth rates under conditions of relatively high mortality, and no effect on present population growth rates if mortality declines. This dilemma requires some systematic consideration.

2. See, for example, K. Davis, ''Fertility Control and the Demographic Transition in India,'' *The Interrelations of Demographic, Economic, and Social Problems in Selected Underdeveloped Areas* (New York: Milbank Memorial Fund, 1954), pp. 65–89.

3. D. J. Bogue, ''Some Tentative Recommendations for a 'Sociologically Correct' Family Planning Communication and Motivation Program in India,'' *Research in Family Planning*, ed. C. V. Kiser (Princeton: Princeton University Press, 1962), p. 503.

In countries like India mortality is declining enough to provide a high rate of demographic increase—as far as we know, over two per cent annually. But even so, mortality remains shockingly high, and improvements may be spotty. Although surveys show that Indians normally desire three, four, or five children, it is still true that in India many births are required to guarantee this result. Presumably Indian parents want their children to survive at least through their own reproductive periods. This dependency of birth-reducing motives on confidence in mortality improvements is widely recognized as a principal reason for the lack of success to date of family planning programs.[4]

But even if continuously spectacular improvements in mortality were to be made and births were proportionately reduced, population growth rates would remain high unless the *desired size of the planned families* were itself greatly curtailed. Developing peoples may not wish to have an unlimited number of offspring, but survey data gathered so far do not turn up excessively modest family-size desires either. For example, available data on ideal family size in India show that the mass of the people prefer an average of close to four (presumably surviving) children.[5] Moreover, high proportions (30–45 per cent) either refuse to answer the question or are not asked it,

---

4. *Ibid.*, p. 528. Although the direction of the relationship is not made clear, E. D. Driver presents for Central India some suggestive data on births and child mortality. He shows that the larger the number of births in a family the larger the proportion of children who have died. Doubtless some of this association is due to the independent effect of high fertility on child mortality as well as to the fact that large families will have older children who may have lived out a normal adult span for India and then died. The ages at death were not recorded. See E. D. Driver, *Differential Fertility in Central India* (Princeton: Princeton University Press, 1963), Chap. 6. For a discussion of the "realization lag" respecting mortality, see H. Leibenstein, *Economic Backwardness and Economic Growth* (New York: Wiley, 1957), p. 166.

5. See, for example, Driver, *op. cit.*, Chap. 6. In this study 30 per cent of the couples had no interest at all in limiting the size of their families. This percentage ranged from 23 per cent for couples where the wife was under 25, to 38 per cent where she was 45 or more. The data on ideal family size were only obtained from the couples interested in limiting. Also, United Nations, *The Mysore Population Study* (New York: United Nations, Population Studies No. 34, 1961), Chaps. 9–12; V. M. and K. Dandekar, *Survey of Fertility and Mortality in Poona District* (Poona: Gokhale Institute, 1953), Chap. 7; close to one half of the respondents in both urban and rural districts answered in terms of "any number" or that they "could not say."

often because they do not wish even to consider limiting births. The averages may therefore have a downward bias, although a countervailing tendency for subfecund couples to refuse to answer may also exist. In Latin America, the four-child preference has also been found in a large study of Santiago, Chile and in Taiwan, Freedman and his colleagues have found four children to be the ideal.[6] In all these cases, such an average typically means that close to 60 per cent of the respondents consider four *or more* children to be ideal. To be sure, these desires represent a wish for a family of only moderate size, and in general the ideals are lower than the actual numbers of births, but for reducing population growth under conditions of low mortality the desires are not low enough. They are on the whole somewhat higher than the actual family size of the overseas European countries (the United States, Canada, Australia, and New Zealand) and these countries have been experiencing population growth rates which, if continued, will result in a doubling of their populations every 30–40 years. Family-size aspirations such as these among peoples who characteristically marry and reproduce even earlier than overseas Europeans, will, if realized in practice, result in higher rates of population growth (at comparable mortality levels), because the mean length of a generation is shorter thereby allowing more generations to be squeezed into a given unit of time.

Can family planning programs solve this dilemma by introducing not only contraceptive means but more modest family-size desires? In answer we can only say that to date we have no compelling reason to believe that developing peoples will ever be merely propagandized or "educated" into wanting really small families—slightly more than two children on the average—regardless of the level of mortality. It does not seem as if their desires for larger families will succumb to flipcharts, flannelboards, message movies, group leaders, or "explanations"

6. L. Tabah and R. Samuel, "Preliminary Findings of a Survey on Fertility and Attitudes Toward Family Formation in Santiago, Chile," *Research in Family Planning*, ed. C. V. Kiser (Princeton: Princeton University Press, 1962), pp. 289–91. Out of 1,970 respondents only 12 did not answer and 14 said "an unlimited number." Also, R. Freedman, J. Y. Peng, Y. Takeshita, and T. H. Sun, "Fertility Trends in Taiwan: Tradition and Change," *Population Studies*, XVI (March, 1963), p. 232.

about the "advantages" of few children. As we shall see, this expectation is so discontinuous with our existing knowledge of the institutionalization of reproduction as to be virtually incongruous.

Have we then exhausted the alternatives available for reducing population growth by means of direct policy? The answer is, I think, that we have not yet begun to explore them. But if we are to bring them to light, we must review what is known of reproductive motivation through research concerning family-size declines and present levels in industrial countries. In doing so we shall find that an analysis in terms of the social and economic factors affecting reproduction does not necessarily only result in indirect choices for population policy such as economic development. This type of analysis is just as capable of generating possibilities for direct action regarding family size.

HISTORICAL PERSPECTIVES ON FAMILY SIZE

Concomitant with improved mortality, the desire for smaller families among Western industrializing peoples appears to have resulted from a complex of factors (among them urbanization, increased opportunities for social mobility, separation of work from residence, compulsory education, child labor laws) that diminished the economic utility of offspring (as income producers and security in old age) leaving simply their noneconomic utility for parents to take into account. This complex not only decreased the range of utilities but augmented the costs of children, both direct and indirect. Parents had to undergo increased direct costs such as those for compulsory education, food, recreation, and space in crowded urban circumstances. They also suffered an extension of indirect or opportunity costs since expanding economies offered them unprecedented opportunities for upward mobility and investment, and a modern, urban, middle-class way of life opened up virtually unlimited nondomestic avenues of recreation and interest.[7] In sum, this

7. This highly generalized statement of the elements in declining family-size goals may be found in Leibenstein, *op. cit.*, Chap. 10. Other statements of the same basic idea by sociologists and demographers have usually been in terms of particular features of modernization—urbanization, educational levels, social mobility, etc.—

account amounts to a delineation of how modernizing and urbanizing societies affected the family and its articulations with socioeconomic structure, and how couples reacted by altering the number of their "hostages to fortune." [8]

In utilizing this outline of Western experience for clues as to the determinants of very modest family-size ideals, we must however beware of two potential fallacies: the *particularistic fallacy* and the *economic fallacy*. The particularistic fallacy occurs when one turns one's attention entirely to the associations between particular variables—urbanization, education, social mobility—and declining family-size goals, instead of utilizing the associations to trace out the basic and more general mechanisms involved. Thus our real concern seems to be with factors making children more and more useless to parents and increasingly expensive (both directly and indirectly). The exact nature of these factors will necessarily vary between historical periods and among societies, although we may expect to find some recognizable patterns and repetitions. But we must be sensitized to search for this common element of decreased utilities and increased costs in a wide diversity of events. Otherwise, we are operating in demography as epidemiologists did prior to bacteriology—we mistake the vector for the agent. [9]

On the other hand, although the framework of utilities and

------

and have seldom attempted to differentiate clearly among utilities, direct costs, and opportunity costs. See, for example, F. W. Notestein, ''The Economics of Population and Food Supplies,'' *Proceedings of the Eighth International Conference of Agricultural Economists* (London: Oxford University Press, 1953), pp. 13–31, and by the same author, ''Population—The Long View,'' *Food for the World*, ed. T. W. Schultz (Chicago: University of Chicago Press, 1945). For recent efforts to document the important role played by opportunity costs, see, J. A. Banks, *Prosperity and Parenthood* (London: Routledge and Kegan Paul, 1954) and K. Davis, ''The Theory of Change and Response in Modern Demographic History,'' *Population Index*, XXIX (Oct., 1963), pp. 345–366, and, by the same author, ''Population,'' *Scientific American*, CCIX (Sept., 1963), pp. 63–71.

8. The theory also accounts for other related adjustments such as delayed marriage and nonmarriage, but these need not concern us here. The phrase ''hostages to fortune'' is Francis Bacon's, from *Essays or Counsels, Civil and Moral* (1625).

9. This in effect has been one of the principal criticisms of so-called ''demographic transition theory,'' namely that it represents a more or less unweighted and nonspecific collection of associations between broad social trends and fertility (as well as mortality) with little attempt to assess common factors and their actual connection with fertility. See L. Van Nort and B. P. Karon, ''Demographic Transition Re-Examined,'' *American Sociological Review*, XX (Oct., 1955), pp. 523–527.

costs outlined above is reasonable as far as it goes, it becomes very limited in its applicability if we are led to assume that the *noneconomic* utilities of offspring are somehow not very important or meaningful, as is implied when we say that children have become mere "items of consumption." If we fall into this line of reasoning, then we are expecting the theory to explain some of the most social aspects of human motivation, without giving these aspects independent status in the formulation. Thus, as the theory is stated in the "economic development" school of thought, the family plays an almost completely passive role in the formulation. It is assumed throughout that the family is acted upon and that it only indirectly affects individual calculation regarding familial investment. Yet one can readily point out that the family has powerful sources of resistance to its own demise. Socialization is not simply "a function" that the family "performs" for "the society," it is a primary mechanism of indoctrination and control. Individuals who are socialized in families will be likely to want families themselves, to enforce norms and sanctions regarding families, and to take pleasure in acting out familial roles. This means that the family complex is itself a goal—the utilities represented by children are not merely economic or affectional but socially structured in a powerful manner. Moreover, societies with long familial traditions have powerful sanctioning and ideological systems which help to keep parents from being discouraged by direct reproductive costs, or distracted by indirect ones. It is hardly surprising therefore that in its purely economic form the theory led social scientists to extreme conclusions. The idea arose that the desire for children was on the way to disappearing altogether from Western societies, and this expectation made the subsequent "baby boom" a source of never-to-be-forgotten embarrassment.

Unfortunately, the lesson of the reproductive renaissance seems to have concluded with the rediscovery that social institutions like the family are adaptive to change and hence (without direct intervention) are neither transformed readily nor obliterated rapidly. The relevance of family-size declines up to the "baby boom" is not extended to an analysis of possibilities for further declines in family size—that is, from moderate to small numbers of offspring. This disjuncture is due primarily to the inability of the theory, when stated in purely economic terms, to deal with variability within the moderate to small family range. Such variation is categorized as "short-term fluctuation," and no long-term institutional determinants of small families are postulated.[10] This truncating of the theory is, moreover, buttressed by the fact that long-term and widespread institutional influences leading to small families may well not actually exist in any major societies today. Even if this is the case, it does not argue against the scientific and practical advantages of extending the theory to logical closure. In fact, even if it appears that modern, industrial societies typically generate desires for a moderate, rather than a small family, this very fact should give us some insights into the types of factors that to date *prevent* families from stablizing at few children. Let us examine then one of the principal existing differences in fertility among modernized countries—the family-size differential between Western European and overseas European countries (the so-called "frontier" countries).

FAMILY SIZE VARIATIONS AMONG MODERNIZED PEOPLES— WESTERN EUROPE AND THE OVERSEAS COUNTRIES

For some years the overseas or "frontier" countries (the United States, Canada, Australia, and New Zealand) have been exhibiting a noticeable difference from Western Europe in family-size ideals and desires, as well as in actual family size itself. Table 1 indicates that with the possible exception of the Netherlands, Western Europeans for whom we have data consider between two and three children "ideal," whereas respondents in the frontier countries are more inclined to place their ideals at three to four offspring. Moreover, the difference in proportions replying in terms of two or more children between the two sets of countries is striking.

10. For example, Leibenstein, *op. cit.*, p. 169, only discusses the theory with reference to the demographic revolution up to the point of achieving some undefined level of relatively low fertility. He says, "This point refers to the stage at which per capita output is quite high, considerably beyond the subsistence level, and where the economy has overcome the major obstacles to sustained growth. Usually, this is a point at which the gap between mortality and fertility rates closes gradually. In this situation the business cycle is likely to be a significant determinant of economic and social phenomena. Since we are not concerned, in this essay, with short-term fluctuations we shall not enter into analysis of fertility determinants under such circumstances."

TABLE 1

Ideal Number of Children. Selected Western European and Overseas European Countries at Various Survey Dates, 1936–1960

Country	Date	Average ideal number of children *	Per cent saying 4 or more
Austria	1960 [b]	2.0	4.0
Belgium	1952 [a]	2.64	25.0
Finland	1953 [a]	2.84	22.0
France	1944 [a]	3.17	34.0
	1945 [a]	2.92	24.0
	1946 [a]	2.70	20.0
	1947 [a]	2.77	23.0
	1947 [a]	2.88	23.0
	1959–60 [b]	2.77	16.9
Italy	1951 [a]	2.80	19.0
Netherlands	1947 [a]	3.66	46.0
	1960 [b]	3.3	38.7
Norway	1960 [b]	3.1	25.0
Switzerland	1960 [b]	2.9	22.4
Great Britain	1938 [a]	2.94	25.0
	1939 [a]	2.96	29.0
	1944 [a]	3.00	33.0
	1947 [a]	2.84	25.0
	1952 [a]	2.84	26.0
	1960 [b]	2.8	23.2
Sweden	1947 [a]	2.79	22.0
West Germany	1950 [a]	2.21	11.0
	1953 [a]	2.28	11.0
	1958 [c]	2.6	12.0
Australia	1947 [a]	3.79	64.0
Canada	1945 [a]	4.06	60.0
	1947 [a]	3.91	55.0
	1960 [b]	4.2	70.1
United States	1936 [a]	3.17	34.0
	1941 [a]	3.42	41.0
	1945 [a]	3.61	49.0
	1947 [a]	3.37	43.0
	1949 [a]	3.91	63.0
	1953 [a]	3.33	41.0
	1960 [b]	3.6	50.6

[a] J. Stoetzel, "Les attitudes et la conjoncture démographique: la dimension idéale de la famille," *Proceedings of the World Population Conference, 1954*, VI (New York: United Nations, 1955), pp. 1019–1033.

[b] D. V. Glass, "Family Limitation in Europe: A Survey of Recent Studies," *Research in Family Planning*, ed. C. V. Kiser (Princeton: Princeton University Press, 1962), pp. 244–245.

[c] R. Freedman, G. Baumert, and M. Bolte, "Expected Family Size and Family Size Values in West Germany," *Population Studies*, XIII (Nov., 1959), pp. 141-142.

* As reported in original publications cited above.

Turning to recent trends in actual family size we must rely on a series of age-adjusted birth rates (in this case we have used Gross Reproduction Rates [GRR]) to document the trends since the 1950's (Table 2). It is not yet possible to bring together recent cohort data on family size for a large number of the countries in question. The overall contrast between the frontier

TABLE 2

Recent Gross Reproduction Rates for Western European and Overseas European Countries

Western European countries	1955	1956	1957	1958	1959	1960	1961
With rising rates							
Austria	1.08	1.17	1.20	1.23	1.26	1.28	—
Belgium	1.16	1.18	1.19	1.22	1.26	1.24	—
West Germany	1.03	1.08	1.12	1.12	1.16	1.17	—
Netherlands	1.48	1.48	1.50	1.51	1.54	1.52	1.58
Norway	1.33	1.37	1.37	1.38	1.39	1.38	—
Switzerland	1.10	1.12	1.14	1.14	1.15	—	—
England & Wales	1.08	1.15	1.19	1.22	1.23	1.29	—
With stable rates [a]							
Denmark	1.24	1.26	1.24	1.23	1.21	1.24	—
France	1.31	1.30	1.32	1.31	1.34	1.33	—
Sweden	1.09	1.10	1.11	1.08	1.08	1.06	—
With falling rates							
Finland	1.42	1.37	1.38	1.29	1.31	1.29	—
Overseas European countries							
Australia	1.59	1.61	1.66	1.67	1.68	1.68	1.73
Canada	1.86	1.87	1.91	1.89	1.92	1.90	1.87
New Zealand	1.82	1.84	1.89	1.93	1.95	1.97	2.03
United States (whites)	1.67	1.72	1.76	1.73	1.73	1.72	—

[a] This category also used for cases of no discernible trend.
Source: *Population Index,* XXIX (April, 1963), pp. 196–207.

and European countries constitutes about a one-child difference in favor of the overseas group (remembering that the GRR refers to girls only and that the differentials must therefore be roughly doubled). This difference between period data from the two sets of countries seems to be a continuation of earlier trends that were beginning to show up in marriage cohort data from censuses around 1950 (Table 3).

TABLE 3

Number of Live Births per 100 Marriages Existing at Census Date by Duration of Marriage—Around 1950

Western European countries	Census year	Number of years after marriage			
		0–4	5–9	10–14	15–19
Lower than overseas European countries					
Belgium [a]	1947	69	146	182	—
France [b]	1946	84	169	211	231
West Germany [c]	1950	73	137	178	214
Great Britain [d]	1946	57	134	182	209
Norway [e]	1950	81	174	217	240
Switzerland [f]	1950	81	182	221	237
Higher than overseas European countries					
Finland	1950	106	210	274	320
Netherlands [g]	1947	72	200	275	322
Overseas European countries					
Australia [h]	1947	66	164	225	271
United States [i]	1950	79	168	220	253

[a] Includes families headed by a widow or widower, but excludes divorced couples.

[b] First marriages only. Includes marriages where the woman was widowed or divorced at the age of 45 or over. All children born alive to the woman, including children born before marriage.

[c] Federal Republic of Germany excluding Berlin. Including stillbirths. Excludes marriages where the couple was separated, e.g., the husband was missing or a prisoner of war.

[d] First marriages only. Excludes marriages where the woman was 45 or over at marriage. Includes marriages where the woman was widowed or divorced at 45 or over. All children born alive to the woman (including children born before marriage). Adjusted for understatement of childlessness.

[e] Excluding marriages where the woman was aged 45 or over at marriage.

[f] All legitimate and legitimized children born alive.

[g] First marriages only.

[h] Excluding marriages where the couple was permanently separated, legally or otherwise.

[i] White women married once and husband present who were aged 15–49 at date of census.

Source: United Nations, *Recent Trends in Fertility in Industrialized Countries,* ST/SOA/Series A/27 (New York, 1958), p. 60.

Are there dissimilarities between the two sets of countries that may lead to long-term stabilization of the family-size differential? If this is the case, Western Europe may contain significant clues to the institutionalization of the small family as a way of life. Indeed, Freedman has suggested that analysis of the institutional settings for this difference may provide such guidance! [11] Still, before we embark on such a mammoth undertaking, let us consider how reasonable it is to assume that the differential is at all stable. It is initially sufficient to deal with one set of countries alone. If these promise to be unstable, there is no need to go further. We shall start with Western Europe because it offers the nearest hope for clues to small-family desires.

First, to judge from actual period data (see Table 2 on GRR) fertility is rising somewhat among the European countries that previously experienced the very lowest rates, and it appears to be stabilizing among others like Denmark.[12] Second, the average "ideal" number of children given by Europeans (like the ideals given by Americans) is typically in excess of actual behavior or of expectations. This excess is particularly marked when the question refers to the number desired under better financial or living conditions if these were available. Finally, both ideal and actual family size in some European countries have been showing either a U-shaped or a direct linear relationship with socio-economic status.

The Discrepancy Between Fertility Ideals and Expectations or Behavior

The discrepancy among modernized peoples between the number of children they say they consider "ideal" and the number they personally intend to have, or in fact do have, has been noted in the literature for many years. In his 1954 summary of

---

11. See R. Freedman *et al.*, "Expected Family Size and Family Size Values in West Germany," *Population Studies*, XIII (Nov., 1959), pp. 136–137 and 142–143; and R. Freedman, "American Studies of Family Planning and Fertility: A Review of Major Trends and Issues," *Research in Family Planning*, ed. C. V. Kiser (Princeton: Princeton University Press, 1962), p. 216 and pp. 226–227.

12. See, for example, the discussion by R. Pressat, "Tendances récentes de la fécondité en Europe occidentale," *International Population Union Conference*, 1961, Paper Number 93 (mimeographed).

existing European survey data on "ideal" family size, Stoetzel
was struck by the discrepancy between actual European fertility
in the reporting countries and "ideal" fertility.[13] A recent study
in West Germany that found the same type of excess of ideals
over actualities, was fortunately designed so that an explicit
analysis of the differences in reply to three related questions
was possible. These were the number of children actually expected, the "ideal size of the average family in Germany," and
the number of children personally desired "if financial and
other conditions of life were very good?" German respondents
expected fewer children than they considered ideal for "average Germans," and they desired for themselves (under good
conditions) more children than they thought the average German family should have, and hence more than they expected.[14]

TABLE 4

*Mean Number of Children Expected and Desired, by Occupation and Education of
Head of Family. West Germany, 1958* [a]

Occupation of family head	Mean number of children expected		Mean number of children desired (good conditions)	
Professional	2.5	(37)	2.9	(37)
Businessman	2.1	(167)	2.7	(176)
White collar workers	2.1	(305)	2.7	(314)
Officials	2.1	(136)	2.7	(145)
Skilled laborers	2.1	(581)	2.6	(598)
Unskilled laborers	2.3	(304)	2.8	(887)
Education of family head				
Elementary school	2.2 (1,429)		2.7 (1,491)	
Secondary school or high school without *abitur*	2.0	(220)	2.7	(228)
High school with *abitur* or university	2.3	(59)	2.9	(62)

[a] R. Freedman, G. Baumert, and M. Bolte, "Expected Family Size and Family
Size Values in West Germany," *Population Studies*, XIII (Nov., 1959), p.145.

13. J. Stoetzel, "Les attitudes et la conjoncture démographique: la dimension
idéale de la famille," *Proceedings of the World Population Conference, 1954,* VI
(New York: United Nations, 1955), pp. 1019–1033.
14. R. Freedman *et. al., op. cit.,* p. 141. The differences between the expected
number and the number desired under good conditions are not accounted for merely
by the fact that couples expecting to be childless actually desired some children. For
example, the percentage expecting three or more children was 31.9, but 49.5 per cent
would have desired that many if conditions were good.

The German study is particularly valuable in presenting these data by socioeconomic indictators (Table 4). At all nonfarm occupational levels there is a discrepancy between expected and desired family size. Although the professional class desires the most children, the discrepancy for them is the smallest because they expect the most as well. On the other hand, most other nonmanual workers desire over 25 per cent more children than they expect to have. The stability of this gap for most of the population comes out clearly when we look at the data broken down by education level.

These data suggest that there is among Western European populations that have been experiencing very low fertility since the Second World War or before, what we might call a latent child hunger that would be satisfied under some more favorable financial and living conditions. Moreover, it is of interest that in desiring or idealizing more children than they expect to have, Western Europeans are similar to Americans.[15] The Europeans apparently do not have some stabilized low fertility ideology that their recent behavior expresses. Let us now test the idea that Europeans would desire and have larger families under what they conceive to be better conditions by looking at European ideal and actual family-size data according to socioeconomic indicators. If the hypothesis has any validity we should find that better situated Europeans both idealize and are beginning to have larger families than less advantaged groups.

Differential "Ideal" and Actual Fertility Among
West Europeans

As far back as the late 1940's and early 1950's when systematic data on ideal family size in selected European countries

15. For a discussion of the Growth of American Families Study data on this topic, see R. Freedman, P. K. Whelpton, and A. A. Campbell, *Family Planning, Sterility and Population Growth* (New York: McGraw-Hill, 1959), pp. 220–226. Also, similar findings have been reported for the Detroit Area Study and for the Indianapolis Study. See R. Freedman, D. Goldberg, and H. Sharp, " 'Ideals' about Family Size in the Detroit Metropolitan Area: 1954," *Milbank Memorial Fund Quarterly*, XXXIII (April, 1955), pp. 187–197, and L. V. Pratt and P. K. Whelpton, "Social and Psychological Factors Affecting Fertility XXX. Extra-Familial Participation of Wives in Relation to Interest in and Liking for Children, Fertility Planning, and Actual and Desired Family Size," *Milbank Memorial Fund Quarterly*, XXXIV (Jan., 1956), pp. 1245–1279.

begin, there have been noticeable exceptions to the inverse relationship between these ideals and socioeconomic status. Table 5 shows that many of the highest socioeconomic groups express a family-size ideal of around three children. Among different educational levels and nonfarm occupations, the materials indicate a positive association between social advantage and family-size goals. On the economic variable, Sweden and France evince a direct relationship with familial ideals, and Britain and Germany a U-shaped one—the middle-income groups have the lowest reproductive ideals. It seems possible that West Europeans of the upper strata have for many years desired a family of relatively modest size. In fact, some upper-status European groups come close to idealizing the same number of children as was found for Americans of all classes in the Growth of American Families Study—3.3 (minimum) or 3.5 (maximum).[16]

The pertinence of these differentials in reproductive ideals is suggested by the recent trends in *actual* fertility for selected European countries (where we have data), which show the same types of variation with status indicators. Special studies in Great Britain, Sweden, and the Netherlands indicate that the family size of the better educated is "clearly above the average rates for these countries."[17] In Britain, Norway, and the Netherlands, the professional class no longer has the lowest fertility. The latter is found among civil servants and other white collar employees.[18]

It thus seems unlikely to us that Europeans are on the road to permanent adjustment of family size at approximately two children. Like Americans they typically desire at least two, and there is an apparent backlog of motivation for more under better cirumstances. That this desire is meaningful seems to be illustrated both by the very recent upturn in period rates and by

16. The average "minimum" and "maximum" figures come from using the lower and upper limits of answers giving a range of children—i.e., "two or three," or "three or four." See Freedman, Whelpton, and Campbell, *op. cit.*, pp. 220–226.

17. G. Z. Johnson, "Differential Fertility in European Countries," *Demographic and Economic Change in Developed Countries*, National Bureau of Economic Research (Princeton: Princeton University Press, 1960), p. 53.

18. *Ibid.*, p. 59, and D. H. Wrong, "Class Fertility Differentials in England and Wales," *Milbank Memorial Fund Quarterly*, XXXVIII (Jan., 1960), pp. 37–47.

TABLE 5

Ideal Family Size by Economic, Occupational, and Educational Levels, Selected European Countries, 1939–1958

| Country | Date | Economic Level | | | |
		Impoverished	Poor	Middle class	Rich
West Germany	1950 [a]	2.18	2.20	2.14	2.33
	1953 [a]	2.34	2.30	2.21	2.35
	1958 [b]	2.8 [c]	2.6	2.4–2.5	2.6
France	1944 [a]		2.92	3.72	
	1946 [a]	2.54	2.77		3.15
	1947 [a]	2.70	2.90		3.27
United Kingdom	1939 [a]	3.00	2.90		3.07
	1947 [a]	2.92	2.79	2.93	2.89
	1952 [a]	3.10	2.79	2.81	2.92
Sweden	1947 [a]	2.72	2.89		3.41

| Country | Date | Occupational Level | | | | | | |
| | | Farmers | Laborers | | | Industry—commerce staff | | Free professions |
			Farm laborers	Clerical		Officials		
West Germany	1950 [a]	2.88	2.20	2.03	2.11	2.37	2.23	2.08
	1953 [a]	2.71	2.44	2.17	2.23	2.49	2.31	2.44
	1958 [b]	2.9		2.5–2.6	2.6	2.6	2.6	2.8
Belgium	1952 [a]		3.45	2.25	2.44		2.69	2.80
Finland	1953 [a]	3.10	2.65	2.71		2.98	3.15	
France	1944 [a]		3.74	2.70		2.80	2.95	
	1945 [a]		3.15	2.60		3.03	2.78	3.34
	1947 [a]		3.33	2.67		2.79	2.94	3.32
	1947 [a]		3.09	2.73		2.76	2.87	3.47

| Country | Date | Educational Level | | |
		Primary	Secondary	Higher
West Germany	1950 [a]	2.26	2.18	2.22
	1953 [a]	2.26	2.31	2.42
	1958 [b]	2.6	2.5	2.7
Finland	1953 [a]	2.75	3.16	3.24
France	1947 [a]	2.77	3.15	3.35

[a] J. Stoetzel, "Les attitudes et la conjoncture démographique: la dimension idéale de la famille," *Proceedings of the World Population Conference, 1954,* VI (New York: United Nations, 1955), pp. 1019–1033.

[b] R. Freedman, G. Baumert, and M. Bolte, "Expected Family Size and Family Size Values in West Germany," *Population Studies,* XIII (Nov., 1959), p. 145.

[c] As reported in original publications cited above.

the larger families desired and achieved among higher socio-economic groups.

Hence the one-child difference between European and frontier countries may be due not to some fundamental differences in reproductive or social and economic goals, but to the fact that Europeans have, during the past 25 years, experienced a heavier dose of the cost factors involved in reproduction than the overseas countries. Although Europeans operated within the same modern context as other industrialized peoples (being subject to the modern costs of childrearing, plus the need to maintain their own positions and assure themselves of security later in life), they underwent a relatively long period of deprivation during which the realization of these goals was very difficult. No one factor can necessarily be said to be crucial. Differences in per capita income between Western Europe and the overseas countries have long been unfavorable to Europe, and Europe suffered the principal direct devastations of war and its aftermath. Moreover, it is more densely settled, there are apparently fewer opportunities for social mobility, and more clogging and insufficiency of channels of mobility such as education.[19] It hardly seems surprising in terms of existing

---

19. The difficulty of constructing international indicators of living levels is widely recognized, but per capita income is highly correlated with other well-known indicators such as those suggested by the United Nations, *Expert Report on International Definition and Measurement of Standards and Levels of Living* (New York: United Nations, 1954). For a recent discussion of historical and present differences between the frontier and North West European countries in per capita income, see L. J. Zimmerman, "The Distribution of World Income," *Essays on Unbalanced Growth*, ed. E. de Vries ('S-Gravenhage: Mouton, 1962), pp. 28–41. It is of some interest that in recent years the disparity in per capita income between Europe and the other countries is lessening because of increasing rates of growth in Europe and relative slowness in North America. For discussion of this point, see Zimmerman. Information on trends on intergenerational occupational mobility in the United States may be found in B. Barber, *Social Stratification* (New York: Harcourt, Brace, 1957), Chap. 16; E. Chinoy, "Social Mobility Trends in the United States," *American Sociological Review*, XX (April, 1955), pp. 180–186; J. A. Kahl, *The American Class Structure* (New York: Rinehart, 1957), Chap. 9; G. Lenski, "Trends in Intergenerational Mobility in the United States," *American Sociological Review*, XXIII (Oct., 1958), pp. 514–523; W. Petersen, "Is America Still the Land of Opportunity?" *Commentary* (Nov., 1953), pp. 477–486; N. Rogoff, *Recent Trends in Occupational Mobility* (Glencoe: Free Press, 1953); G. Sjoberg, "Are Social Classes in America Becoming More Rigid?" *American Sociological Review*, XVI (Dec., 1951), pp. 775–783; W. L. Warner and J. Abegglan, *Occupational Mobility in American Business and Industry, 1928–1952* (Minneapolis: University of Minnesota Press, 1955). For comparison of occupational mobility in Europe and the

theory that the frontier peoples should feel more carefree about having an extra child or two than Europeans, since they have enjoyed unprecedented wealth, a halcyon period of suburbanization, high rates of social mobility, and a great expansion of educational opportunity.

POPULATION POLICY AND THE SMALL FAMILY PATTERN

Modernization alone, therefore, has nowhere in the world to date had an abiding and drastically downward effect on family-size desires. Peoples of the wealthy overseas countries have sustained a prolonged boom in births not merely because of intrinsic demographic factors (age structure, shifts in age at marriage, or changes in the age patterning of childbearing), but because they have come close to realizing their wishes for families of three to four children. Europeans seem clearly to be attempting to bridge the gap between their desires for a moderate-size family and their modest achievements of the last quarter of a century. Yet it is certainly true that the modern world exacts the high direct and indirect costs for reproduction that have been attributed to it.

Why do adults buck the pressures against childbearing to the extent that they do? To understand this paradox it seems necessary to return to the noneconomic utilities of children which appear to be powerful forces outweighing the impact of direct and indirect costs. Although it cannot be denied that

---

United States, see S. M. Lipset and R. Bendix, *Social Mobility in Industrial Society* (Berkeley: University of California Press, 1959), Chap. 2. Using a manual/nonmanual breakdown, the authors find that total vertical mobility for nonfarm sons is approximately the same in the United States and Germany, Sweden, France, and Switzerland. However, their conclusion that ''. . . total mobility in these countries is practically the same'' seems to be an overstatement, because they fail to take into account the higher agricultural proportions in the European countries they discuss. For example, in the early 1950's France had over a quarter of its population still engaged in agricultural pursuits, Sweden and Germany more than 20 per cent, and Switzerland over 15 per cent; J. F. Dewhurst *et al.*, *Europe's Needs and Resources* (New York: Twentieth Century Fund, 1961), Chap. 3. The United States, on the other hand, had less than 13 per cent in agriculture in 1950. Moreover, for our purposes the manual/nonmanual breakdown on an intergenerational basis is too crude an indicator of differential opportunity, since chances for mobility in nonmanual careers are fully as important as is opportunity to cross the blue collar line intergenerationally. In this connection, see C. A. Anderson, ''The Social Status of University Students in Relation to Type of Economy: An International Comparison,'' *Transactions of the Third World Congress of Sociology* (London: International Sociological Association, 1956) V, pp. 51–63.

modernization has brought about many changes in family organization, the complex of roles and goals we call the family is still a major focus of individuals' expectations and activities. This means, by definition, that children are high on the list of adult utilities. Offspring are not simply outlets (and inlets) for affection, they are the instrumentalities for achieving virtually prescribed social statuses ("mother" and "father"), the almost exclusive avenues for feminine creativity and achievement, and the least common denominator for community participation—to give but a few examples.[20] Parents (and potential parents) are thus motivated to create and respond to seemingly superficial arguments for an extra child or two. Childhood mortality risks, desires for a boy, for a girl, for companionship for the youngest—such arguments prevail because parental motivation is already socially structured in terms of having children. This structuring also blunts the sense of deprivation in things foregone (the indirect costs of additional offspring). It even permits the rationalization of direct costs, particularly if the latter are the sort that the children rather than the parents suffer—outgrown and worn clothing, educational limitations, crooked teeth, congenital defects that have a high probability of occurring—the list is not difficult to lengthen. That parental rationalization does not carry the day in modern societies is testimony to the strong social pressures for "doing a good job" at parenthood, and the aforementioned difficulty of finding outside sources of relief from the costs of this privileged status.

This analysis clearly begs the further question of why individuals are still so oriented toward achieving familial statuses in such a seemingly nonfamilial world. One suggested answer is that the family as a social group has certain attributes uniquely suited to the individual's needs in a modern, urban, mobile society.[21] This view is certainly stimulating as far as it goes, but

20. A systematic account of the noneconomic utilities of children would be well worth considering. For instance, they allegedly prevent marital boredom and premature aging and "stodginess," as well as providing couples with a "common interest" and topics of conversation with their own parents. The further one extends the list, the more one becomes aware of how explicitly the marital institution is structured in terms of reproduction.

21. For instance, R. Freedman says, ". . . I suggest that with all its loss of functions, the family in a highly mobile, specialized society continues to have a unique set of core functions. It is, in the first place, the only continuing primary

to understand the family's unique powers we must pay some attention to the types of control mechanisms that channel the quest for satisfactions in the direction of children (and not something else) and families (and not some other social groupings). In a sense, the answer has already been suggested. A strong parental orientation is readily perpetuated through a prolonged period of youthful socialization. Beyond this, the *de facto* primacy of the family provides mechanisms for excluding viable alternative affiliations and satisfactions. Implementation of such alternatives—even popular discussion of them—is ridiculed, or at the worst branded "immoral." Insofar as such alternatives are thrown open for consideration at all, it is typically with reference to clearly disadvantaged or despised choices (celibacy, prostitution, homosexuality, the "don juan" complex), descriptions of which make traditional family roles seem overpoweringly advantageous by contrast. The family thus seems to be uniquely well-suited to modern life in part because functional rivals (competing roles, satisfactions, and activities) are effectively relegated to the sidelines.

It seems therefore that a stabilized reduction in the family-size desires of both prosperous and poor countries will require a significant lessening of involvement in familial roles. Otherwise, policy is bucking a motivational syndrome that has a built-in "righting reflex" in the face of antinatalist blows. The family complex may bow to depression, stoop to war, and shrink into an urban apartment, but until nonfamilial roles began to offer significant competition to familial ones as avenues for adult satisfaction, the family will probably continue to amaze us with its procreative powers.

Yet policy directed at reducing rates of population growth has

---

group that a man takes with him in his travels in space and in society. It is the unit which specializes in nonspecialized relationships in a highly specialized society. It is, therefore, the only social unit which can provide dependably the emotional support and stable orientation man needs in a kaleidoscopic, mobile, specialized world. . . . The family performs a correlated and equally important function in serving as the center which organizes the impersonal socialized services of the economy and the society for consumption on a personal basis by its members. This important function increases the family's strength as a source of nonspecialized orientation and emotional support." "Comment" on G. Z. Johnson, "Differential Fertility in European Countries," *Demographic and Economic Change in Developed Countries*, National Bureau of Economic Research (Princeton: Princeton University Press, 1962), pp. 74–75.

to date failed to come to grips with this predicament. It has either enjoined institutional changes such as economic development that are once-removed from the family, or it has taken off toward purely technical and instrumental consideration respecting birth control. In neither case is there direct manipulation of family structure itself—planned efforts at deflecting the family's socializing function, reducing the noneconomic utilities of offspring, or introducing nonfamilial distractions and opportunity costs into people's lives. In neither case is there genuine leadership out of the demographic dilemma posed by declining mortality.

The question may well be raised, however, whether we have other than purely theoretical reasons for believing that direct policy affecting family structure would also affect family-size desires and their implementation? For example, would deflection from important familial roles lead individuals to desire smaller families? A full answer to such a question will require a wide variety of research endeavors. But, fortunately, demographers and sociologists have already devoted fairly intensive study to this problem in their research on female labor force participation and family size.

FAMILY SIZE AND WORKING WIVES

From the standpoint of the theory discussed in this paper, the employment of women outside the home constitutes one of the most likely sources of a desire for small families. Such employment will often entail satisfactions alternative to children (companionship, recreation, stimulation, and creative activity), or the means to such satisfactions in the form of financial remuneration. Foregoing employment will frequently be experienced as a cost—one of the costs of having children. Thus employment is a means of introducing into women's lives the subjective awareness of opportunity costs involved in childbearing—an awareness that traditional feminine roles and activities are well-designed to circumvent.

In actual fact, female labor force participation has long been known to bear one of the most impressive relationships to family size of any variable—typically in Western countries it has been equaled or exceeded in strength only by Catholic-non-Catholic religious affiliation. An inverse relationship between the labor force participation of married women and their family size has been suggested by census data for Western Europe and the United States for many years.[22]

Recently, Collver and Langlois found a high negative association of fertility with women's participation in work (other than domestic service). For 20 countries of varying modernization levels (having data available) the Pearsonian correlation was —.60. The regression equation shows that the number of children per 1,000 women declined by seven for each one per cent increase in the work participation rate.[23] Jaffe and Azumi contrasted the smaller families of both Puerto Rican and Japanese wives employed outside the home with the families of wives not in the labor force or engaged in cottage industry. Among Puerto Rican women it was possible to control for women's educational levels and the relationship still was maintained.[24]

Furthermore family-size ideals, desires, and expectations have also been related to women's work behavior. A number of American studies discovered that the longer the work experi-

22. These data for married women during the 1930's and 1940's have been summarized by the United Nations. United Nations Population Division, *The Determinants and Consequences of Population Trends,* Population Studies, Number 17, ST/SOA/Series A/17 (New York, 1953), pp. 88–89.

23. A. Collver and E. Langlois, ''The Female Labor Force in Metropolitan Areas: An International Comparison,'' *Economic Development and Cultural Change,* X (July, 1962), pp. 381–384.

24. A. J. Jaffe and K. Azumi, ''The Birth Rate and Cottage Industries in Underdeveloped Countries,'' *Economic Development and Cultural Change,* IX (Oct., 1960), pp. 52–63. The authors say (p. 62), ''what implications can be drawn from these findings? First, it is clear that cottage industries are not an unmixed blessing, even if it can be proven—which is doubtful—that they are economically advisable. By maintaining high fertility levels together with relatively low levels of worker productivity they simply help perpertuate a system of rapid population growth together with a rate of economic growth which at best barely manages to keep abreast of population growth. Traditional forms of social and family relationships are maintained (one of the important elements involved in sustaining traditionally high fertility levels) and no or little progress is made toward transforming the entire socioeconomic structure into that of a rapidly growing modern economy. . . . From the population viewpoint, perhaps the most desirable industries to be introduced into an underdeveloped country would be those using large quantities of female labor away from home, in modern factories, stores, offices, etc. If enough women were so occupied the birth rate would be lowered considerably.'' See also A. J. Jaffe, *People, Jobs and Economic Development* (Glencoe: Free Press, 1959), Chap. 10. The same type of relationship between women working and family size is suggested by data from a survey on fertility and attitudes toward family formation in Santiago, Chile. See L. Tabah and R. Samuel, *op. cit.,* pp. 281–282.

ence of fecund wives since marriage (holding constant age of wife or duration of marriage or both) the smaller the family size expected.[25] Moreover the difference in desired or expected family size between wives who have had no work experience and those having "much" (five years or more) is about one child—a difference as great as is typically found between Catholics and non-Catholics and usually greater than any other single difference.[26] A recent study in West Germany discovered a similar association.[27]

Although this association between married women working and family size is generally acknowledged to be one of the strongest, most persistent over time and space, and most theoretically reasonable, questions must be raised about the nature of the causal relationship. It seems clear by now that the relationship is not due simply to the fact that involuntarily infecund or subfecund wives are more inclined or able to work. The association holds among fecund wives. However, from none of these studies is it clear whether the small-family ideal is solely a *result* of labor force participation by women (a result of their becoming socialized to earning their own living, a nondomestic way of life, etc.), or whether the *intention* of working precedes the desire for small families (or coincides with it in youth), before either family experience or intensive work experience is undergone. Fortunately, data now being analyzed at the University of California, Berkeley, allow us to examine this very point, because the sample was drawn from high school and

25. L. V. Pratt and P. K. Whelpton, "Social and Psychological Factors Affecting Fertility XXX. Extra-Familial Participation of Wives in Relation to Interest in and Liking for Children, Fertility Planning and Desired Family Size," *Social and Psychological Factors Affecting Fertility, V*, ed. P. K. Whelpton and C. V. Kiser, (New York: Milbank Memorial Fund, 1958), pp. 1245–1280; and J. C. Ridley, "Number of Children Expected in Relation to Non-Familial Activities of the Wife," *Milbank Memorial Fund Quarterly*, XXXVII (July, 1959), pp. 277–296; R. Freedman, D. Goldberg, and D. Slesinger, "Current Fertility Expectations of Married Couples in the United States," *Population Index*, XXIX (Oct., 1963), p. 377.

26. R. Freedman, D. Goldberg, and D. Slesinger, *op. cit.*, p. 384. The 1955 and the 1962 studies have shown that the difference between the religious groups contrasts with increased length of wifely work experience. In the 1962 study, wives with five or more years experience evinced a Catholic-non-Catholic difference of 0.6 in expected family size, whereas those with no such experience since marriage showed a religious difference of 1.2 expected children, or double the other figure.

27. R. Freedman, G. Baumert, and M. Bolte, *op. cit.*, pp. 145–149.

TABLE 6

Mean Number of Children Desired and Percentage Distribution of Children Desired by Work Intentions after Marriage and Selected Social and Economic Characteristics, Gallup Study of High School and College Students, 1961. White Females Only

| Selected characteristics | $\overline{X}$ Desired children | Percentage distribution—desired number of children | | | | |
		0–1	2–4	5+	Total	n
Work intentions after marriage						
Does not intend to work	4.1	2.2	67.8	30.0	100	270
Intends to work until family	3.8	1.3	79.9	18.8	100	149
1–2 years	3.7	0.8	82.0	17.2	100	239
3 years	3.5	1.6	79.5	18.9	100	127
4 years	3.4	2.1	87.5	10.4	100	48
5 or more years	3.3	6.9	81.0	12.1	100	173
Occupation of household head						
Professional & business	3.6	2.2	81.0	16.8	100	417
Clerical & sales	3.8	1.4	75.0	23.6	100	148
Skilled	3.8	4.4	69.6	26.0	100	135
Semi-skilled & service	3.7	1.8	81.8	16.4	100	171
Laborers (nonfarm)	3.5	0.0	84.6	15.4	100	26
Farmers/farm laborers	4.3	5.1	70.9	24.0	100	64
Education of household head						
Less than 8	3.5	1.8	85.5	12.7	100	55
8–11	3.6	3.4	77.7	18.9	100	238
12, H.S. graduate	3.7	3.0	74.7	22.3	100	305
Some college	3.9	0.6	77.7	21.7	100	152
College graduate	3.4	3.1	80.1	16.8	100	131
Professional, etc.	3.6	2.7	78.5	18.8	100	149
Religious affiliation						
Catholic	4.3	1.6	61.3	37.1	100	248
Protestant	3.5	3.0	81.8	15.2	100	664
Jewish	3.3	0.0	94.0	6.0	100	50
None	3.4	4.8	83.3	11.9	100	42
Region of country						
East	3.7	1.7	76.0	22.3	100	346
Midwest	3.8	3.5	73.9	22.6	100	310
South	3.5	3.6	79.6	16.8	100	225
West	3.5	1.3	86.7	12.0	100	158
Age						
14–15	3.8	0.7	75.7	23.6	100	148
16–17	3.7	2.7	76.9	20.4	100	333
18–19	3.5	3.5	78.9	17.6	100	142
20–21	3.6	3.0	78.8	18.2	100	363
22–23	3.7	1.1	79.1	19.8	100	91
Grade						
H.S. sophomore	3.6	2.8	78.1	19.1	100	320
H.S. senior	3.7	2.6	76.2	21.2	100	302
College junior	3.7	2.0	80.7	17.3	100	249
College senior	3.5	3.3	88.9	7.8	100	234

college students who were asked about both their work intentions after marriage and about their family-size ideals.[28] As may
be seen from Table 6, whether girls intend to work for any
prolonged period of time outside the home after marriage exerts
approximately as important an influence on their family-size
desires as does their religious affiliation—probably the other
single most important influence we will be able to show. The
importance of most socioeconomic variables other than religious
affiliation is relatively slight.

These data should serve to illustrate that already existing
research on one of the possible means of reducing the noneconomic utilities of children, and increasing the opportunity costs
in childbearing, shows considerable promise for reducing family
size. From the standpoint of population growth, the potential
influence of policy designed to deflect women from family
participation lies not only in the direction of reducing family-
size desires, but of lengthening the period between generations
through later marriage and delayed childbearing. Further,
policy designed to increase feminine labor outside the home will
often involve few direct governmental outlays, but rather
merely the abolition of legal restrictions and informal barriers.
Even actual investment in such policy (for example, in-service
training for women) would have social and economic functions,
rather than solely helping to reduce family size. Finally, work in
factories and other organized situations outside the home makes
women readily (and inexpensively) accessible to all types of
educational influences, including (in developing countries) those
that will help them to reduce infant and child mortality as well
as undesired fertility.

In view of the advantages just cited, it is surprising that a
country like India where impressive amounts are being in-
vested in family planning campaigns) is not taking advantage of
this structural means of influencing family-size motivation. If
anything, the cumulative effect of governmental policy has been
one of discouraging rather than encouraging the employment of

28. The data are from the Gallup Youth Study, 1961. Their analysis is part of a
project being conducted by the author and Kingsley Davis at International
Population and Urban Research on family formation attitudes in the United States.
This project utilizes survey data from a variety of agencies. I wish to thank Glen
Elder for allowing us to make use of some of his tabulations.

females. While trends in long-term employment of women in India are difficult to evaluate, there does seem to have been a decided decrease in the proportion of women classified as working in census reports during the first half of the century.[29]

SUMMARY

To date efforts at curtailing population growth in developing countries have been bipolarized into the "economic development" approach on the one hand, and the family planning approach on the other. The first sees decreases in family size as the long-range resultant of a complete socioeconomic overhauling which, in turn, leads to a desire for fewer children. The second overlooks the institutionalization of reproduction entirely and assumes that education and communication regarding birth control will eventually reduce births to a level in keeping with low mortality. Neither approach seems to be practical taken alone, nor do they even appear to be adequate in combination. Population growth is clearly impeding economic development in many poor countries, rather than itself being reduced through the modernization process. Family planning programs are not lowering birth rates among the mass of the people in such countries, and their failure is understandable in view of their superficialty. We are thus led to ask whether additional types of direct action for reducing family size cannot be incorporated into population policy.

In answer, we have taken the position that the limitation of

29. A recent study of female employment in India claims that "the number of working females declined from 43 million in 1911 to 40.7 million in 1951, while the female population during the period increased from 149.9 million in 1911 to 173.4 in 1951. In other words, there was a decrease of about 2.3 million working females as against the actual increase of 23.5 million female population," *Women in Employment, 1901–1956.* A Joint Study by the Labour Bureau, Simla, and the Labour and Employment Division, Planning Commission (Government of India, August, 1958), p. 10. See also Labour Bureau, Ministry of Labour, Government of India, *Economic and Social Status of Women Workers in India* (Delhi: Ganga Printing Press, 1953), p. 12, and Padmini Sengupta, *Women Workers of India* (Bombay: Asia Publishing House, 1960), p. 26. See R. G. Gokhale, *Summary of Workmen's Service Records* (Bombay: The Millowners' Association, 1941) and *The Bombay Cotton Mill Worker* (Bombay: The Millowners' Association, 1957) as quoted in R. C. James, "Discrimination Against Women in Bombay Textiles," *Industrial and Labor Relations Review,* XV (Jan., 1962), p. 211.

alternatives is more a function of insufficient thought and analysis than actual circumscription of choice. For example, theory and research accounting for declining family size in Western societies is as relevant for direct action concerning reproduction as it is for indirect action respecting family size (such as economic development). It is instructive to analyze the present-day preference in industrial societies for approximately three children from the standpoint of the institutional barriers to further declines. We then see that the purely economic assumptions concerning the utility of children discount too readily the importance to individuals of the noneconomic benefits involved in reproduction. These far exceed simple affectional or companionship elements, since they are built into the achievement of familial statuses and the success of marriage. When one analyzes further why modern, urban, mobile individuals are so familially oriented, one cannot discount the advantages of the family group in a modern world. But one must also take into account the strong social controls which isolate individuals from alternative roles and satisfactions and, hence, bolster their intense feelings of dependency on the family, and *a fortiori* on having children.

It would thus appear that policies expressly related to family roles, and opportunities for legitimate alternative satisfactions and activities, constitute the crux of future reduction in family size because they directly assault the motivational framework of reproduction. Moreover, many of these policies for influencing the family do not depend on prior economic development, they can be implemented concomitantly with modernization strategies. Regardless of the level of development, policy can undermine the utilities found in offspring (thereby allowing a sense of increased costs to prevail) and can structure itself in terms of crucial existing foci of change in the society. We have used female labor force participation as an example because it met both of these criteria—a lessening of family involvement on the part of a disadvantaged (and hence potentially revolutionary) group. Numerous additional facets of policy come to mind, one such being rigidly compulsory education of children which would remove them as potential economic utilities (even as household help on anything but a token level), all the while effectively putting intellectual barriers between them and the past generation. Regardless of the specific paths taken by population policy, its designers cannot afford to overlook the lesson already available to them in the substantial family-size desires and actualities to be found in presently industrial countries. Modernization and birth control alone will clearly not bring family size into line with modern levels of mortality unless this reproductive institution is itself modified to make the small family a way of life.

ACKNOWLEDGEMENTS

Research for this paper was conducted at International Population and Urban Research, Institute of International Studies, University of California, Berkeley, under a grant from The Equitable Life Assurance Company. The author wishes to thank Kingsley Davis for his criticisms and suggestions.

M. Brewster Smith

MOTIVATION, COMMUNICATIONS RESEARCH, AND FAMILY PLANNING

INTRODUCTION

The fertility of a population can be viewed as the resultant of many individual acts and decisions, made within a framework of biological and environmental constraints. Questions of human motivation and motivational change thus have an important bearing on the viability of efforts to attain social control over population growth. Such questions enter the picture in two logically separable respects. On the one hand, the number of children desired by fecund couples varies from society to society, and, over time, within the same society. What factors lead parents to aspire to a particular size of family, and how may their desires be influenced in the direction of the small families required for slowly growing populations in an era of low mortality? On the other hand, couples differ in the extent to which they are motivated to employ rational and effective means of limiting their families to the size they desire. What motivational factors are involved in the acceptance and effective use of birth control, and how may the more effective use of birth control procedures be promoted?

70

These two kinds of motivational questions are thus respectively concerned with the private ends and means that affect fertility and population growth. So long as the sizes of families that actually prevail in a population exceed the size that is typically desired—as when effective birth control techniques are not generally employed—the second type of question, concerned with the promotion of birth control, should have the top priority because of its strategic relevance to population growth. But in populations (typical of the economically well-developed countries) in which birth control has gained widespread acceptance, questions concerning the motivation of desired family size become increasingly important from the standpoint of population policy. The main body of this paper is focused on the first problem: What implications can be drawn from social psychological research and theory that can contribute to the acceptance and promulgation of effective birth control practices? At the end, I will revert to the problem of desired family size in connection with a discussion of research needs.

Practitioners and scientists in other fields often look to the student of human motivation for near-magical solutions to problems that *they* cannot handle—and are ready with contempt when the magical solution is not forthcoming. If he is mindful of these ambivalent expectations, the social psychologist who ventures into the strange territory of population control and family planning will be wise to assume a posture of extreme modesty. In order to appreciate what research on communications and motivation *can* contribute, we had best begin by examining some of the reasons why such modesty is called for—not by way of apology, but to clear the ground so that relevance can be established.

TYPES OF COMMUNICATIONS RESEARCH

The years since World War II have seen the burgeoning in the United States of research on persuasive communication, and the emergence of a body of tentative empirical generalizations that Nathan Maccoby[1] has dignified as "the new scientific rhetoric." In spite of substantial progress in this field, however,

1. N. Maccoby, "The New 'Scientific' Rhetoric," *The Science of Communication,* ed. W. Schramm (New York: Basic Books, 1963).

communications research has been addressed to much easier problems than those confronted in the motivational aspect of family planning, and its empirical propositions have been worked out in much simpler, more promising settings.

One impressively cumulative research tradition has used controlled experimentation to identify factors that determine the effectiveness of communication once the recipient has been exposed to the message.[2] This body of work on "captive audiences," primarily the contribution of psychologists, has yielded a considerable array of generalizations. But apart from the simplification involved in starting with the captive audience, research in this tradition has characteristically chosen its ground so as to increase the likelihood of obtaining substantial effects, which facilitate the comparison of various factors in the modification of attitudes and practices. It has dealt more with short-term effects than with long-term ones, more with trivial or superficial issues than with emotionally laden and central ones, and more with changes in beliefs and feelings than with consequential behaviors. It has also been heavily based on conveniently available American student populations. Thus, we cannot be sure that the same variables will remain important or have the same weights when communication with widely differing kinds of audiences on very different topics is at issue, but we can certainly expect that the magnitude of effects achieved will often be substantially smaller than in these experimental studies.

A second tradition, to which sociologists have been the main contributors, has used techniques of interview survey research in field studies of the effects of the mass media.[3] In contrast with the results of experimental studies, the typical finding in these field studies of "free" audiences has been one of rather minimal

2. A key reference in this tradition is C. I. Hovland, I. L. Janis, and H. H. Kelley, *Communication and Persuasion* (New Haven: Yale University Press, 1953). The more recent literature is reviewed, and a selection of empirical generalizations provided, in I. L. Janis and M. B. Smith, "Effects of Education and Persuasion on National and International Images," *International Behavior: A Social Psychological Interpretation*, ed. H. C. Kleman (New York: Holt, Rinehart, and Winston, 1965).

3. See J. T. Klapper, *The Effects of Mass Communication* (Glencoe: Free Press, 1960), for a recent review of findings from this research tradition. An attempt at reconciling the general trend of results in experimental and in field studies is made by C. I. Hovland, "Reconciling Conflicting Results Derived From Experimental and Survey Studies of Attitude Change," *American Psychologist*, XIV (Jan., 1959), pp. 8–17.

effects, primarily in the direction of reinforcing or activating existing attitudes, not of conversion. Again, the research has been primarily on Amercian publics, and the range of issues explored has not been great. Voting and purchasing, as identifiable acts, have nevertheless made available a research focus on consequential behavior that goes beyond attitudes and beliefs.

Field research in this tradition becomes most relevant to population planning when it has been directed at the role of communications in the promulgation and diffusion of new techniques and practices. Converging evidence seems to point to a two-step linkage in which the public media have their effect primarily upon a limited subpopulation of "opinion leaders" (it turns out that they are different people depending on the issue), who in turn spread the message in their own spheres of personal influence.[4] But the kinds of decisions involved in buying a new product, adopting a new drug, introducing a new farming practice (all topics of studies in this vein) are a large step from those involved in family planning.

Even the most cursory thought about family planning highlights ways in which its motivational context differs so radically from the setting of most recent communications research as to represent a difference in kind, not in degree. The neutral language in which family planning is discussed scientifically and professionally should not let us forget that we deal here with sex and the marriage bed, around which surely are woven some of the strongest and least rational motives, the most intimate and private relationships, and the firmest institutional norms and taboos known to man. The very idea of introducing planful rationality in this "sacred" area could initially have been conceived only in a society trained to give unprecedented priority to rational-technical considerations by long experience with them in more public, less emotionally charged spheres of urban and industrial life.[5] Yet we are under imperatives to promote birth control in traditional societies that are just

4. E. Katz, "The Diffusion of New Ideas and Practices," *The Science of Communication*, ed. W. Schramm (New York: Basic Books, 1963); E. Katz and P. F. Lazarsfeld, *Personal Influence: The Part Played by People in the Flow of Mass Communication* (Glencoe: Free Press, 1955).

5. Methods of population control have of course been practiced in many traditional societies. But the use of such methods may reflect adaptations gradually developed in the culture, rather than deliberate decisions of rational planning.

beginning to attain a modicum of rationality in their public, economic, and political spheres! Any attempt to extrapolate to the motivation of family planning from research on other topics runs the risk of sheer fatuity.

On this appraisal, the social psychologist who shares concern with the population problem has several options. On the one hand, he may proclaim the irrelevance of existing social psychological research and call for an enormous expansion of basic research on the motivation of change in birth-producing or birth-limiting decisions and behavior. It always seems both easy and virtuous to ask for more research, and more is obviously needed here, but I will nevertheless reject this option with respect to the promotion of family planning. For all its limitations, existing research has its relevance in ways I hope to suggest below. And I agree with Berelson[6] that given the current urgencies and limitations of resources, the highest priorities for investment ought to be assigned in other directions.

A second option that I will follow in part is to draw cautiously on the results of existing research for hypotheses that seem relevant to social intervention in population control. The research will seldom warrant prescriptive advice to the practitioner. It may help to sensitize him, however, to potentially important factors that he has not considered explicitly. Particularly the negative conclusions of communications research—conclusions about circumstances in which persuasive communication is likely to be *ineffective*—may, *a fortiori*, help him to avoid wasted effort in the more difficult case of family planning. To the extent that action programs incorporate features extrapolated from the results of research on other topics and contexts, these action hypotheses need to be checked in program evaluation—but so do all the hunches and insights around which programs are built, whatever their source.

In addition, the present fund of research experience can be drawn upon for aid in the better *theoretical* definition of the practical problem. Often to redefine a problem is to see the

---

6. B. Berelson, ''Communication, Communications Research, and Family Planning,'' *Emerging Techniques in Population Research* (New York: Milbank Memorial Fund, 1963), pp. 159–171.

contingencies that bear upon its solution in a different light. My impression is that in the present modest state of research in motivation and communication, the greatest probable contribution of social psychology lies in this direction. With these preliminaries behind us, I therefore begin with an attempt to illustrate this third option.

SOME THEORY WITH PRACTICAL IMPLICATIONS

A little theory can often cast a useful searchlight upon silly practice. My favorite example comes from a wartime venture in venereal disease control, so far as I know unrecorded. The American troop information officers in Manila—high-ranking recruits from Madison Avenue—had the inspiration of modelling their appeals over Armed Forces Radio on a recently notorious and perhaps successful campaign of cigarette advertising, in which the advertisers of Lucky Strikes had filled the media for weeks with the unexplained slogan, LS/MFT, at long last announcing—after suspense had presumably built up to the point of nationwide breathlessness—LS/MFT: Lucky Strikes Mean Fine Tobacco. The Manila version, also repeated sententiously for weeks, went: VD/MT. . . . VD/MT—with the final elucidation to a supposedly breathless audience: VD/MT . . . Venereal Disease . . . Means Trouble! A moment's theoretical consideration of the radically different behavioral objectives involved in raising the saliency for smokers of one among many closely similar alternative brands, and in motivating soldiers to avoid intercourse or employ prophylactic measures, should have stopped this pretentious effort.

The modification of birth-producing practices is a special and difficult case of the more general problem of the induction of another's behavior by an outside agent. One of the most cogent analyses of the psychological processes involved in such "behavior induction" remains that of Dorwin Cartwright,[7] which he presented in the context of selected findings from research on the sale of United States war bonds in World War II. To quote Cartwright:

7. D. Cartwright, "Some Principles of Mass Persuasion: Selected Findings of Research on the Sale of United States War Bonds," *Human Relations*, II, No. 3 (1949), pp. 253–267.

What happens psychologically when someone attempts to influence the behavior of another person? The answer, in broad outline, may be described as follows: To influence behavior, a chain of processes must be initiated within the person. These processes are complex and interrelated, but in broad terms they may be characterized as (i) creating a particular cognitive structure, (ii) creating a particular motivational structure, and (iii) creating a particular behavioral (action) structure. In other words, behavior is determined by the beliefs, opinions, and 'facts' a person possesses; by the needs, goals, and values he has; and by the momentary control held over his behavior by given features of his cognitive and motivational structure. To influence behavior 'from the outside' requires the ability to influence these determinants in a particular way.

It seems to be a characteristic of most campaigns that they start strongly with the first process, do considerably less with the second, and only lightly touch upon the third. To the extent that the campaign is intended to influence behavior and not simply to 'educate,' the third process is essential.[8]

Cartwright's entire analysis is so pertinent that if space permitted, I would like to summarize it at greater length. He points out that to *create the desired cognitive structure*—gain acceptance for the relevant facts and beliefs—the message must first reach the sense organs of the persons to be influenced. Once it is received, whether the message is accepted or rejected will depend on how the person identifies it with more general categories to which it appears to belong. He will tend to fit new messages into his stock of categories in ways that serve to protect him from unwanted changes in his cognitive structure (change is resisted). *Creation of the required motivational structure* in a person involves getting him to see the given action as a step toward some desired goal—the more goals that are seen as attainable by a single path, the more likely the path is to be taken. Finally—and it is the implications of this last step that I want to develop here—*creating the required behavioral structure* so that the given action will in fact occur depends on establishing conditions such that the appropriate cognitive and motivational systems gain control of the person's behavior at a

8. *Ibid.*, p. 255.

particular point in time. Cartwright suggests and illustrates three subprinciples in this connection:

> The more specifically defined the path of action to a goal (in an accepted motivational structure), the more likely it is that the structure will gain control of behavior.
>
> The more specifically a path of action is located in time, the more likely it is that the structure will gain control of behavior.
>
> A given motivational structure may be set in control of behavior by placing the person in a situation requiring a decision to take, or not to take, a step of action that is a part of the structure.[9]

In the case of war bond sales, the advantages of specifying the path of action concretely (the first two of the foregoing principles) were illustrated by the substantially greater effectiveness of campaign appeals that said, in effect, "Buy an extra $100 bond during the drive from the solicitor where you work," than of appeals of an earlier, expensive campaign that in substance merely recommended, "Buy War Bonds." The effective technique of personal solicitation, which required the solicited person to make a decision to buy or not to buy a bond then and there, embodied the third principle. It is easy to think of parallels in communications advocating birth control.

But the search for parallels reveals instructive differences between the two cases. Buying a bond is a single well-defined act, to which the principles just noted can be readily applied; the barrage of wartime appeals and solicitation was designed to make it easy to buy, difficult to refuse. By the technique of payroll deduction, moreover, one decision can be made to commit the person to a whole series of purchases, which become equivalent to a single act rather than a set of independent actions. Once committed, the war bond subscriber has to make a separate decision to terminate his purchases—and the promotional campaign, of course, does nothing to encourage *such* decisions. In the sphere of birth control, however, all of the methods that depend on modifying the conditions of each specific act of sexual intercourse fall outside the scope of ready influence, according to these principles. It is simply not possible

9. *Ibid.*, pp. 264–265.

to arrange the equivalent of war bond solicitation to guide the decision processes affecting each separate act of intercourse. Neither is it possible, where these methods are at issue, to secure the kind of externally binding commitment to their practice that is represented by payroll deduction. The behavioral objective for their advocates must therefore be *not* the motivation of specific acts, but rather the establishment of consistent habits or the development in people of strong and consistent internalized controls. Both of these objectives are intrinsically much more complex and difficult to achieve. It is dubious whether even the best planned promotional campaigns can often attain them.

The present analysis therefore highlights the probable relevance of a dimension along which techniques of birth limitation may vary, ranging from fully committing single acts (male and female sterilization), through infrequent acts the motivation of which can be separately induced (the insertion of intrauterine rings, long-term medication, perhaps abortion), to the entire range of chemical-mechanical procedures that must be carried out daily or before each occasion of intercourse. Included in this last, least promising category are not only the rhythm method and withdrawal, but also the daily "pill," since each of these techniques requires multiple decisions to act or refrain from acting.

The initial middle-class leadership of the birth control movement has favored techniques that fall in the latter category, perhaps just because they seem to maximize voluntary decision —planfulness—about parenthood and thus appeal to middle-class values. It should be recognized, however, that any procedure that maximizes and multiplies voluntary decisions is *disadvantageous* from the standpoint of permitting coordinated social intervention to limit births. If, as seems likely, promotional methods cannot instill sufficiently consistent contraceptive habits and self-discipline in enough people to achieve acceptable target reductions in birth rates, consideration might well be given to focusing promotion on more attainable goals. Sterilization and chemical or mechanical procedures that require attention only at infrequent occasions would seem to be more feasible subjects for promotional campaigns.

Note in passing that the dimension I have been emphasizing is closely related to one emphasized by Berelson [10] in his grid of three main factors which he proposes for the orientation of field experiments on the promotion of birth control. Berelson ventures that the practically important variables which in combination define a framework for the planning of program testing are, first, the nature of the *society* (traditional or modern), second, the nature of the *contraceptive method* (hard to use or easy), and, finally, the nature of the *approach* (through whom the informational, educational, or promotional campaign is addressed, saying what, to whom).

For his second variable, he contrasts the traditional methods of withdrawal, condom, foam tablet, rhythm, etc., with the steroid pill and intrauterine device, saying that:

> What makes [the former] methods hard to use is the requirement for sustained motivation, the need in most cases to do something preparatory at the time of intercourse, and in some cases the sheer bother and nuisance value. Beyond such problems is the further difficulty that such methods are not always effective—so that the user or potential user may feel justified in thinking that the result is not going to be worth the effort.

Berelson calls for field studies aimed at providing an adequate basis for such gross administrative decisions as whether the "hard" methods can be effectively promoted in traditional societies, even with maximum effort.

Clearly Berelson is making much the same distinction as mine. But his unduly pessimistic dismissal of motivational theory leads him to couch the distinction in the more commonsense terms of "hard" vs. "easy," which in turn leads him to neglect ways in which male sterilization (easy) and female sterilization (hard) both carry one feature of his "easy" list to an even higher degree.

The kind of motivational theory that I have borrowed from Cartwright differentiates analytically the cognitive, attitudinal, and decisional components of the problem of motivating a change in behavior. One may also look at the process temporally. In their generally perspicacious distillation of the literature of

10. Berelson, *op. cit.*, pp. 163–165.

communication research for the guidance of written communication on birth control, Bogue and Heiskanen [11] offer as their first principle that "The complete adoption of a new idea or a new mode of behavior is not a simple act, but is a PROCESS comprised of several steps or stages." For the adoption of birth control practices, they suggest the following four stages as a useful framework:

> Stage I. *Awareness and Interest.* This stage includes *learning that birth control is possible, respectable, and practical; becoming interested in it; and wanting to learn about it.*
>
> Stage II. *Information-Gathering, Evaluation, and Decision to Try.*
>
> Stage III. *Implementation.* This stage includes *taking action, learning how to use, correcting mistakes, and overcoming wrong ideas.*
>
> Stage IV. *Adoption and Continued Use.* This is the stage of full adoption. Couples who arrive at this stage feel that birth control is right and normal. They would be uncomfortable or fearful to have sex relations without it unless they positively wanted a pregnancy to occur.[12]

While such a scheme of stages certainly does not represent an ambitious level of theorizing, it again illustrates the advantage that even low-level theory can provide; it functions as a scanning device in terms of which judgments are called for that might otherwise be neglected. Thus, we are reminded that individuals and populations will be located at different steps along this continuum: the planning of communication strategy obviously requires information about the target population in this respect. Special surveys may be required. Further, the advantages become apparent of developing materials and approaches geared to the readiness and interests characteristic of a particular stage—and of finding or devising channels of distribution that match the materials to the readiness of the recipient. Once such a scheme is proposed, the consequences are obvious.

SOME IMPLICATIONS OF RESEARCH ON COMMUNICATION

Of all the results of communications research, the central finding that ought to be kept before all would-be communicators

11. D. J. Bogue and V. S. Heiskanen, *How to Improve Written Communication for Birth Control* (Chicago: University of Chicago Family Study Center, and New York: National Committee on Maternal Health, Inc., 1963).

12. *Ibid.*, pp. 7–9.

is the fact of resistance. In general, people's beliefs, attitudes, and behavior tend to be stable. Demands and arguments for change, uncomfortable new facts that do not fit neatly into accustomed categories, are likely to be resisted. Whenever communications attempt to change pre-existing beliefs, attitudes, and habits that engage important goals and values, strong resistances are likely to arise at each stage of the communication process. Thus, some communications are so strongly resisted that they fail to achieve even the first step of eliciting audience *exposure* to the message. The self-selective tendency by which audiences become restricted to the already informed and converted is a recurring and major source of frustration to organizers of persuasive campaigns.[13] Other communications that are somewhat more successful at the outset may end up by being just as ineffective because resistances are mobilized in members of the audience while they are exposed to the message, which interfere drastically with *attention, comprehension,* or *acceptance.*[14] No change or even "boomerang effects" may occur as a consequence of selective inattention to disturbing ideas, misperception of the message, or subsequent selective forgetting.[15] And as we have seen, even when a persuasive message is accepted, the recipient may fail to act upon it or lack the skill to act effectively.

Much effort is wasted in futile persuasive efforts because this paramount fact of resistance is neglected or underestimated. Before any major campaign in the difficult area of human reproductive practices is embarked upon, the would-be communicator should consider his chances of overcoming resistance sufficiently to justify his investment. Some pilot testing of materials and approach is normally called for before any substantial outlay of funds and effort is warranted.

One touchstone for distinguishing promising from unpromising situations is suggested by Hovland, Janis, and Kelley[16] in their analysis of an essential difference between instruction and persuasion. They point out that in communication consensually

13. H. H. Hyman and P. B. Sheatsley, "Some Reasons Why Information Campaigns Fail," *Public Opinion Quarterly*, XI, No. 3 (1947), pp. 412–423.
14. Hovland, Janis, and Kelley, *op. cit.*, pp. 287–293.
15. Klapper, *op. cit.*, pp. 18–26.
16. Hovland *et al.*, *op. cit.*, pp. 293–298.

defined as instructional, in which acceptance is more readily elicited, the setting is typically one in which the recipients anticipate that the communicator is trying to help them, that his conclusions are incontrovertible, and that they will be socially rewarded rather than punished for adhering to his conclusions. In situations commonly regarded as persuasive, on the other hand, interfering expectations are likely to be aroused which operate as resistances. These interfering expectations seem to be of three major kinds: (1) expectations of being manipulated or exploited by the communicator (distrust); (2) expectations of being "wrong"—out of tune with reality as they understand it; and (3) expectations of social disapproval (from people important to them whose norms do not accord with the communicator's position).

The situations encountered by communicators in the sphere of population control surely cover the full range between these two ideal types. The more that inculcation of the desired knowledge and practices can be conducted via the established educational, medical, and religious institutions of the community, the more the "instructional" conditions should apply. Conversely, the more the campaign is seen as a foreign body at variance with the natural and established order, the more closely the "persuasive" type is approximated under conditions that maximize the likelihood of resistance. To the extent that the latter conditions prevail, it is always an open question whether the effort is warranted.

Janis and Smith [17] summarize the research evidence concerning the major sources of resistance to persuasive communication, classifying them under two rubrics: resistance due to the anchorage of a person's attitudes and practices in his group affiliations, and resistance due to anchorage in personality needs. Factors related to the former source of resistance have been extensively studied, documenting the obvious but important point, among others, that the more strongly attached a person is to his group, the more he is likely to resist "counternorm communications" at variance with the standards and precepts of the group to which he belongs. Techniques of

17. Janis and Smith, *op. cit.*

persuasion that emphasize a community orientation, legitimation by established leaders, discussion and group support and the like are intended to take these sources of resistance into account.[18]

Resistance to change anchored in personality needs arises inevitably from the fact that each person has a major investment in his own pattern of beliefs, attitudes, and behaviors that he has worked out in the give-and-take of living or adopted from his parents and mentors. Attitudes and practices are particularly obdurate to rational persuasion insofar as they form part of the person's armament for dealing with his unrecognized inner problems, containing and allaying his anxiety, and helping him to maintain adequate "face" toward self and world. It is in this respect that strong personality-anchored resistances may especially be anticipated in the intimate and emotionally charged area of sexual beliefs and practices. One implication, to the extent that such defensive sources of resistance are otherwise likely to be evoked, is that those techniques of birth control that dissociate the contraceptive decision from the intimacy of sexual life should meet with less resistance than others: the oral "pill" and, to a lesser extent, the implanted intrauterine device (which is associated with the sexual anatomy but not with specific sexual acts). And here, of course, lies the great obstacle to sterilization, where the motivational advantage that it requires only a single act of decision is counterbalanced by the fantasies of impotence, castration, or defeminization that it may invoke.

We have already noted a special source of personal and perhaps cultural resistance that becomes particularly relevant as efforts at population control are directed toward the rural and urban poor of traditionally oriented societies, or even of modern ones. Rationality, planfulness, capacity for delayed gratification, and broad time perspectives, all middle-class virtues that are called for by some approaches to birth control, become psychological luxuries that the extremely deprived, the

18. See R. Lippitt, J. Watson, and B. Westley, *The Dynamics of Planned Change* (New York: Harcourt, Brace, 1958), for a well-conceptualized account of a group-oriented approach to the induction of planned change, with consideration of relevant evidence.

hope-foresaken of the "culture of poverty"[19] can ill afford. Culturally supported attitudes of resignation, fatalism, and present—rather than future—orientation are presumably clung to because they permit a measure of equanimity in the face of predictable frustrations; gratifications are grasped heedlessly when they are available because there is no warrant for confidence that forbearance will pay off. Programs aimed at reducing birth rates in such populations will obviously encounter the passive resistance of apathy and erratic performance, if they make demands on resources of planfulness and committing decision-making that are unavailable.[20]

The emphasis in the foregoing has advisedly been placed on obstacles and resistances to persuasive communication as an avenue toward population control, since an over-valuation of the power of the "persuader" seems to be a contemporary culture trait shared by professionals and laity alike. Yet research does suggest circumstances under which persuasive efforts are likely to meet with more success.

One such type of situation is that to which Katz and Schanck called attention a number of years ago, with the label *"pluralistic ignorance."* "People will stay in line because their fellows do, yet, if they only knew that their comrades wanted to kick over the traces too, the institutional conformity of the group would quickly vanish. . . ."[21] Where there are taboos or strong barriers against free communication, as is so likely to be the case in regard to sexual matters, states of pluralistic ignorance are especially likely to develop. Surveys of individual attitudes in the area of family planning will often turn up such instances, which then suggest points of vulnerability in the traditional norms that persuasion can capitalize upon.

19. O. Lewis, *Five Families: Mexican Case Studies in the Culture of Poverty* (New York: Basic Books, 1959); J. Blake, *Family Structure in Jamaica* (Glencoe: Free Press, 1961); L. Rainwater, *And the Poor Get Children* (Chicago: Quadrangle Books, 1960).

20. As noted in other papers in this Symposium, the increasingly uprooted urban concentration may be more amenable than a traditional peasantry to innovation. Other accompaniments of modernization such as the reduction of high infant mortality and compulsory education may make individuals more accessible to new ideas, and freer from the restraints of group-anchored resistances.

21. D. Katz and R. L. Schanck, *Social Psychology* (New York: Wiley, 1938), pp. 174–175.

Thus in their Puerto Rican survey, Hill, Stycos, and Back unearthed pluralistic ignorance that was giving vulnerable support to the *machismo* tenet that men are expected to want large families, especially of sons, as a proof of their masculinity. In fact, however, the men turned out to be even more oriented than their wives to small families. Their wives were unaware of this fact.[22] To the extent that such constellations of misinformation prevail, programs that seek to induce freer communication can contribute to the emergence and stabilization of more appropriate norms.

A second class of situations that affords optimal opportunities for influence involves the "captive audience." We noted at the outset, as a limitation on the generalizability of psychologists' experimental studies, that they have tended to focus on captive audiences with which exposure to the intended message is guaranteed. Certainly, results from such studies cannot be generalized to situations in which people are freely exposed to competing messages in the mass media, but there *are* important types of situations in which one can count on people receiving the desired message. In these situations there are many reasons to expect communications to be more effective, especially when the circumstances permit prolonged and repeated exposure under favorable institutional auspices. An ideal case is provided when the schools are available for instruction in family planning or for the promulgation of small-family values. Whatever messages can be channelled through the classroom not only have the advantage of a guaranteed audience; they participate in the context of "instruction" which as we have seen is likely to circumvent the resistances to which "persuasion" is vulnerable.

While no other case comes to mind that presents equivalent opportunities, there are others that share some of its advantages. For example, a program that enlists the participation of the specialists who officiate at childbirth—be they physicians, nurses, or midwives—gains access for communicating with

22. R. Hill, J. M. Stycos, and K. W. Back, *The Family and Population Control: A Puerto Rican Experiment in Social Change* (Chapel Hill: University of North Carolina Press, 1959).

women during a period when they may be expected to be especially receptive to information about family planning.

POLITICAL AND LOGISTICAL CONSIDERATIONS AS STRATEGIC FACTORS

This selective and speculative survey points to tentative conclusions that come to me almost as a surprise. Existing knowledge, for all its uncertainty, calls into serious question the effectiveness of current effort and practice to attain population control by persuasive means. Even were the many "pilot" ventures to be regularized and multiplied, it seems to me unlikely that enough people would be reached, enough persuaded, enough confirmed in consistent birth-limiting practices, to achieve the socially desirable degree of reduction in birth rates. These doubts follow from the minor impact of persuasive campaigns under most circumstances, the major fact of resistance, and the motivational complexity of many of the widely-recommended techniques of birth control. The most strategic class of factors that govern the effectiveness of persuasive communication in this application seem to me to be essentially *political,* not scientific or technical.

Thus, access to the schools and other respected and central social institutions—particularly medical—for the free and legitimate communication of facts and recommendations about family planning is clearly a political matter. Where the dissemination of birth control information is illegal, common agreement would see the strategic problem as one of how to get the law changed—not as a need for research on how to achieve more effective clandestine dissemination. So with the school: there is good reason to believe that schools could play a much more effective role than presently available channels; the political problem of access thus becomes more strategic than research on how to achieve more effective persuasion outside the legitimate institutional framework.

Political considerations are also involved in social decision about the acceptability of particular techniques of birth control, regardless of their effectiveness. The acceptability of the rhythm method and the inacceptability of all others to the Catholic Church is of course a matter of engrossingly strategic politics outside and within the Church. But quite parallel issues involve non-Catholics in value conflicts and potentially political disputes about such undoubtedly effective means as abortion and voluntary sterilization.

Gains on the political front would permit persuasive efforts to be directed to a larger extent than is presently the case in most countries toward objectives and via channels that have a fair chance of circumventing human resistances and producing substantial differences in people's reproductive habits and attainments. *Logistical* problems would then emerge as a close second to political ones in strategic relevance. Well supplied and staffed clinics must be readily available if favorable motivation is to be converted into the desired action. Health educators in large numbers would be needed to convert existing pilot programs into operational ones. Not least, persuasive efforts toward population control will be immeasurably furthered by the cheap and ready availability of chemical and mechanical means of contraception that are designed to fit the specifications of human motivation as well as of human reproductive physiology. The more effectively the design problem is solved, however, the more strategic will political factors become in determining the logistical availability of the perfected techniques!

THE NEED FOR RESEARCH

In spite of the uncertain and far from adequate state of psychological knowledge about persuasive communication, therefore, I cannot assign high priority in the grand strategy of population control to basic research in this area. There are too many greater urgencies. But there is great need for the feeding back of dependable knowledge of results to guide the development of more effective persuasive programs, and equal need for dependable knowledge about the relevant beliefs, attitudes, and practices of each population that becomes the target of persuasion. The efforts that are called for fall at various locations on the continuum between informal observation and appraisal, systematic surveys and evaluations, and well-controlled experimentation in the field. A limited number of full-scale field experiments—the Puerto Rico study [23] is in many respects a model—should amply repay the investment required, in providing the grist from which fresh insights can be developed into the

23. *Ibid.*

processes by which limitation in birth rate can be induced. But the larger share of investment should go toward incorporating modest provisions for fact-finding, pre-testing, and evaluation into all major action programs. Were this investment made (at a level of ambitiousness roughly proportional to the scope of the associated action program), wasted efforts could be avoided and cumulative wisdom developed about sound practice.

Applied research and program evaluation, then, fits the short-term urgencies concerning the promulgation of birth control techniques. The other motivational problem noted at the outset —that of individual goals for family size and how they may be modified—acquires its priority in a broader time perspective. There is time for basic research on this problem, and there is need. If, as has been suggested, American couples are converging on preference for families of two to four children, what are the factors that tip the decision (which in the long run has vast consequences for population growth) toward the higher or the lower number? How may these preferences be modified? Surveys on American samples provide some leads.[24] Other hypotheses have been suggested in speculative essays by psychologists [25] and by popular writers.[26] Elsewhere in this volume, Judith Blake [27] advocates an indirect approach via the encouragement of female employment outside the home. Basic research now by psychologists and sociologists could provide knowledge that will be badly needed when effective birth control programs have succeeded in narrowing the gap between desire and achievement in family size.

CONCLUDING REMARKS

Apart from the priorities that I see as inherent in the field of population control, I hope that my colleagues in psychology will

24. See R. Freedman, P. K. Whelpton, and A. A. Campbell, *Family Planning, Sterility, and Population Growth* (New York: McGraw-Hill, 1959); C. Westoff, R. G. Potter, P. Sagi, and E. Mishler, *Family Growth in Metropolitan America* (Princeton: Princeton University Press, 1961); C. Westoff, R. G. Potter, and P. Sagi, *The Third Child* (Princeton: Princeton University Press, 1963).

25. E.g., L. W. Hoffman and F. Wyatt, ''Social Change and Motivations for Having Larger Families: Some Theoretical Considerations,'' *Merrill-Palmer Quarterly*, VI (1960), pp. 235–244.

26. E.g., B. Frieden, *The Feminine Mystique* (New York: Norton, 1963).

27. See J. Blake, this volume.

move the field of population research to a position considerably higher in their own scheme of priorities than the less than marginal position which it presently occupies. Because of the intimacy with which fundamental human passions and relationships are involved, the motivational and decisional processes associated with human fertility should provide a rewarding context in which psychologists may come to grips in research with important aspects of personality and social psychology.

ACKNOWLEDGEMENT

I am indebted to Mr. Richard Gardner for bibliographic assistance.

PART II

Natality Patterns and
Programs for Effecting Change

W. Parker Mauldin

APPLICATION OF SURVEY TECHNIQUES TO FERTILITY STUDIES

INTRODUCTION

Interest in fertility levels, differentials, and trends has grown during the past two decades, and this interest has quickened during the past decade. But curiously, there has been a rather slow response in the field of fertility studies to the forces growing out of two revolutions that have taken place since World War II: a revolution in mortality which has seen declines in death rates three to five times as rapidly as before the war; and a revolution in the hopes and aspirations of man that is highlighted in the creation of new nations and in the popularization of new phrases such as Five Year Plans, development economies, and economic take-off.

Birth rates in the developing countries now average 40–45 (per 1,000 population per year). To bring these down to the European level of 17 or 18 would mean a drop of some 25 points in the birth rate. Given a population of more than two billion people in the developing areas, this implies a reduction of some 50 million births per annum, if the reduction were accomplished at this time. If the reduction is postponed until the end of the century, the figures will have doubled, and a reduction of 100 million births per year will be needed.

The decline of the birth rate in Europe took 60 to 70 years— from 1880, when reductions in the birth rate became general in Western Europe, until the 1940's when moderate levels of fertility were to be found throughout most of Europe. For some countries the shift from moderately high to low birth rates took longer.

Birth rates are higher in the developing areas now than they were in Europe just before the major declines that brought fertility rates to their current lows. It is clear that the tempo of the European demographic transition is too slow if Asia and Africa and Latin America are to realize their hopes and aspirations, at least if this is to be done during the twentieth century.

This is an era in which it is generally acknowledged that the world has a population problem and that something must be done about it. There is still a sizeable body of intellectuals and moralists who feel that economic development is the key to the problem and that fertility declines will follow economic advancement. They reason that economic advancement brings with it increased education, increased vertical mobility, increased urbanization, and all those unspecified processes that are assumed automatically to trigger fertility declines. There was considerable institutional opposition in Europe and America to family planning and such opposition may have retarded declines in fertility. Today governments are taking action in the field of population in advance of the people themselves, and perhaps this new climate of opinion can speed up the transition from high birth rates to more modest ones. As Kirk has phrased it:

> The European demographic transition occurred in a much less favorable atmosphere with reference to family planning than exists in the world today. Family planning spread among European populations in spite of the specific opposition of restrictive legislation, religious opposition (including not only Catholic but Protestant opposition), and in what might be called a "conspiracy of silence" with reference to sexual matters and birth control. There were of course militant fringe groups advocating birth control, but the prevailing middle class morality prevented free public discussion.

The formal position of governments was generally pronatalist and in some cases an increase in the birth rate was made a specific governmental policy; as in Nazi Germany, in Fascist Italy, in Communist Russia and in Nationalist Japan. While most of these disappeared with the war and military defeat, even a decade ago the communist doctrinal opposition to family planning and population control was rigid and belligerent.

By contrast, no government in the underdeveloped areas today has a specific pro-natalist policy.[1]

India, Pakistan, Korea, Taiwan, Turkey, and Tunisia have adopted national policies of encouraging family planning; other countries are subsidizing private family planning efforts; and a third group is giving government support to family planning programs even though reduction of the rate of population growth is not now a formal national policy.

At the same time, Communist doctrinal opposition has faded. The Soviet Union and the countries of Eastern Europe have liberal polices regarding abortions and use of contraceptives. The Communist Government of China provides family planning services justified on health and welfare grounds rather than on doctrine.

Governments in Asia, and many of those in the Middle East, are favorably oriented toward the study of population problems, and encourage discussion in this field. Even in Latin America, where low densities and religious orientation combine to impede consideration of population problems, there is a growing and widespread concern, especially about the problem of abortion, which seems to be rapidly increasing among Latin American populations.

Increasingly governments and research institutions are studying population trends, examining fertility patterns, and conducting studies to learn what the people know, what they think, and what they do about family planning. This paper is concerned with examining some of the methodological problems and some of the substantive results from such studies.

---

1. D. Kirk, ''Prospects for Reducing Natality in the Underdeveloped World,'' *Conference on Demographic and Economic Trends in the Developing Countries*, New York, October 10–12, 1963 (mimeographed).

FERTILITY STUDIES

Censuses and registration systems furnish basic data for studies of fertility. Good censuses permit analysis of fertility levels, patterns, and differentials by characteristics such as age, marital status, marriage duration, age at marriage, place of residence, education, occupation, industry, color, and economic status.

In the developing countries, however, censuses frequently do not contain as much information on socioeconomic characteristics as is needed for fertility analysis, and such data often are tabulated by hand, and many cross-classifications are lost to musty files. Also response errors are serious, both on the part of respondents and of enumerators. Registration data are sadly deficient, as is indicated by the estimate that during 1951–1955 only 42 per cent of births in the world were registered, according to a United Nations estimate.[2]

Carefully designed, more narrowly focused surveys using more qualified, better trained interviewers have been used to supplement census and registration data in the developed world, and to help fill the large gap of nonexistent or inadequate censuses and registrations in the developing countries. Such surveys are useful in studying relationships between socioeconomic factors such as race and religion, and demographic behavior, including fertility. They are particularly useful in studying recent trends, and can easily focus on special groups, urban or rural, the educated, the elite, etc. But their promise exceeds their performance to date. Even so, a number of fertility surveys have been carried out over the past few years so that comparable data are now available, or shortly will be, from no fewer than 24 countries throughout the world—from Ceylon, Chile, Czechoslovakia, Ghana, Greece, Hungary, India, Indonesia, Israel, Italy, Jamaica, Japan, Korea, Lebanon, Mexico, Pakistan, Peru, Puerto Rico, Taiwan, Tunisia, Turkey, the United Arab Republic, the United Kingdom, and the United States. In addition to the above studies, the United Nations Demographic Center in Santiago is sponsoring a series of fertility studies in urban areas of several countries, including Argentina, Brazil, Colombia, Costa Rica, Mexico, Panama, and

2. *United Nations Demographic Yearbook, 1956.*

Venezuela. To the best of my knowledge, incidentally, this is the most substantial set of comparative social data ever collected across such a range of societies. Moreover, a few of the pilot projects in the field of family planning are among the most elaborate and extensive social experiments ever carried on in the natural setting. This is so even though rather few of the studies of fertility attitudes and performance have been based on national samples; only in Czechoslovakia, Hungary, Jamaica, Turkey, the United States, and the United Kingdom has such coverage been achieved. Also in India studies of fertility performance, but not of attitudes, have been based on a probability sample of rural areas.

As the results show, many of the attitude studies undertaken in the developing countries have been hastily put together. Indeed, I think it useful to think of them as "sorting" questionnaires rather than as base-line studies inasmuch as their prime purpose, certainly their prime utility, often has been to divide a population into two groups, one of which says it is interested in learning about family planning. Most of these studies have not profited from the Puerto Rican and Jamaican studies of Hill, Stycos, and colleagues, nor from the more sophisticated studies including the Indianapolis study, the Growth of American Families, and the Princeton studies. There is also, and unfortunately, a considerable gap between initiation and publication of such studies. The Puerto Rican study was undertaken mostly in 1953, but the book reporting results was not published until 1959; a number of articles were published prior to this date, to be sure. Most major studies have taken four to five years for publication. The United Nations Mysore study was published nine years after the major field work was done. It is not surprising, therefore, that many investigators in developing countries have not profited from the more sophisticated studies. There are notable exceptions, such as Poti's study of the prevalence of contraceptive practice in Calcutta.[3]

---

3. S. J. Poti, C. R. Malaker, and B. Chakraborti, ''An Enquiry into the Prevalence of Contraceptive Practices in Calcutta City (1956–1957),'' *The Sixth International Conference on Planned Parenthood*, London, 1959; S. J. Poti, B. Chakraborti, and C. R. Malaker, ''Reliability of Data Relating to Contraceptive Practices,'' *Research in Family Planning*, ed. C. V. Kiser (Princeton: Princeton University Press, 1962), pp. 51–65.

RELIABILITY AND VALIDITY

We know in a general way that verbal and nonverbal behavior often are not closely related. Opinion polls, however, have been very accurate in predicting voter behavior, and, when properly used, accurately forecast consumer expenditures. But in the sensitive area of fertility behavior, will people tell about their behavior, and will they tell the truth? How useful are such surveys? Even with reference to the simple statistic, how many births has a woman had, there is great difficulty in obtaining correct information. People in many cultures are neither time nor numbers conscious and tend to forget the number of children born, those born within a specified time, and even the number of living children they now have.[4]

With respect to attitudes or to more intimate aspects of fertility behavior, it would be surprising if accurate data could be obtained. The sophisticated American and British studies have given good results on past performance (number of children born), moderately good results on the number of children expected to be born within a few years, but rather disappointing results on most other subjects. For example, significant relationships between psychological factors and fertility simply have not been found. Perhaps the relationships do not exist. Certainly it has been possible to interview persons about all aspects of their beliefs and behavior. Indeed some investigators say that the American public is more sensitive to answering questions about income than about sexual behavior. The major barrier in obtaining such information seems to be timidity of the interviewers themselves. Ten years or so ago questions about the number of children desired, the number expected, knowledge about contraceptive methods, use of contraception, and the like were seldom asked. But today the situation is much changed and such studies are being undertaken in almost all areas of the world, developed and developing. It is well to recall, however, that the first representative study in this field in the United

4. R. K. Som, ''On Recall Lapse in Demographic Studies,'' *International Population Conference*, Vienna, 1959; A. J. Coale, ''The Population of the United States in 1950, A Revision of Census Figures,'' *Journal of the American Statistical Association*, L (March, 1955), pp. 16–54; U.S. Bureau of the Census, *The Post-Enumeration Survey: 1950*, Technical Paper No. 4 (Washington, D.C.: 1960).

States was undertaken only in 1955,[5] and this study, "in many ways a model of design, focused upon current reproductive behavior, thus restricting the age-range of women covered and sacrificing data on changes in incidence over time."[6] The earlier studies in the United States, such as the Indianapolis study, were not designed to be representative of women in the United States in general.

How meaningful is an answer to a question about desired family size, and how reliable are data on recollection of family size desired at the time of marriage? In the mid-1930's Kelly conducted a study of marital compatibility among 300 engaged couples. In 1953–54, almost 20 years later, a special investigation was made of those couples neither spouse of which had married more than once, who had reported no problems of sterility, and had not adopted children. The authors conclude that though the estimate of the number of children is fairly accurate, the correlation between the desired and actual family size is quite low, only 0.30.

> The high level of accuracy of the aggregate prediction appears to be a statistical artifact resulting from the sample proportions of couples who planned all pregnancies and those who did not. Recall of originally stated preferences after passage of time and intervening experience reveals considerable error, associated with both success in planning and actual size of family. . . . Correlations between actual number of children and recalled family-size preferences are seriously inflated.[7]

These results are not reassuring—highly educated young persons on the eve of marriage are not good predictors of the number of children they will eventually have, even though they think they know how many they want. Further, 20 years later they cannot recall with accuracy what they thought about family size 20 years before, but they think they can remember. We can

5. R. Freedman, P. K. Whelpton, and A. A. Campbell, *Family Planning, Sterility and Population Growth* (New York: McGraw-Hill, 1959).

6. D. V. Glass, "Family Limitation in Europe: A Survey of Recent Studies," *Research in Family Planning*, ed. C. V. Kiser (Princeton: Princeton University Press, 1962), p. 231.

7. C. F. Westoff, E. G. Mishler, and E. L. Kelly, "Preferences in Size of Family and Eventual Fertility Twenty Years After," *The American Journal of Sociology*, LXII (March, 1957), pp. 491–497.

be slightly comforted by the fact that individual errors tended to cancel out and the aggregates were fairly accurate.

The situation may be even worse among an illiterate population unaccustomed to thinking in terms of planning, and largely uninformed about how to determine the number of children that one has. Such people are unfamiliar with the idea of family limitation, unfamiliar with verbalizing some of their wants, certainly unfamiliar with answering the questions of a stranger.

Another study in the United States reinforces the view that reliability in responses over a period of time is only moderate. Among a sample of mothers initially interviewed shortly after a second birth and then reinterviewed three years later, 20 per cent gave contradictory replies as to the use or nonuse of contraception during the interval between marriage and the first birth. For the period between the first birth and the second pregnancy, 15 per cent gave contradictory replies. In each instance, the contradictions were about equally divided in their direction. Among those reporting a miscarriage, three quarters gave contradictory answers. Mainly, these involved an inconsistency as to the month when the miscarriage was said to have occurred; one third of them involved a discrepancy in the number of miscarriages reported.[8]

In the Ramanagran [9] study (a rural area in India), 75 per cent (811 of 1,008 couples) expressed an interest in learning a method of family planning, and 25 per cent (277 couples) said they were unwilling to learn. Later when the action program began, 10 per cent (98 couples) were unwilling to learn when the opportunity was offered, although earlier they said they were willing to learn. Indeed, only 14 per cent of the "want-to-learn" couples in Ramanagran learned the method. It was estimated that about 25 per cent of the couples who said they wanted to learn a method of family planning might be eligible for and would want to use the rhythm method if the action program were to continue.

In the developing countries, at least in some cultures, there is

8. C. F. Westoff, R. G. Potter, Jr., and P. C. Sagi, "Some Estimates of the Reliability of Survey Data on Family Planning," *Population Studies,* XV (July, 1961), pp. 52–69.

9. World Health Organization, *Final Report on Pilot Studies in Family Planning* (New Delhi: W. H. O. Regional Office for Southeast Asia, Sept., 1954), pp. 20, 49, 81.

evidence that women are shy and are reluctant to talk about family planning. The data shown in Table 1 from a study in Lodi Colony, India, are revealing.

At the time of a visit to a clinic 80 per cent of the women in this subsample said they had previously used contraception, but

TABLE 1

Distribution of Contraceptive Methods Reported in Use in Lodi Colony, India

Method	Per cent of women reporting use in attitude survey (all women)	Responses of 328 women who came to clinic	
		In the survey (Per cent)	Later, at the clinic (Per cent)
Condom	41	33	23
Rhythm	17	10	5
Abstinence	14	18	3
Withdrawal	11	17	30
Chemicals	6	4	2
Diaphragm or diaphragm and cap	4	3	1
Sterilization	5	—	—
Combination of different methods	—	16	37
Not given	2	—	—
Any method	35	51	80
Number reporting use	443	169	262
Number interviewed	1,274	328	328

Source: World Health Organization *Final Report on Pilot Studies in Family Planning* (New Delhi: W. H. O. Regional Office for South East Asia, Sept., 1954), pp. 61–62.

at the time of the initial survey only 51 per cent of them had admitted such use. Surveys in Great Britain, Pakistan, Turkey, and Korea lend support to the view that women understate contraceptive use, but studies in India sometimes support, sometimes cast doubt on this interpretation. In Mysore, India, only three per cent of rural couples and 12 per cent of urban couples were judged to have practiced contraception, but females were about twice as likely as males to report such use.

The responses obtained from men indicated generally somewhat smaller percentages of users of family limitation methods, with variations among the different areas that followed on the whole the pattern of the women's responses. In comparing the figures for men and women it must be considered that mis-statements may have resulted from the shyness of respondents and their reluctance to discuss personal matters with strangers. The investigators who interviewed the men may not have been able to get the same co-operation as those who interviewed the women; the latter had, as a rule, more time to establish good rapport with the respondents. The main difference between the responses of men and women was that the latter more frequently reported the use of abstinence.[10]

Both in Korea and in the Dacca Growth Study, data are available on husband and wife reports of contraceptive usage. In Dacca, 96 husbands and wives both reported use of contraception; 98 husbands reported such use but their wives did not; and only 17 wives reported use of contraception when their husbands did not. There was no marked difference in reporting of husbands and wives by type of method.[11] In Korea, the numbers are smaller, but the results are in the same direction. Among 94 couples reporting use of contraception, only 25 husbands and wives gave the same report; 59 husbands and 10 wives gave such reports but their spouses did not.[12]

The most detailed study of husband-wife differences in reported use of contraception was made in the Calcutta area. Poti in 1956–57 found that husbands' reports on contraceptive usage were much more valid than reports of wives. His sample design was quite similar to that of the Indianapolis Study, and it consisted of 1,018 couples from three broad social classes in Calcutta. There was complete agreement in husbands' and wives' reports on contraceptive usage in only one fifth to one seventh of the cases, with slightly higher agreement among the lower social classes. After editing, 50 to 60 per cent of the interviews were in agreement. In most cases the reconciliation achieved by editing accepted the husband's report. In the

10. United Nations, *The Mysore Population Study* (New York: United Nations, 1961).

11. D. Yaukey, B. Roberts, and W. Griffiths, ''Husbands' vs. Wives' Responses to a Fertility Survey,'' *Population Studies*, XIX (July, 1965), pp. 25–31.

12. Sook Bang, Man Gap Lee, and Jae Mo Yang, ''A Survey of Fertility and Attitude Toward Family Planning in Rural Korea,'' *Yonsei Medical Journal*, IV (1963), pp. 77–102.

remaining 40 to 50 per cent of the cases the subjects were again interviewed by either male or female supervisors or both and necessary amendments were made on the basis of information collected at the reinterview. After the reinterview, a comparison was made of the husband's and wife's initial responses with the responses that were considered correct by the reinterview. These data show that the reports of wives were only one half as accurate as those of husbands. Table 2 gives the percentage of

TABLE 2

Reliability of Reporting on Use or Nonuse of Contraceptives, by Social Class in Calcutta

	Social Classes		
	High	*Middle*	*Low*
Per cent of interpregnancy intervals correctly reported by:			
Husbands	71	62	72
Wives	44	36	30
Per cent of months of exposure to risk, correctly reported by:			
Husbands	75	78	76
Wives	40	33	30

Source: S. J. Poti, B. Chakraborti, and C. R. Malaker, "Reliability of Data Relating to Contraceptive Practices," *Research in Family Planning*, ed. C. V. Kiser (Princeton: Princeton University Press, 1962), pp. 57, 59.

intervals and the percentage of months of contraceptive usage correctly reported by husbands and wives.

The results of this study have revealed that the reports of the husbands are more dependable than those of the wives. The female investigators frequently reported that the wives felt too shy to report the use of contraceptives, particularly in large households where it was difficult to hold the interview in privacy. The husbands, with few exceptions, were cooperative and consequently their reporting errors were mostly ascribable to lapse of recall, and could be considerably reduced to appropriate amendments effected by re-interview. There were difficulties in verifying whether a pregnancy occurred as a result of failure of contraceptive or whether it was a planned one because of a subsequent change of attitude towards child birth. As this is a crucial question in the determination of pregnancy rates for different types of contracepted exposures, a more thorough investigation of the problem is essential.[13]

Other data on knowledge and attitudes could be given, though these are more difficult to interpret. In general such studies show that men have more knowledge about family planning methods, men report greater use of contraceptives, but women say they are more interested in family planning. This latter finding has led many investigators to conclude that women are more interested in family planning than are men, and to suggest that KAP studies (Knowledge about, Attitudes toward, and Practice of family planning) and action programs can more profitably be directed toward women. The evidence for this is ambiguous, at best, and perhaps contradictory. In developing countries it may be true that the male is actually dominant; he certainly is the breadwinner, the migrant, the more educated, etc. Perhaps we are safe in ignoring the male in studies of fertility in developed countries, as is now done; but this seems foolhardy in developing countries. Now let us turn to an examination of what the data show.

DESIRED FAMILY SIZE

Table 3 summarizes results from a variety of studies about desired family size, including the reported average number of children desired and the percentages of respondents saying they want four or more, and five or more children. These data are presented in spite of the fact that they are not entirely comparable, and, even if they were, there is serious question as to how meaningful they might be. Hill, Stycos, and Back say that ''posing simple questions which elicit 'yes' or 'no' answers to problems as complex as attitudes about family size and birth control may no longer be justified. The techniques of progressive cross-classification and specification described . . . show that there are many facets to these innocent-appearing topics.''[14] Stycos and Back show that large proportions of respond-

13. S. J. Poti, B. Chakraborti, and C. R. Malaker, ''Reliability of Data Relating to Contraceptive Practices,'' *Research in Family Planning*, ed. C. V. Kiser (Princeton: Princeton University Press, 1962), p. 65.

14. R. Hill, J. M. Stycos, and K. W. Back, *The Family and Population Control, A Puerto Rican Experiment in Social Change* (Chapel Hill: University of North Carolina Press, 1959), p. 3.

ents are inconsistent in their replies to attitudinal questions about the desirability of large and of small families, and conclude that in Jamaica "attitudes on family size, while generally favorable to the small family, are characterized by ambivalence and lack of intensity." [15]

The questions asked varied considerably. Some examples are:

United States	"What do you think is the ideal number of children for the *average* American family?"
	"Just before you were married, how many children did you think you would want during your married life?"
	"A year after your first child was born how many children did you want to have altogether?"
	"If you could have (more) children in coming years how many children would you want to have altogether (counting those you have now)?"
India (Mysore Study)	"How many children make an ideal-sized family?"
Korea	"What would be an ideal number of children, if you could control the number as you wish?"
Puerto Rico	"Supposing you were about to get married again for the first time. How many children would you want to have?"
Jamaica	"If you could live your life over, how many children would you like to have?"
Lebanon	"Suppose you have a very close friend, in the same circumstances as yourself, and she asked you for advice on the convenient number of children for her. What is the number of children you would advise her to have, if she could?"

15. J. M. Stycos and K. W. Back, *Prospects for Fertility Reduction, The Jamaica Family Life Project, A Preliminary Report* (New York: The Conservation Foundation, Oct., 1957), p. 14.

TABLE 3

Number of Children as Reported in Surveys of Developed and Developing Countries [a]

Area	Date	Sex of respondent	Type of sample [b]	Size of sample	Average number children	Range of one standard deviation around average [c]	Per cent wanting 4 or more children	Per cent wanting 5 or more children
Austria [1,d]	1960	F	GP	na	2.0	na	4	na
West Germany [1]	1960	F	GP	na	2.2	na	4	na
Czechoslovakia [2]	1959	F	PN	3,192	2.3	na	na	na
Hungary [3]	1958–60	F	PN	6,732	2.4	0.8–4.0	13	6
Great Britain	1960 [1]	F	GP	na	2.8	na	23	na
Great Britain	1946 [19]	F	PN	10,000	2.1	0.6–4.8	25	15
France [1]	1960	F	GP	na	2.8	na	17	na
	1956	F	N	10,645	2.2	na	na	na
Japan [16]	1961	F	PN	2,753	2.8	1.5–4.1	22	8
Switzerland [1]	1960	F	GP	na	2.9	na	22	na
Puerto Rico [7]	1947	F	PN	5,475	3.0	na	19	na
	1953	F	N	888	3.0	(2.4–3.2)	19	na
	1953	F	Clinic	3,000	3.0	(2.4–3.9)	12	na
						(2.2–4.1)		
Italy [1]	1960	F	GP	na	3.1	na	18	na
Norway [1]	1960	F	GP	na	3.1	na	25	na
Netherlands [1]	1960	F	GP	na	3.3	na	39	na
United States	1960 [4]	F	PN	2,414	3.3	1.7–4.9	40	15
	1955 [5]	F	PN	2,684	3.4	2.1–4.7	49	8
	1945 [5]	F	GP	na	3.3	2.2–4.4	41	10
	1941 [5]	F	GP	na	3.0	1.8–4.2	27	6
Ceylon [22]	1963	M	R	302	3.2	na	25	12
Jamaica [6]	1957	F	U/R	1,368	3.4/4.2	na	48	19
Turkey [12]	1963	M	PN	2,387	3.8	2.1–5.5	48	32
	1963	F	PN	2,735	3.2	1.7–4.7	36	18
South Africa [9]	1957–8	F	U	1,022	3.6	2.4–4.8	54	10
Taiwan [18]	1962–3	F	U	2,432	3.9	2.9–4.9	62	22
	1962	M	U	241	3.8	2.7–4.7	57	19
	1962	F	U	241	3.8	2.8–5.2	57	18
Pakistan [13]	ca. 1960	M	U	989	4.0	2.3–5.5	66	26
	1960	F	U	1,007	3.0	5.5	64	25

TABLE 5 (continued)

Area	Date	Sex of respondent	Type of sample[b]	Size of sample	Average number children	Range of one standard deviation around average[c]	Per cent wanting 4 or more children	Per cent wanting 5 or more children
Chile[8]	1959	F	U	1,970	4.1	2.6–5.6	58	26
Canada[1]	1960	F	GP	na	4.2	na	70	na
India (Mysore)[14]	1952	M	U	1,011	3.7	na	na	na
	1952	F	U	793	4.1	na	na	na
	1952	M	R	392	4.7	na	na	na
	1952	F	R	323	4.6	na	na	na
Central India[15]	1958	M & F	U/R	2,314	3.8	2.2–5.4	57	25
New Delhi[21]	1957–60	M	R	311	4.1	2.7–5.5	60	34
	1957–60	F	R	765	4.2	3.0–5.4	63	33
Indonesia[20]	1961–62	M & F	R	2,208	4.3	na	66	36
Korea[17]	1962	M	R	914	4.3	3.1–5.6	73	42
	1962	F	R	970	4.4	3.3–5.5	80	45
Ghana[10]	1963	M	U	296	5.5	na	89	67
	1963	F	U	341	5.1	na	88	56

[a] Percentages not specifying number of children are excluded from the base in calculating percentages wanting a specified number. Excluded percentages are: Hungary, 5; Jamaica, 3; Puerto Rico, 1.9 for Hatt's sample, 16.1 among out-patient department respondents, and 5.3 in the stratification sample of Hill and colleagues; Chile, 1; South Africa, 1; Egypt, 45 in completed families, 34 in incompleted families; Lebanon, 75 among rural uneducated to a low of 10 among the urban educated; Turkey, 7 among men, 15 among women; Pakistan, 24 among men, 26 among women; Central India, 30; Japan, 1; Korea, 1 for men and 1 for women; Taiwan, 2 for women, 1 for men.

[b] Type of sample:
GP   Gallup Poll
PN   National probability sample
N   National but not a probability sample
R   Rural area
U   Urban area
Clinic   Patients coming to a hospital clinic

[c] Range: Figures in parentheses refer to the middle 50 per cent of the range; it was not possible to calculate the standard deviation because of the way in which the data were presented.

[d] The numbers in superscripts refer to correspondingly numbered sources in Appendix.

Although the data are not strictly comparable, they are interesting! We are fond of saying that almost everywhere people share, or are coming to share, the small family ideal. The average number of children desired varies from two to more than six, and people in developed areas want smaller families than do people in developing areas. If we use 3.5 as a cutting point, only Canada among the developed countries is above, and only Puerto Rico among the developing areas is below this number. In Europe the average desired family is smaller than three in most countries—Italy, Norway, and the Netherlands being the exceptions. To the extent that these data are valid, it is evident that the small family ideal is not yet a part of the culture of many in the developing countries. This is highlighted if one looks at proportions of people saying they want four or more children. In Europe typically less than one fifth of the married couples want four or more children, and only one country, the Netherlands, shows a figure higher than 25 per cent. But among the developing countries, typically more than one half of the people want four or more children, and in Pakistan and Korea more than two thirds of the people say they want at least four children. The notable exceptions to these generalizations are the United States and Canada, where many still desire moderately large families, and in the developing areas, Jamaica and Puerto Rico, where small families are rapidly becoming the ideal.

DESIRE TO LIMIT FAMILY SIZE

Perhaps it is more relevant for persons interested in introducing family planning to examine the figures in Table 4, which shows the proportions of respondents who say they do not want additional children. Replies to questions about wanting or not wanting additional children can be grouped into three categories: want more children, do not want more children, and indifferent or uncertain. For convenience in comparing replies of populations from different areas, this table shows only the percentage saying that they do not want more children. Where the question was not asked but where replies were given to ideal family size, persons having *n* children are counted as not wanting more if they gave *n* or a smaller number as the ideal. It should be added that though no claim is made as to completeness of coverage, the relative scarcity of countries listed in Table 4 is an indication of the lack of information on this item.

Respondents in Japan, Hungary, and Puerto Rico share the distinction of wanting to limit family size the most. Similarly, respondents in Pakistan and India are least interested in limiting family size. Ceylon and Taiwan give somewhat varying responses, dependent upon whether one examines replies of those having three, four, or five or more children. Suffice it to say that there are sizeable proportions of those having four or more living children who do not want more children. Among a majority of countries listed, at least one half the married couples with three or more children say they do not want more children.

KNOWLEDGE, ATTITUDE, AND PRACTICE

Knowledge about birth control methods, physiology of human reproduction, and the rhythm theory is hard to measure and is highly variable by geographic area and socioeconomic status; such information is seldom reported and the meager information that is available is not reported in anything approaching a standard format. Typically it is assumed, and with reason, that in developed countries almost everyone has some knowledge about birth control methods. Questions about rhythm typically are asked only of those who object to other methods on moral grounds. In the developing countries, when questions about knowledge of contraceptive methods are asked, the proportions who have such knowledge typically are so low that almost any vague answer is accepted as positive information. Even so, the scattered available data show that knowledge is greater among those groups where one would expect to find more information: among men more than women, urban dwellers more than rural, the educated more than the uneducated, the well-to-do more than the poor, and so on. In India, where there has been a large number of studies, proportions expressing approval of the idea of family limitation range from about two thirds to four fifths, for example, 80 per cent in Singur, 70 per cent in Central India,

TABLE 4

Per Cent of Persons Reporting They Do Not Want More Children

Area	Date	Re-spondent	Sample Type	Sample Size	Among those having				Among all persons inter-viewed
					2 living children	3 living children	4 living children	5 or more living children	
Puerto Rico [7,a,*]	1953	F	N	885	na	—	87 (3 or 4)	93 (5 or 6)	87
Jamaica [6,b]	1957	F	U/R	1,368	56	68	80 (4 or 5)	84 (6 or more)	—
Hungary [3,c]	1958–60	F	PN	6,732	85	92	95	93	62
Turkey [12,d]	1963	M & F	PN	5,100	5	23	44	66	59
East Pakistan [23,e]	1963	M	U	543	28	48	57	54	45
	1963	F	U	543	15	51	55	73	51
West Pakistan [13,c]	ca. 1960	M	U	1,098	13	32	68	71	41
	ca. 1960	F	U	989	29	45	66	75	46
India [15]	1958	M & F	U/R	2,314	27	42	75	85	37
India [21,e]	1957–60	M	R	311	26	40	71	92	44
	1957–60	F	R	734	20	48	75	91	44
Ceylon [24,f]	1962	F	R	758	29	57	69	88	44
Taiwan [25,g]	1962–63	F	U	2,432	24	54	76	88 (5 children)	—
Japan [16,g]	1961	F	PN	2,897	76	95	98	97	72

a The figures shown are calculated as 100 minus those reported as "Want more or don't care;" the only other category shown on the questionnaire was "Does not want more."

b The preliminary report gives only the per cent who want more children. The figures shown in this table are 100 minus those who do not want more children, and therefore probably are too high inasmuch as they probably include those who don't care, etc.

c Those desiring the same number or fewer children than they have.

d Per cent saying ideal number is fewer or the same as the number of children they have.

e Per cent saying they hope they will not have any more children.

f Respondents were only those expressing an interest in family planning—70 per cent of total interviewed; data were not available for persons having five or more children, but only for persons having five or six children.

g The figures shown are calculated by subtracting reported percentages of persons saying they want more children from 100; the report does not show the proportion expressing no opinion.

63 to 72 per cent in Trivandrum. But the percentages saying they have knowledge of some contraceptive method are much smaller, varying from 11 among females in rural areas in Mysore, 15 among males in rural areas in Mysore, 28 among females in six villages near Delhi, 38 among both males and females in Bangalore, and 43 among males in three villages near Delhi. Similar figures are to be found in many of the developing areas, and, of course, knowledge of contraceptive methods ranges upward to the high 90's in developed countries such as Japan.

Sometimes questions are asked about a desire to learn about a family planning method, and a large majority of respondents usually say they would like to learn more about this subject. In part such answers probably reflect a real desire for more information about how to limit family size, but in part the "yes" answer is a generalized expression of wanting to learn about a new topic, with the respondent not being quite sure what it is all about. Thus it should be no surprise that the proportion of persons who learn about and adopt a method of family limitation is much smaller than the proportion saying they would be willing to learn about such methods. Caldwell,[16] in his study among the more advantaged urban classes in Ghana, attempted to get more realistic answers by asking a series of questions which may be summarized as follows:

	Per Cent Expressing Approval	
	Males	*Females*
"If you were told by a doctor of some way (or a better way) to avoid having a baby, would you use it?"	72	63
"If the method were complicated, would you use it?"	37	26

In almost all studies that have been conducted, an overwhelming majority of respondents approve the idea of family planning, a large majority express some interest in learning more about this subject, and in the developing countries very few have detailed information about birth control, since only small

16. Unpublished data provided to the author by J. C. Caldwell, Associate Professor of Sociology, Population Council Post, University of Ghana.

proportions have used such methods. Proportions who have used them vary widely: 1 per cent in rural Mysore; 6 per cent in urban Mysore; 3 per cent in Trivandrum; 3 to 8 per cent in villages near Delhi; 8 to 18 per cent in Lahore, Pakistan; 21 to 36 per cent in Dacca, Pakistan; 4 to 9 per cent in Korea; 24 per cent in Turkey; 1.5 per cent in rural Egypt; 12 per cent in semi-urban Egypt; and 17 per cent in urban Egypt.

CONTRACEPTIVE METHODS

It is generally agreed that women, more than men, want to limit the number of children they have. Survey results support this view, though there are some exceptions, and the differences usually are not very great. Indeed, an examination of data shows that women more than men want small families in Jamaica, Ghana, Turkey, Mysore, and perhaps Lahore. No differences between men and women were found in Japan, Korea, Taiwan, South Africa, Ceylon, and in many areas of India such as Trivandrum, Madras, Singur, Poona, and villages in North India. It is not sufficiently recognized, however, that male methods of contraception are used far more than are female methods. Indeed, probably only in Japan has the major means of reducing fertility rates been by use of female methods, and there the method has been abortion. The case is not clear in Puerto Rico although female sterilizations have been numerous and may have been a major factor in reduction of fertility rates. Table 5 groups contraceptive methods by male, female, and combined methods such as rhythm and abstinence. The data presented in Table 5 show that male methods are used much more than female methods in most countries of the world; even in the United States male methods are almost as popular as female methods. In Puerto Rico and Trivandrum female sterilizations are important methods of family limitation, but the proportion of users in Trivandrum is very small, less than four per cent.

As already noted, in most societies where attitude studies toward family planning have been conducted, males report the use of contraception to a greater extent than do females. This is true with respect both to male and female methods of contraception.

TABLE 5

Per Cent Reporting Use of Contraceptives by Method in Selected Countries

Methods	United States, 1955[b],[*]	United States, 1960[4]	Great Britain[25], 1950–1960	Jamaica[6]	Puerto Rico[7] (clinic patients)	Puerto Rico[7] (stratification)	Czechoslovakia[1]	Hungary[8]	Japan, 1961[18]	Japan, 1960[27]	Greece[28]	South Africa[11]	Turkey[12] M	Turkey[12] F	Pakistan,[13] Lahore	Korea[17]	Ceylon[24]	India,[30] Lodi Colony	India,[29] Trivandrum
All male methods	58	67	91	72	33	28	88	94	48	52	91	83	113	86	37	23	58	52	42
All male-female methods	36	39	19	11	4	16		15	39	27		28	42	63	46	10	13	31	10
All female methods	74	79	32	44	62	56		37	23	45		72	23	22	10	71	29	17	48
Unspecified	2	1					12	1	1	10	9	1			7	7		2	
Male methods																			
Coitus interruptus	15	17	44	59	17	11	67	64	7	13	65	32	59	52	8		7	11	
Condom	43	50	49	13	16	17	21a	30	40	39	25	51	54	34	29	23	51	41	3
Male and female methods																			
Rhythm	34	35	16	3	4	16		11	39	27		26	20	11	12	10	13	17	10
Abstinence	2	4	3	8				4				2	3	11	34			14	
Female methods																			
Appliance																			
Diaphram	36	38	11	4	3	3		7	4	6		18	0	0	5	9	8	4	2
Other	4		10					2	1	4		15							
Chemical																			
Jellies and cream	6	11	3	4	1	2		2	7	16		16	2	1	5	44	21	2	
Foam tablets			3	28				8	5	14		4	15	11					
Other		6										6	8	4					
Miscellaneous																			
Douche	28b	24	3	7	6	4		18	1			13	17	46		18			
Sterilization				1	52c	47c			5	5			0	1				5	38
Other			2										26	27					
Total **	170	186	145	127	100	100	100	147	100d	134d	100	184	181	174	100	111	100	100	100
Number of users	1,901	1,948	1,444	165	1,165	329	2,403	3,875	1,974	1,623	2,501	838	566	774	436	96	499	443	616
Total sample	2,713	2,414	2,338	1,368	3,000	888	3,200	6,732	2,897	5,579	3,838	1,022	2,387	2,735	1,098	1,884	758	1,274	17,750

a This is a minimal figure inasmuch as 24 per cent of the couples reported using coitus interruptus and other methods, with the method being the condom.
b Does not include 306 wives who reported douche for cleanliness only.
c Reports of females; it was assumed that all reported sterilizations were of females.
d Excludes sterilizations and abortions.
* The numbers in superscripts refer to correspondingly numbered sources in Appendix.
** Where percentages add to 100, the base is total of all methods used; where percentages exceed 100, the base is total persons who have used any method.

CONCLUDING REMARKS

The above comments on indications of low reliability on some questions and lack of validity on others should not obscure the fact that much useful information has been obtained from fertility surveys. And much more useful information can be obtained. It is clear that substantial proportions both of men and of women say they want to limit family size, particularly after three or four children. The figures vary somewhat from place to place, and their over-all validity is reinforced by surveys such as those in rural Ghana where it is evident that people have not yet begun to think in terms of family limitation. There, respondents say they want more than 10 children, on the average, but in the city among the economically more fortunate, desired family size is about one half that number.[17] But in the developing areas of the world, desired family size is smaller than in Ghana; this is true in Asia, in South America, in the Caribbean, and particularly in Europe, Japan, and the United States. Such information is not generally known to the intellectuals, the middle and upper grades of government servants, the elites in countries such as Pakistan, Turkey, and the United Arab Republic, or in South America. One of the important functions of such studies is to inform various publics, and indeed to determine attitudes among various elites as well as among a cross section of the population.

Time has not permitted an adequate treatment of many methodological questions such as differences between expected and desired family size, the use of scaling techniques in establishing base-line measures, the need for applying moderately sophisticated techniques that have been known for at least 10 years, problems of collecting accurate vital statistics, and many others. For example, the methodological problems associated with application of the Chandrasekaran-Deming model of collecting vital statistics is currently receiving a practical test on a national basis in Pakistan.[18] Similarly, the thesis of Kamat [19]

17. *Idem.*
18. N. Ahmed and K. J. Krotki, ''Simultaneous Estimations of Population Growth,'' *The Pakistan Development Review,* III (Spring, 1963), pp. 37–65.
19. M. Kamat and R. G. Kamat, ''Diet and Fecundity in India,'' *The Sixth International Conference on Planned Parenthood,* London, 1959.

and Mahalanobis [20] that fecundity has been reduced in India as a result of seriously inadequate diets deserves attention, particularly so inasmuch as there is some evidence by Das Gupta [21] and colleagues that fertility in India is increasing. Also many surveys indicate quite clearly that differential fertility has begun to operate in a number of countries where census data have not previously shown such differentials.[22]

This is an era of ferment, of social experimentation, of rapid social change. There is a tendency to depend too much on censuses to measure change, but these cannot adequately reflect rapid and recent changes. There is a tendency to rely on governmental statistics for an indication of success or failure of national programs, but in the field of family planning, governmental programs may be primarily catalytic agents rather than the total effort. Surveys can help bridge the gap, but they must be used more often, on a broader base, with more sophistication, and the data must be processed more rapidly.

The studies partially summarized in this paper do not reflect use-effectiveness studies of newer methods of birth control. They do not tell us anything about the use of Emko [23] in Puerto Rico, of the widespread use of oral tablets in the United States, and perhaps in the United Arab Republic and other places, or the adoption of intrauterine devices in the United States, Chile, India, Pakistan, Taiwan, Tunisia, Korea, and Japan. The development of better contraceptive methods, in a wider range, undoubtedly will do much to speed up the adoption of such methods. Repeated surveys will be needed to ascertain the extent to which people are informed or misinformed about such methods, and the extent to which such methods are available at a

20. P. C. Mahalanobis, foreword to *Couple Fertility* by A. Das Gupta, R. K. Som, M. Majumdar, and S. N. Mitra, The National Sample Survey No. 7 (Calcutta: Statistical Publishing Society, 1956).

21. A. Das Gupta, R. K. Som, M. Majumdar, and D. N. Mitra, *Couple Fertility*, The National Sample Survey No. 7 (Calcutta: Statistical Publishing Society, 1956).

22. See, for example, J. C. Caldwell's study of Ghana; H. Rizk's unpublished thesis on "Differential Fertility in Egypt" (Princeton, 1959); D. Yaukey, *Fertility Differences in a Modernizing Country* (Princeton: Princeton University Press, 1961); and E. D. Driver, *Differential Fertility in Central India* (Princeton: Princeton University Press, 1963).

23. A foaming intravaginal cream manufactured by Emko Company.

reasonable cost and without embarrassment to the potential user.

There are increasing indications of differential fertility in almost every country of the world. Surveys will aid greatly in understanding the factors associated with such differentials; they could tell us whether lack of information or lack of motivation is the principal barrier to the spread of family planning. The evidence is overwhelming that only a small proportion of people in the developing countries have moderately good knowledge of various methods of family planning. And there is almost a pathological fear of the use of mass communication and advertising to inform the poor and the uneducated of what the well-to-do and the educated already know, that there are a number of safe, reliable, simple methods of limiting one's family. Surveys should continue to give us information about the extent to which the masses are learning about methods of family limitation.

APPENDIX

List of sources for Tables 3, 4, and 5

1. D. V. Glass, "Family Limitation in Europe: A Survey of Recent Studies," *Research in Family Planning*, ed. C. V. Kiser (Princeton: Princeton University Press, 1962), pp. 231–261.

2. V. Srb, M. Kucera, and D. Vysusilova, "Investigation Concerning Marriage, Birth Prevention and Abortion (1959)," *Demografie*, III, No. 4 (1961), pp. 311–330.

3. Kozponti Statisztikai Hivatal, *Main Results of the Hungarian TCS-Study* (Budapest, 1963). Data in Table 3 from p. 115; in Table 5 from p. 7.

4. Data from the 1960 survey, Growth of American Families, furnished by A. A. Campbell, Scripps Foundation for Research in Population Problems.

5. R. Freedman, P. K. Whelpton, and A. A. Campbell, *Family Planning, Sterility and Population Growth* (New York: McGraw-Hill, 1959). Data in Table 3 from p. 223.

6. J. M. Stycos and K. Back, *Prospects for Fertility Reduction, The Jamaica Family Life Project, A Preliminary Report* (New York: The Conservation Foundation, Oct., 1957). Data in Table 3 from p. 9.

7. R. Hill, J. M. Stycos, and K. W. Back, *The Family and Population Control, A Puerto Rican Experiment in Social Change* (Chapel Hill: University of North Carolina Press, 1959). Data in Table 3 from p. 72 and p. 133; in Table 5 from p. 170.

8. L. Tabah and R. Samuel, "Preliminary Findings of a Survey on Fertility and Attitudes Toward Family Formation in Santiago, Chile," *Research in Family Planning*, ed. C. V. Kiser (Princeton: Princeton University Press, 1962), p. 289.

9. E. Higgins, "Some Fertility Attitudes Among White Women in Johannesburg," *Population Studies*, XVI (July, 1962), pp. 70–78.

10. Unpublished data provided to the author by J. C. Caldwell, Associate Professor of Sociology, Population Council Post, University of Ghana.

11. L. T. Badenhorst, "Family Limitation and Methods of Contraception in an Urban Population," *Population Studies*, XVI (March, 1963), p. 294.

12. B. Berelson, "The Turkish Survey on Population," *Turkish Seminar on Population* (Istanbul, April, 1964).

13. Social Sciences Research Centre, University of Panjab, *Knowledge of and Attitudes Toward Family Planning* (Lahore: Family Planning Association of Pakistan, not dated), Preface by M. K. H. Khan.

14. United Nations, *The Mysore Population Study* (New York: United Nations, 1961).

15. E. D. Driver, *Differential Fertility in Central India* (Princeton: Princeton University Press, 1963).

16. The Population Problems Research Council, *Sixth Opinion Survey on Family Planning and Birth Control* (Tokyo: The Mainichi Newspapers, 1962).

17. Sook Bang, Man Gap Lee, and Jae Mo Yang, "A Survey of Fertility and Attitude Toward Family Planning in Rural Korea, *Yonsei Medical Journal*, IV (1963), pp. 77–102.

18. R. Freedman, J. Y. Peng, Y. Takeshita, and T. H. Sun, "Fertility Trends in Taiwan: Tradition and Change," *Population Studies*, XVI (March, 1963), pp. 219–236. The data for the larger sample were furnished to the author by R. Freedman in a letter dated May 4, 1964.

19. D. V. Glass and E. Grebenik, *The Trends and Patterns of Fertility in Great Britain*, Papers of the Royal Commission on Population, VI, Part 1, Report (London: Her Majesty's Stationery Office, 1954).

20. H. Gille, letter of May 8, 1964 to the author.

21. S. N. Agarwala, Demographic Section, Institute of Economic Growth, University of Delhi, *Family Planning in Selected Villages* (Asia Publishing House, 1962).

22. A. Kinch, letter of May 20, 1964 to the author.

23. Data from Public Health Education Project—Dacca Family Growth Study.

24. A. Kinch, ''A Report on Some Experiences in the Sweden-Ceylon Family Planning Project,'' *The Seventh International Conference on Planned Parenthood* (Singapore, Feb., 1963).

25. B. Berelson and R. Freedman, data from Taichung Survey, personal communication.

26. R. M. Pierce and G. Rowntree, ''Birth Control in Britain, Part II,'' *Population Studies,* XV (Nov., 1961), pp. 121–160.

27. The Population Problems Research Council, *Public Opinion Survey on Birth Control in Japan* (Tokyo: The Mainichi Newspapers, 1952).

28. V. G. Valaoras, A. Polychronopoulou, and D. Trichopoulos, *Control of Family Size in Greece, The Results of a Field Survey* (unpublished).

29. *Final Report on Pilot Studies in Family Planning* (New Delhi: W. H. O. Regional Office for South East Asia, 1954), p. 61.

30. *Family Planning Communication Research Programme, Report on Preliminary Survey* (Trivandrum: University of Kerala, 1963).

David Goldberg

FERTILITY AND FERTILITY DIFFERENTIALS:
SOME OBSERVATIONS ON RECENT
CHANGES IN THE UNITED STATES

Two features appear to distinguish the past eight or ten years of research on fertility from previous periods. First, the amount and scope of nongovernmental research activity has picked up considerably. Among the studies in this category, the ones referred to most often in this paper are the 1957 Princeton Study of two-parity women and its follow-up, usually identified as the 1957 and 1960 Family Growth in Metropolitan America Study (1957 and 1960 FGIMA), the 1955 and 1960 Growth of American Families Studies of national samples of married women aged 18–39 (1955 and 1960 GAF), the 1962 and 1963 national studies of married women aged 18–39 originating from the Population Studies Center and the Survey Research Center of the University of Michigan (1962 and 1963 UMPSC), and the 1962 Detroit Area Study of zero-, one-, two-, and four-parity wives (1962 DAS). A second feature that appears to be characteristic of the present research as contrasted with past efforts is the growth in the number of variables used to measure fertility behavior and the shift to variables which presumably reflect a greater part of the entire reproductive span—the expected number of children, ideal number, desired number, and birth intervals. In several respects, the "new" collection of fertility variables represents an attempt to avoid the problems of period measurement and provide substitute cohort measures.

The studies mentioned and the continuing efforts of the Bureau of the Census and the National Vital Statistics Division provide us with an exceptionally detailed description of American fertility. Briefly, the major trends and characteristics during the postwar period are: (1) a declining age at marriage which is probably linked to an increasing incidence of illegitimate conception, (2) an apparently casual approach to contraception and spacing of children which, more easily measured, appears as a set of decreasing birth intervals, and (3) a concentration of fertility desires focused on the two to four child range and greater incidence of performance within this range across nearly all major strata of the population.

Various bits of evidence during the past six years suggest that the pattern described above may be changing. The crude birth rate has declined 14–15 per cent between 1957 and 1963. The proportion of women married at the youngest ages may have declined slightly. And 1960 GAF results indicate that the expected number of children in the most recent cohorts is lower than in the preceding cohorts. Whether these movements of data reflect a genuine change in cohort behavior or a stabilization in some of the timing patterns of cohorts is not fully understood yet.

With the exception of certain types of historical data, American fertility patterns are probably better documented than in any other country. To document a pattern, however, does not explain it. On the whole, our understanding of fertility differentials is negligible. Moreover, what we thought we knew in the past, the relationships we took for granted, are being seriously questioned by some recent research. In fact, the most exciting research on differentials during the past few years has either negated what was thought to be true in the past or has found differentials to be increasing precisely in those areas for which contraction had been predicted.

FERTILITY PATTERN

The general sequence in the timing of events in marriage leading to completed family have not been described until recently.[1] The Marriage Registration Area is far from complete; birth records do not contain data on the timing of previous events; and the specialized fertility surveys with their age cutoff and resulting selectivity do not provide enough marriage or birth cohorts to obtain a historical sense of cohort trends. A significant part of this void in our fertility data was filled by the Current Population Survey of marriage, fertility, and childspacing of 1959.[2]

The data from the 1959 Current Population Survey and estimates for the most recent marriage cohorts drawn from 1955, 1960 GAF Studies [3] and 1962, 1963 UMPSC [4] are displayed in Table 1. Restriction to white women was necessitated by the limited materials available for nonwhites. Median age at marriage appears to have been fairly stable among the marriage cohorts of 1901–10 to 1925–29. The depression and war cohorts married at later ages. This was followed by a sharp decline in median age at marriage among the postwar cohorts. The intervals from marriage to first, second, and third birth follow almost identical patterns—stability in interval for cohorts un-

1. P. C. Glick, *American Families* (New York: John Wiley, 1957); National Office of Vital Statistics, ''Child Spacing as Measured from Data Enumerated in the Current Population Survey: United States, April 1950 to April 1954,'' *Special Reports*, XLVII (Oct., 1958).

2. U.S. Bureau of the Census, ''Marriage, Fertility, and Childspacing: August 1959,'' *Current Population Reports*, Series P-20, No. 108 (July, 1961).

3. The major publication from the 1955 GAF Study is R. Freedman, P. K. Whelpton, and A. A. Campbell, *Family Planning, Sterility and Population Growth* (New York: McGraw-Hill, 1959). The volume describing the results of the 1960 GAF Study is, as yet, unpublished. Some relevant materials from the study have appeared in articles: P. K. Whelpton, ''Cohort Analysis and Fertility Projections,'' *Emerging Techniques in Population Research*, Proceedings of the 1962 Milbank Round Table (New York: Milbank Memorial Fund, 1963), pp. 39–64; and A. A. Campbell, P. K. Whelpton, and R. F. Tomasson, ''The Reliability of Birth Expectations of U.S. Wives,'' *International Population Conference New York 1961*, International Union for the Scientific Study of Population (London: John Wright, 1963), I, pp. 49–57.

4. M. Axelrod, R. Freedman, D. Goldberg, and D. Slesinger, ''Fertility Expectations of the U.S. Population: A Time Series,'' *Population Index*, XXIX (Jan., 1963), pp. 25–31; R. Freedman, D. Goldberg, and D. Slesinger, ''Current Fertility Expectations of Married Couples in the United States,'' *Population Index*, XXIX (Oct., 1963), pp. 366–391.

TABLE 1

Selected Measures of Fertility by Marriage Cohort for White Ever-Married Women

Marriage cohort	Median age at marriage	Median interval: marriage to 1st birth	Median interval: marriage to 2nd birth	Median interval: marriage to 3rd birth	Children ever born or expected number
1960–63	na	na	na	na	(3.0–3.1)[b]
1955–59	20.2	(1.2) [a]	na	na	(2.9–3.0)
1950–54	20.6	(1.3)	(3.9)	(6.5)	(3.0–3.1)
1945–49	21.2	(1.4)	(4.3)	(7.0)	(2.9–3.0)
1940–44	21.4	(1.8)	(5.3)	(8.2)	(2.8–2.9)
1935–39	21.4	1.8	5.2	8.1	2.5
1930–34	21.1	1.8	5.2	8.4	2.4
1925–29	20.7	1.6	4.7	7.5	2.5
1920–24	21.0	1.5	4.1	6.7	2.7
1910–19	20.7	1.4	4.0	6.6	3.1
1900–09	20.2	1.5	4.0	6.6	3.9

[a] Figures in parentheses dealing with birth intervals are estimates made by the author from the necessarily incomplete data provided by the Bureau. Median interval estimates were prepared by estimating the proportion of ever-married women who would eventually have a first, second, or third birth. For example, it was estimated that 94 per cent of the 1955–59 marriage cohort would have a first birth, 83 per cent of the 1950–54 marriage cohort would have a second birth, etc. Should these estimates prove to be high, the actual intervals will be shorter than the estimated intervals.

[b] Estimates of expected number of children for marriage cohorts are shown in parentheses. These estimates were made from published and unpublished materials from the 1955 and 1960 GAF and from the 1962 and 1963 UMPSC. The use of data from all four studies was required because of the selectivity with respect to marriage cohort produced by a sample design that has an age cutoff at 39. The earliest (oldest) marriage cohorts are grossly misrepresented in each of the studies.

Sources: U.S. Bureau of the Census, "Marriage, Fertility and Childspacing: August 1959," *Current Population Reports*, Series P-20, No. 108 (1961); R. Freedman, D. Goldberg, and D. Slesinger, "Current Fertility Expectations of Married Couples in the United States," *Population Index*, XXIX (Oct., 1963), pp. 366–391; unpublished materials from UMPSC 1962 and 1963.

affected by the depression and war followed by a rise associated with these events and a sharp decline since that time. The last marriage cohorts to be relatively unaffected across all the variables shown in the table, including children ever born, were the 1910–19 marriages. It is most striking that the most recent cohort (1950–54) for which all variables can be estimated has a pattern of timing and probably of completed fertility which will closely match the behavior of the 1910–19 cohorts. There is a temptation, with the pattern of these data, to argue that the long-term decline in fertility would have come to an end by the marriage cohorts of 1910–19 and that, the decline after that point was artificially created by the events affecting the succeeding cohorts.

When data are arrayed by marriage cohorts, there is no firm evidence suggesting that the most recent marriage cohorts will have fewer children than their immediate predecessors. The evidence available is from a series of national samples of married women aged 18–39 during the period 1955–63. The 1950–54 cohort will serve to illustrate the procedure employed to estimate completed fertility. In the 1955 GAF Study, the 1950–54 marriage cohort expected eventually to have 2.98 children. This study is particularly appropriate for examining the 1950–54 cohort because it obtained nearly complete coverage of that particular marriage cohort (limiting the sample to women up to 39 years does not seriously affect coverage of the cohort). In contrast, 1960 GAF results show that the 1950–54 marriage cohort expects to have 3.2 children per couple in the sample. The discrepancy in results may reflect any one of several things: (1) women may actually have revised their expectations upward;[5] (2) the difference may be attributed to the fact that these are two different samples of women married at the same point in time; and (3) the selectivity of the two samples differ with respect to age at marriage. A woman who married at age 30 in 1950 was included in the 1955 study, but excluded from the 1960 study.[6] Unpublished data from the 1962 and 1963 UMPSC Studies indicate that the 1950–54 cohort expects 3.1 children (this is an even poorer representation of the cohort in terms of age at marriage). The estimate for the 1950–54 cohort contained in Table 1 is an attempt to reconcile the varying results from what are, in fact, different samples. With corrections for

---

5. Whelpton has argued, on the basis of data comparisons between 1955 and 1960 GAF, that young wives revise their estimates of expectations upward. See P. K. Whelpton, *op. cit.*, p. 52.

6. Actually, the 1960 GAF Study included women aged 40–44 as well as those aged 18–39. The older group of women was included primarily to check on the accuracy of expectation statements given by women aged 35–39 in the 1955 GAF Study. The published materials from the 1960 GAF Study, including those cited in this paper, are based on the age group 18–39.

including all ever married women, an average of 3.0–3.1 eventual births appears to be a reasonable estimate from the available data.

While expected family size may be stabilizing at about three children per couple for marriage cohorts, it is possible that the decline in birth intervals has continued. Data on median age at marriage by year of marriage are not available in a stable form for the past few years. When marriage age is examined by birth cohorts, we find that the median age at first marriage for white women has declined continuously from the 1910–14 cohort (21.9 years) to an estimated 19.8 for the 1935–39 birth cohort.[7] Similarly, the proportion of women ever married by year of birth has increased from .91 for the 1880–89 cohort to a figure of .95–.96 for the 1920–24 cohort and will probably reach .96 in more recent cohorts.

In Table 2, data are presented illustrating the relationship between marriage potential and marriage patterns for the most recent periods. The ratio of the number of females aged 18–21 to the number of males aged 21–24 (including armed forces overseas) is shown for the years 1950–63 together with projections to the year 1980.[8] The index numbers are inversely related to the marriage potential or marriage availability for females. The simple fact that women select older males for marriage can produce highly varying degrees of availability when the size of birth cohorts is altered from period to period. Between 1950 and 1954, the conditions of availability favored the women. Since 1956, the situation has been reversed, as women born in the latter part of the depression were marrying men born in the first part of the depression and as female war babies reached marriage age while their appropriate male counterparts represented the smaller depression cohorts. Today, there are about 14

7. U.S. Bureau of the Census, ''Marriage, Fertility, and Childspacing: August 1959,'' *Current Population Reports*, Series P-20, No. 108 (July, 1961), Table 5.

8. The use of the age range 18–21 and 21–24 was dictated by the age categories available in estimates and projections of population. See U.S. Bureau of the Census, ''Interim Revised Projections of the Population of the United States, 1975 and 1980,'' *Current Population Reports*, Series P-25, No. 251 (1962); U.S. Bureau of the Census, ''Estimates of the Population of the United States, by Age, Color, and Sex: 1950–1962,'' *Current Population Reports*, Series P-25, No. 256 (1963); U.S. Bureau of the Census, ''Estimates of the Population of the United States, by Age, Color, and Sex: July 1, 1963,'' Series P-25, No. 276 (1963).

TABLE 2

Selected Measures of Marriage and Marriage Potential, Total United States Population, 1950–1980

	1950	1952	1954	1956	1958	1960	1961	1962	1963	1965	1970	1975	1980
Ratio: $\frac{\text{female 18-21}}{\text{male 21-24}}$	.96	.93	.96	1.03	1.05	1.07	1.13	1.15	1.14	1.10	1.03	1.02	.98
Female birth cohort	1929–32	1931–34	1933–36	1935–38	1937–39	1939–42	1940–43	1941–44	1942–45	1944–47	1949–52	1954–57	1959–62
Male birth cohort	1926–29	1928–31	1930–33	1932–35	1934–37	1936–39	1937–40	1938–41	1939–42	1941–44	1946–49	1951–54	1956–59
Median age at first marriage													
Bride	—	—	20.3 ᵃ	20.3	20.0	—	—	—	—	—	—	—	—
Groom	—	—	23.2	23.1	22.6	—	—	—	—	—	—	—	—
Per cent ever married													
Female 14–17	6.3	5.6	5.0	6.2	4.7	4.6	4.0	3.8	—	—	—	—	—
18–19	32.1	32.2	29.8	34.0	33.6	29.1	28.3	30.4	—	—	—	—	—
20–24	68.4	70.4	69.3	71.4	71.0	71.1	70.9	70.7	—	—	—	—	—
Male 18–19	7.6	10.1	7.6	8.2	8.4	9.0	7.3	9.3	—	—	—	—	—
20–24	44.2	51.7	45.8	50.8	47.9	45.3	44.9	47.6	—	—	—	—	—

ᵃ Data on median age of bride and groom are for 17 states in 1954 and 22 states for 1956 and 1958.

Sources: U.S. Bureau of the Census, "Interim Revised Projections of the Population of the United States, 1975 and 1980," *Current Population Reports*, Series P-25, No. 251 (1962); U.S. Bureau of the Census, "Estimates of the Population of the United States, by Age, Color, and Sex: 1950–62," *Current Population Reports*, Series P-25, No. 256 (1963); U.S. Bureau of the Census, "Estimates of the Population of the United States, by Age, Color, and Sex: July 1, 1963," *Current Population Reports*, Series P-25, No. 276 (1963); U.S. Bureau of the Census, "Marital Status and Family Status: March or April 1952, 1954, 1956, 1958, 1960, 1961, 1962," *Current Population Reports*, Series P-20, Nos. 44, 56, 72, 87, 105, 114, 122; National Office of Vital Statistics, *Vital Statistics of the United States: 1958, 1959* (Washington, D.C.: U.S. Government Printing Office, 1960, 1962).

per cent more females than males in the selected age categories. This situation will reach its crest in 1967.

The demographic constraints placed on desired marriage patterns may be considerable. As data become available on marriage trends, they should be evaluated in relation to these constraints. There are many possible combinations of marriage patterns which could develop in response to the changing marriage potential. The most obvious ones are increasing marriage age for women, smaller proportions of women marrying, and a decreasing gap in marriage age between men and women. The response to the initial phase of the lessening availability of males was for more women to marry, for their marriage age to decline, and for the difference in the age of bride and groom to decline.[9] This suggests that the changing pattern of marriage is even more striking than it appears to be. During the 1960's, the marital status and family status surveys of the Census Bureau indicate that the proportion of women married at ages 14–19 has declined. It would be premature, given the demographic constraints, to assume that these data reflect a reversal of the patterns of the 1950's. With respect to males, there is too much year-to-year wobble in the data available to evaluate any changes in their marital status by age.

Table 3 supplements the Current Population Survey data on birth intervals with material from the 1957 FGIMA Study and the 1962 DAS Study. The design of the two studies is comparable, in that white women were interviewed about one half year after the event of marriage, first birth, second birth, or fourth birth. Birth interval data from these studies cannot be attached to the series shown in Table 1 because FGIMA and DAS are samples of events whereas the Current Population Survey data are a sample of time. However, first births in the DAS Study certainly represent more recent marriage cohorts than the 1955–59 cohort of the Current Population Survey.

A direct comparison of the 1957 and 1962 studies can be made only for two-parity women. The median interval between mar-

9. There are only very limited amounts of data available on the response of the young population to the changing availability ratio, but it appears that the 1935–39 birth cohort will probably have a higher proportion of women ever married than the 1930–34 cohort. See U.S. Bureau of the Census, ''Marriage, Fertility, and Childspacing: August 1959,'' *Current Population Reports*, Series P-20, No. 108 (July, 1961), Table 5.

riage and first birth and between first birth and second birth is down by about 0.3 years in the 1962 study. The third and fourth intervals from 1962 DAS are lower than anything shown in the 1959 Current Population Survey. These data are at least suggestive of a continuing decline in birth intervals, although they

TABLE 3

Birth Interval by Parity, 1957 FGIMA and 1962 DAS

	Interval								
	Marriage to 1st birth				1st to 2nd birth			2nd to 3rd birth	3rd to 4th birth
Date	1957		1962		1957	1962		1962	1962
Study	FGIMA		DAS		FGIMA	DAS		DAS	DAS
Parity	2	1	2	4	2	2	4	4	4
Years									
				Per cent distributions					
1	29	43	41	45	3	4	10	5	4
1–1.9	35	30	32	33	36	42	52	41	38
2–2.9	15	9	9	11	25	23	24	24	22
3–4.9	15	9	8	7	22	19	11	21	23
5	6	9	10	4	14	12	3	9	13
Total	100	100	100	100	100	100	100	100	100
Median	1.4	1.1	1.1	1.1	2.4	2.1	1.7	2.1	2.3
Vital record median	—	1.0	1.0	1.0	—	—	—	—	—

Sources: Unpublished data 1962 DAS; unpublished data from W. F. Pratt study of premarital pregnancy in the Detroit metropolitan area, supported by United States Public Health Service Grant No. HD-00609-02; C. Westoff, R. G. Potter, P. Sagi, and E. Mishler, *Family Growth in Metropolitan America* (Princeton: Princeton University Press, 1961).

are not the most appropriate set from which to make this judgement. Some of the intervals are exceptionally low. A median of 1.1 years for first births and a median of 1.7 years for the second interval among four-parity women comes fairly close to models of birth intervals for populations in which no contraception is practiced.[10]

Unpublished results from a study by W. F. Pratt, of the first birth interval, obtained by a check of vital records of 91 per cent of the respondents in the 1962 DAS Study, indicate that the first

10. There are several models of birth intervals and its components. For one of the more recent estimates see R. G. Potter, "Birth Intervals: Structure and Change," *Population Studies*, XVII (Nov., 1963), pp. 155–166.

birth interval is actually shorter than reported (bottom row of Table 3).[11] His data show that more than half of the first births of four-parity women occur in less than 12 months of marriage. For one- and two-parity women the median intervals are just over 12 months. About 14 per cent of the respondents in the 1962 DAS inaccurately reported the first birth interval. Half of the reporting errors turned out to be cases of premarital conception.

Pratt's study of DAS couples and his larger study of 1960 marriages in the Detroit area are focused on the incidence of premarital conception, that is, conception, marriage, and birth in that order. Dealing with the DAS sample of legitimate births, he found that about 20 per cent of the first births represented premarital conceptions. Preliminary analysis of the outcomes of 1960 marriages yields almost identical results—about one fifth of the white marriages involve premarital conception followed by a live birth. For nonwhites the comparable preliminary figures suggest a rate twice as high.

Since the National Vital Statistics Division publishes annual data on illegitimate births by birth order, one can determine the per cent of all first live births that are illegitimate. For the period 1947–1962, the percentages of first births reported as illegitimate were: [12]

	White (per cent)	Nonwhite (per cent)
1947	3.2	28.2
1950	3.7	31.9
1955	4.2	36.8
1960	5.6	39.2
1962	6.4	41.3

The proportion of first births that are illegitimate among whites has been rising at an increasing pace, whereas the

11. Unpublished data collected by William F. Pratt, University of Michigan Population Studies Center, United States Public Health Service Grant No. HD-00609-02.

12. J. Schacter and M. McCarthy, "Illegitimate Births: United States, 1938–1957," *Vital Statistics—Special Reports*, XLVII (Sept., 1960); National Vital Statistics Division, *Vital Statistics of the United States, 1950*, II (Washington, D.C.: U.S. Government Printing Office, 1953); National Vital Statistics Division, *Vital Statistics of the United States, 1960*, I (Washington, D.C.: U.S. Government Printing Office, 1962); National Vital Statistics Division, *Vital Statistics of the United States, 1962*, I (Washington, D.C.: U.S. Government Printing Office, 1964).

nonwhite series has been increasing at a declining pace, with the exception of the 1960–62 period. Incomparability in registration completeness and type of marital union, as well as other problems with the data, necessarily result in incomparability of the meaning of the white and nonwhite series, a topic beyond the scope of this paper.

If we now fix on the population of all first births and ask what proportion are illegitimately conceived, whether they result in a legitimate or illegitimate birth, the answer for whites is about one out of four (20 per cent of legitimate first births are premarital conceptions and 6.4 per cent of all first births are illegitimate). Granted that most of the data are from the Detroit area, it would still be surprising if national figures differed substantially. For nonwhites, the comparable value cannot be obtained because there are no data on the proportion of legitimate first births that are premaritally conceived.

We have been accustomed to thinking of the sequence marriage, conception, and birth. It is apparent that for a very substantial part of the population the current sequence is conception followed by birth, with marriage intervening, following birth, or not occurring at all. This may represent a fundamental change in marriage and fertility patterns, but historical comparisons are lacking. An increase in illegitimate conceptions may be largely responsible for the decline in marriage age in the postwar period. Additional research involving the difficult and time-consuming process of matching marriage and birth records from earlier periods is the only approach to reconstructing a demographic history that may be quite different from the impressions we carry.

The decline in birth intervals raises several types of questions about family limitation as it is practiced in the United States. Potter and his colleagues have perhaps raised the most significant question.[13] If women reach their desired family size by about age 27, with many years of fecundity ahead, how many excess births or pregnancies are likely to occur?[14]

13. R. G. Potter, P. Sagi, and C. Westoff, ''Improvement of Contraception During the Course of Marriage,'' *Population Studies*, XVI (Nov., 1962), pp. 160–174.

14. In 1962 the median ages of mothers at the birth of their first, second, third, or fourth children were, respectively, 21.4, 23.7, 26.5, and 28.5 years. See National Vital Statistics Division, *Vital Statistics of the United States, 1962*, I (Washington, D.C.: U.S. Government Printing Office, 1964), Tables 1–12.

They have attempted to answer their own question by showing that there must be a marked improvement in contraceptive efficiency as desired family size is approached if excess pregnancy is to be kept to a fairly low level. Findings from the 1957 and 1960 FGIMA Studies do indicate an improvement in contraceptive efficiency as the gap between live births and desired number of children is closed.[15] This appears to take the form of a reduction in chance-taking in relation to the stage of growth in the family cycle. The continued reduction in birth intervals will necessitate even greater improvement since it will extend the period of fecundity during which no further births are desired.

The emphasized analysis of couples classified as "number and spacing planned" in the Indianapolis Study, as a model of the future, at this point appears to be a poor fit for the United States population and a fit that may be growing poorer each year. The "number and spacing planned" category [16] may actually have been more typical of the cohorts represented in the Indianapolis Study. Although family limitation is almost universally used by the middle years of the childbearing span among fecund couples in the United States, its use is typically casual or delayed until one or two children are already born.[17] Data from FGIMA suggest that spacing standards are extremely vague and that the standards of the husband and wife are not particularly correlated. The authors of *The Third Child* say, ". . . a mother might easily reach the position, some months after the last childbirth, when she has not quite made up her mind to interrupt contraception, yet would not be dismayed

15. P. Sagi, R. G. Potter, and C. Westoff, "Contraceptive Effectiveness as a Function of Desired Family Size," *Population Studies*, XV (March, 1962), pp. 291–296.

16. The number and spacing planned category refers to couples who wanted each of their children and who interrupted the use of contraception to have each child, or those who prevented conception by continuous use of contraception. See P. K. Whelpton and C. V. Kiser (eds.), *Social and Psychological Factors Affecting Fertility* (New York: Milbank Memorial Fund, 1950), II, pp. 225–230.

17. Contraceptive data from the 1960 GAF Study have not been published, with the exception of the per cent of current users—81 per cent as contrasted with 70 per cent in 1955 GAF. See A. A. Campbell, "Concepts and Techniques Used in Fertility Surveys," *Emerging Techniques in Population Research*, Proceedings of the 1962 Milbank Round Table (New York: Milbank Memorial Fund, 1963).

to find herself pregnant.''[18] Their observations seem most appropriate for the DAS Study data as well. Intended intervals are somewhat longer than the intervals realized. The delayed efficiency approach to the control of births presumably results in most fecund couples having the number of children they want. In the 1955 GAF Study it was reported that about one fourth of the fecund couples married at least 15 years did not want their last child.[19] Since these are self-reported data, the fraction is undoubtedly a minimum estimate of the incidence of excess fertility. Whether the current set of couples who have married and had their children at earlier ages are capable of keeping the reported fraction of excess births to the 1955 level is highly questionable.

The final component in the description of fertility is the number of children couples have, want, or expect to have. In several papers, Freedman has referred to consensus among American couples on a family including two to four children.[20] About 90 per cent consider two to four children "ideal for the American family." This has been true for as far back as we have data—about 20 years (Table 4). Expected number of children is also highly concentrated in this range. In four comparable national samples covering the period 1955–63, about 75 per cent of the women interviewed expected two to four children. This is clearly the acceptable and desired range of behavior. Other types of evidence also lead us to the same conclusion. In the 1962 DAS Study, women were asked to rank order their preferences for number of children from zero to six. When a joint scale is fitted to these preferences—a scale of distance which is consistent with the largest number of preference orders—the distance from two to four children represents less than 20 per cent of the distance from zero to six children.[21] Reinterview data with

18. C. Westoff, R. G. Potter, and P. Sagi, *The Third Child* (Princeton: Princeton University Press, 1963).

19. R. Freedman, P. K. Whelpton, and A. A. Campbell, *Family Planning, Sterility and Population Growth* (New York: McGraw-Hill, 1959).

20. For example, see R. Freedman, "American Studies of Factors Affecting Fertility," *International Population Conference New York 1961*, International Union for the Scientific Study of Population (London: John Wright, 1963), I, pp. 67–75.

21. D. Goldberg and C. Coombs, "Some Applications of Unfolding Theory to Fertility Analysis," *Emerging Techniques in Population Research*, Proceedings of the 1962 Milbank Round Table (New York: Milbank Memorial Fund, 1963).

women from the 1962 DAS also show that expectations in the range of two to four children are frequently modified and apparently insignificant to a substantial fraction of the respondents. For example, a woman, who originally expected three or

TABLE 4

Per Cent Distribution of Respondents by Ideal and Expected Number of Children: Selected Studies, 1941–1963

Ideal number of children	1941 AIPO [a]	1945 AIPO	1955 GAF	1960 GAF	1962 DAS [b]			
					0	1	2	4
Under 2	1	1	0	0	0	0	0	0
2–4	93	89	91	92	90	92	93	91
Over 4	6	10	9	8	10	8	7	9
Total	100	100	100	100	100	100	100	100

Expected number of children	1955 GAF	1960 GAF	1962 UMPSC	1963 UMPSC	1957 FGIMA [b,c] 2	1962 DAS [b]			
						0	1	2	4
Under 2	13	11	11	9	0	4	4	0	0
2–4	74	74	75	77	92	80	83	89	55
Over 4	13	15	14	14	8	16	13	11	45
Total	100	100	100	100	100	100	100	100	100

[a] American Institute of Public Opinion.

[b] Numbers listed under 1962 DAS and 1957 FGIMA refer to parity of women interviewed in those studies.

[c] 1957 FGIMA actually did not obtain data on expected number of children in a form comparable to the other studies. The question was, "How many children do you want to have altogether, counting the two you have now?"

Sources: R. Freedman, P. K. Whelpton, and A. A. Campbell, *Family Planning, Sterility and Population Growth* (New York: McGraw-Hill, 1959); R. Freedman, D. Goldberg, and D. Slesinger, "Fertility Expectations in the United States: 1963," *Population Index*, XXX (April, 1964), pp. 171–175; C. Westoff, R. G. Potter, P. Sagi, and E. Mishler, *Family Growth in Metropolitan America* (Princeton: Princeton University Press, 1961); unpublished data, 1962 DAS.

four children, when reinterviewed said she expected three. When asked why she changed, she said, "I wouldn't want more than four—three or four is still what I mean—three is nice too— and I wouldn't want less than two, ever." Although this woman sounded as if she were well rehearsed by one of us, she was fairly typical.

When we turn to the fertility behavior of cohorts, we know

TABLE 5

Mean Expected Number of Children by Birth Cohort for White Wives,
1955–1963

Birth cohort	1955 GAF	1960 GAF	1962 and 1963 UMPSC
1941–45	—	—	3.1
1936–40	—	3.0	3.2
1931–35	3.2	3.4	3.3
1926–30	3.1	3.2	3.1
1921–25	3.0	3.0	—
1916–20	2.9	na	—

Sources: R. Freedman, D. Goldberg, and D. Slesinger, "Current Fertility Expectations of Married Couples in the United States," *Population Index*, XXIX (Oct., 1963), pp. 366–391; unpublished data 1962 and 1963 UMPSC.

that the lowest cumulative fertility will be characteristic of the 1905–15 birth cohorts. For more recent cohorts, data on expectations from 1955 and 1960 GAF and 1962 and 1963 UMPSC provide tentative information about eventual cumulative fertility (Tables 5 and 6). As was the case for marriage cohorts, the data are not completely comparable among the studies because of differential selectivity in age at marriage. For birth cohorts, the earliest (oldest) birth cohorts are most representative of the population that eventually marries. Therefore, in comparing the expectations of different cohorts the reader should concentrate on the entries listed toward the bottom of each study. When this is done and we make the further assumption that expectations

TABLE 6

Mean Number of Live Births and Expected Number of Children by Age for White Wives, 1955–1963

Age in year of study	Mean number of births				Mean additional children expected				Mean total children expected			
	1955	1960	1962	1963	1955	1960	1962	1963	1955	1960	1962	1963
18–24	1.1	1.3	1.3	1.4	2.1	1.7	1.9	1.7	3.2	3.0	3.2	3.1
25–39	2.3	2.6	2.7	2.8	0.7	0.6	0.4	0.4	3.0	3.2	3.1	3.2

Source: R. Freedman, D. Goldberg, and D. Slesinger, "Fertility Expectations in the United States: 1963," *Population Index*, XXX (April, 1964), pp. 171–175.

will accurately estimate behavior, it seems likely that there will be an increase in size of completed family with each group of cohorts from 1915 on, reaching a peak for the cohorts of 1931–1935. Beyond that point we are on much more tentative ground because of the marriage age selectivity involved and the fact that succeeding cohorts have not progressed very far in the family building process. The data on expectations, by themselves, do suggest that there may be a slight decline in total number of children, *relative to the 1931–35 cohort.* There is nothing in the data suggesting families of fewer than three children in the most recent birth cohorts. Given our impressions of contraceptive practices and the data on birth intervals, the absence of a decline or the existence of only a trivial decline from the 1931–35 cohort level must be assigned a fairly high probability value.

DIFFERENTIAL FERTILITY

If there is such a thing as differential fertility in the United States, there must be a dependent variable of some meaning. Now that we are sophisticated enough to recognize the peculiarities of period data in relation to cohort data, largely through the efforts of Ryder and Whelpton,[22] the emphasis in fertility research has shifted to a set of synthetic variables (expectations, ideals, desires), and to birth intervals. Without detracting from the value of the research that has been conducted with these variables, we should be well aware of the difficulties involved in the analysis of these data when individuals represent the units of analysis.

Some of these difficulties have been spelled out by Sagi and Westoff in a recent article.[23] Their analysis indicates that perhaps half of the variance in family size is nonmotivational, attributable to components which are not easily controlled in

22. For example, see P. K. Whelpton, *Cohort Fertility: Native White Women* (Princeton: Princeton University Press, 1954) ; N. B. Ryder, ''Problems of Trend Determination During a Transition in Fertility,'' *Milbank Memorial Fund Quarterly*, XXXIV (Jan., 1956), pp. 5–21.

23. P. Sagi and C. Westoff, ''An Exercise in Partitioning Some Components of the Variance in Family Size,'' *Emerging Techniques in Population Research*, Proceedings of the 1962 Milbank Round Table (New York: Milbank Memorial Fund, 1963).

fertility surveys, even when the synthetic variables are used.[24] In addition, if couples do not consider the difference between two, three, or four children as being significant, then the analytic procedures we have used, such as correlation, will be insensitive to the relationships we seek to find. It is possible that some of the simplest ways of dealing with the dependent variable are the best. A dichotomization of expectations or desires at some critical juncture implied by various scaling techniques may be more meaningful than the assignment of "exact" values—2, 3, or 2.5 as has frequently been done. Similar types of problems exist for data on birth intervals. Westoff *et al.*, find that more than half of the variance in birth intervals is a function of separations, pregnancy wastage, and conception delays.[25] Add to these the misreporting of intervals, which is typically a one year error in a 1.5–3.0 year average interval, and we are dealing largely with statistical noise when the objective is to find social and economic differentials among individuals by a variance technique. Our criteria of the importance of independent variables should more often include consistency in simple subgroup summary measures, rather than heavy emphasis on "explained" variance. The combination of unreliability, misreporting, accidents, and the lack of meaningful differences to respondents within a certain range of fertility behavior yield a set of fertility variables for which it is almost impossible to find high correlations at the individual level. More flexibility in analytic techniques and in definition of the dependent variable is probably required. For example, if we seek out our independent variables from among those that may be in conflict with fertility, counting children may be less appropriate than noting the time required to complete the family. With the current set of birth intervals, women are having more children but with less time consumed in birth and early child care than was the case during the smaller family pattern of the depression period. In this respect, the historical pattern of fertility may be represented by an almost un-

24. We know little about the reliability of data on family size desires or expectations. When women are asked about the number of children they expect to have, unknown and perhaps highly varying estimates of their fecundity and contraceptive effectiveness are built into their answers.

25. C. Westoff, R. G. Potter, P. Sagi, and E. Mishler, *Family Growth in Metropolitan America* (Princeton: Princeton University Press, 1961), pp. 107–111.

interrupted decline in the proportion of married life devoted to care of young children.

The independent variables that have received the most attention in recent studies of differential fertility are religion and socioeconomic status. On the basis of the findings of several studies, it has become apparent that these two dimensions cannot be separated in a discussion of fertility differentials. Their interaction with respect to fertility is considerable.

Data from 1955 GAF and the 1957 Current Population Survey [26] revealed no differences in actual number of children among Catholics and Protestants of comparable groups. However, 1955 GAF data and 1957 FGIMA data showed relatively large differences in the number of children expected or desired. There are now large differences in actual as well as expected fertility.[27] The Detroit Area studies of 1952–1959 document the change that took place during the decade in that metropolitan area. Surveys of married persons under 40, made between 1952 and 1955, show that live births among Catholic couples exceeded those of Protestants by only 0.1 child. In the 1956–57 surveys the difference had grown to 0.3. By 1958–59 the difference was about 0.5.[28] The difference in live births had reached 0.6 children and the difference in expectations nearly one child according to the results of the 1962 UMPSC Study. The development of such a large differential over a short period of time must reflect some significant structural or normative changes. As one of the few cases of a widening gap in a period of contraction of most other fertility differentials, some understanding of this phenomenon could provide information which would be helpful in locating significant independent variables.

Perhaps out of habit or because we are convinced that changing economic status must bear some relationship to fertility, we turn to it first as an explanation of the newly developed differential by religion. Using only data already tabulated for

26. U.S. Bureau of the Census, *Statistical Abstract of the United States, 1958* (Washington, D.C.: U.S. Government Printing Office, 1958), p. 41.

27. R. Freedman, D. Goldberg, and D. Slesinger, ''Current Fertility Expectations of Married Couples in the United States,'' *Population Index*, XXIX (Oct., 1963), pp. 366–391.

28. These data are reported by G. Lenski, *The Religious Factor* (Garden City, N.Y.: Doubleday, 1963), p. 240.

other purposes, I could find no significant difference in the rates at which economic status has advanced for Catholics and non-Catholics for the period 1955–1962 as represented in 1955 GAF and 1962 UMPSC samples. Between 1956 and 1959 there appears to be almost no difference in the income changes of Catholics and Protestants according to data from the 1960 FGIMA Study. This should not rule out an economic explanation. It is possible that the generally rising economic level of the country has enabled Catholics to achieve, for the first time, a high fertility potential which may have been constrained in previous periods.

A second avenue that seems worth investigating is more directly concerned with the changing linkage of the Catholic population with the Catholic Church. In the 1955 GAF Study, regularity of church attendance was not clearly related to fertility. In 1957 and 1960 FGIMA, 1962 UMPSC, and 1962 DAS studies, it was one of the better predictors of fertility. Along the same lines, I do not know of data which would be sensitive to changes in the proportion of parochially educated Catholics among the relevant cohorts involved.

One of the most sensitive studies of religious differences in fertility was recently completed by Smit, using 1955 GAF Study data.[29] Smit's study is a precision matching on six variables (occupation, education, income, residence, farm background, and duration of marriage) of 380 Catholic and Protestant couples. The matching process results in an increase of religious differences in fertility for all dimensions of fertility used, as compared with the original differences in the GAF Study. Standardization of these differences on a wide variety of population models, including the United States population, does not reduce the differences.

Table 7 summarizes some additional results from the 1957 FGIMA Study and the 1962 DAS with respect to religious differences in fertility. Though some of the individual relationships are weak, every measure of church related association and involvement in the Catholic community is positively related to desired (FGIMA) or expected (DAS) number of children.

29. F. W. Smit, ''A Matched Group Study of Religious Differences in Fertility and Family Planning'' (unpublished dissertation, University of Michigan, 1964).

TABLE 7

Correlations of Socioeconomic and Religiosity Indexes with Desired Number of Children for 1957 FGIMA and with Expected Number of Children for 1962 DAS, by Religion, by Parity

Selected socioeconomic and religiosity indexes	1957 FGIMA 2 Parity		1962 DAS 0 Parity		1 Parity		2 Parity		4 Parity	
	Cath.	Prot.	Cath.	Non-Cath.	Cath.	Non-Cath.	Cath.	Non-Cath.	Cath.	Non-Cath.
Wife's education	.28	−.03	.33	.02	.10	.14	.15	−.06	.22	−.13
Husband's education	.24	.04	.28	.04	.14	.17	.20	.05	.09	−.08
Husband's income	.03	−.15	.09	−.10	.02	−.04	.03	−.02	−.01	−.18
Occupational prestige	.13	.05	.10	.06	.06	.15	.20	.08	.07	−.10
Wife's feeling of economic security	.11	−.08	—	—	—	—	—	—	—	—
Index of SES	.22	.00	—	—	—	—	—	—	—	—
Wife's church attendance	.30	.05	.17	.06	.27	.08	.26	−.16	.22	−.08
Husband's church attendance	—	—	.19	.11	.21	.09	.31	−.08	.18	−.09
Informal religious orientation	.22	.04	—	—	—	—	—	—	—	—
Religiosity	.27	.02	—	—	—	—	—	—	—	—
Frequency of communion (C), prayer (NC)	—	—	.29	−.20	.33	.08	.49	−.07	.37	.07
Wife's mother's religious interest	—	—	.16	−.25	.13	.05	.17	−.05	.15	−.05
How "close" to others of same religion	—	—	.13	−.09	.09	.09	.24	−.03	.02	−.12
Interest in welfare of others of same relig.	—	—	.06	.06	.17	.03	.26	−.02	.13	−.11
Per cent relatives of same religion	—	—	.14	−.13	.06	.08	.17	.00	.14	−.03
Per cent closest friends of same religion	—	—	.23	−.23	.08	.08	.18	−.05	.09	−.14
Wife's Catholic education	—	—	.24	—	.11	—	.27	—	.30	—
Husband's Catholic education	—	—	.34	—	.24	—	.31	—	.14	—
Expected Catholic education for children	—	—	.21	—	.30	—	.32	—	.32	—

Sources: C. Westoff, R. G. Potter, P. Sagi, and E. Mishler, *Family Growth in Metropolitan America* (Princeton: Princeton University Press, 1961); C. Westoff, R. G. Potter, and P. Sagi, *The Third Child* (Princeton: Princeton University Press, 1963); unpublished data, 1962 DAS.

Among Protestants, the measures of communal and religious involvement are not consistently related in a given direction to the measures of fertility employed. The unpublished DAS data are consistent with the published FGIMA Study data.

These two investigations are also consistent in showing an interaction of religion and socioeconomic status with respect to fertility. In both studies there is a modest positive relationship between economic status and fertility among Catholics and

TABLE 8

Correlations of Socioeconomic Measures with Selected Activity Patterns, by Religion, for Two Parity Women

	Catholics				Non-Catholics			
Activity	Hus-band income	Hus-band educ.	Wife educ.	Occupa-tional prestige score	Hus-band income	Hus-band educ.	Wife educ.	Occupa-tional prestige score
Number of meetings attended by wife	.06	−.03	.15	.00	.22	.22	.20	.28
Per cent of leisure activities that are non-home centered	.06	−.03	−.04	.01	.22	.22	.20	.20
Frequency wife goes out for an evening	−.02	.04	.01	.03	.24	.18	.17	.16
Frequency of seeing relatives	−.08	.00	−.02	−.07	−.10	−.12	−.21	−.11
Frequency of seeing friends	.03	.17	.08	.18	.18	.24	.19	.16

Source: Unpublished data, 1962 DAS.

essentially no relationship between these variables for the Protestants. A potential source of explanation for the interaction effect is shown in Table 8. This table illustrates differences in the relationship between economic status and the activity pattern of the wife for Catholics and non-Catholics. In the latter group, economic success and higher education result in activities which are competitive with child rearing. A high status non-Catholic wife is more likely to be involved in activities that remove her from roles associated with home and family than the wife of lower status. She spends a greater part of her time outside the home in both formal and informal activities and she spends relatively more of her time with friends rather than kin. In contrast, status differences do not produce substantial activity differences for Catholic wives. The differential impact of status on fertility for the two religious categories now appears to be reasonable. Although a Protestant woman with higher income can more easily afford an additional child, the higher income leads to activities which would make it more difficult for her to have the child. For the Catholic the higher income appears simply to result in more available resources. A difference in response, by religion, to the changing economic conditions at the societal level appears more plausible with data of this kind.

Another interaction effect that may have considerable value for interpreting trends in differentials is the interaction of economic status and farm background in relation to fertility. Studies of completed families in Detroit and Indianapolis, as well as a study of expectations from the 1955 GAF Study, all show that the traditional inverse relationship between fertility and economic status in the total population may be largely attributed to the negative relationship between those variables among farm-reared elements of population.[30] These results have now been confirmed with data from a national sample of couples who have completed their fertility.

The data shown in Table 9 are from the March, 1962 Current Population Survey, in which a questionnaire containing information about father's occupation was obtained from respondent households. The sample of about 6,000 represents a group of married couples with wives born in the 1900–1919 period. Fertility data from this study were provided by O. D. Duncan.[31] Each couple was classified by residence and farm background as measured by questions about occupations of both fathers. The mean number of children by education follows the pattern of earlier studies. The inverse relationship between fertility and education is confined to couples of nonfarm residence having some farm background and to couples of farm residence. The strength of the inverse fertility differentials in the total popula-

---

30. D. Goldberg, ''The Fertility of Two Generation Urbanites,'' *Population Studies*, XII (March, 1959), pp. 214–222; D. Goldberg, ''Another Look at the Indianapolis Fertility Data,'' *Milbank Memorial Fund Quarterly*, XXXVIII (Jan., 1960), pp. 23–26; R. Freedman and D. Slesinger, ''Fertility Differentials for the Indigenous Non-Farm Population of the U.S.,'' *Population Studies*, XV (Nov., 1961), pp. 161–173.

31. O. D. Duncan, ''Farm Background and Differential Fertility,'' paper read at the meetings of the Population Association of America, June, 1964.

tion at different points in time may reflect only the proportion of farm-reared couples in the total population. As we move toward the present, the declining proportion of couples with farm background may, to some extent, be accounting for the contraction of socioeconomic differentials in fertility.

TABLE 9

Mean Number of Children Ever Born for Married Couples, Spouse Present, Wife 42 to 61, by Educational Attainment of Wife and Residence and Farm Background of Couple, March, 1962

| Education | Nonfarm Residence | | Farm Residence |
	Husband and wife nonfarm background	Husband or wife farm background	
Elementary			
0–4	2.3	4.2	5.2
5–7	2.4	3.4	3.8
8	2.4	2.8	3.5
High school			
1–3	2.3	2.5	3.3
4	2.1	2.0	2.7
College			
1–3	2.0	2.2	2.6
4	2.0	1.9	2.2

Source: O. D. Duncan, "Farm Background and Differential Fertility," paper read at the meetings of the Population Association of America, 1964.

Other data have begun to illuminate the complexity of the relationship between economic status and fertility. For example, D. Freedman has noted a double-edged effect of income on children ever born in a subsample of fecund planners married ten or more years taken from the 1955 GAF Study.[32] She finds that the husband's actual income is negatively related to fertility, whereas the husband's relative income (a ratio of actual income to expected income based on occupation, education, and age) is positively related to children ever born. These findings are most striking because they are suggestive of the possibility that increasing income results in a life style which may be competitive with large families, but that given distinctive styles of life or distinctive fertility values associated with income,

32. D. Freedman, "The Relation of Economic Status to Fertility," *The American Economic Review*, LIII (June, 1963), pp. 414–426.

relative economic ease is more likely to result in additions to the family. Findings of this type may be exceptionally useful in untangling the varied effects of the components of status. The absence of a strong relationship between economic status and fertility appears to be masking a host of canceling effects of the individual dimensions.

At the outset of the paper it was stated that little is known about differential fertility. This position seems justified on several counts. The nearly axiomatic expression of an inverse relationship between fertility and socioeconomic status has now been questioned by a series of studies, from which some of the data apply to fertility performance well prior to the depression period. This, in turn, raises many questions about the traditionally held views of the sequence in the use of contraception by the social classes. The recent emergence of large religious differentials in fertility is basically unexplained. In addition, the social mobility—fertility hypothesis,[33] frequently used to account for several types of fertility differentials, simply has not stood up when put to the test of some data from cross-sectional populations. However, a real sign of progress in any discipline is the elimination of false hypotheses. This is being achieved as a result of the new research freedom enjoyed by the analysts of fertility data. There are numerous studies of fertility in which the researcher is free to use his imagination in measurement and analysis, rather than relying on published materials gathered for other purposes. The initial results of this process may be a bit painful but it will eventually yield the product sought.

The absence of two key publications prevents us from obtaining a more complete description of fertility differentials in the American population. The forthcoming Census Bureau special report on fertility and the volume containing the major results of the 1960 GAF Study will add important information on current fertility differentials.

---

33. The social mobility–fertility hypothesis states that the demands of occupational mobility are incompatible with the demands of childrearing. Therefore, upwardly mobile couples are expected to have relatively few children. An elaboration and summary of this position is found in C. Westoff, "The Changing Focus of Differential Fertility Research: The Social Mobility Hypothesis," *Milbank Memorial Fund Quarterly*, XXXI (Jan., 1953), pp. 24–38.

Jeanne Clare Ridley

RECENT NATALITY TRENDS IN
UNDERDEVELOPED COUNTRIES

G eneral recognition that the rapid growth of the populations of underdeveloped countries is hampering their
ability to achieve higher standards of living has focused attention on their birth rates. As long as natality continues at a high
level while mortality declines, growth rates will continue to
climb, aggravating the difficulties met by these populations in
their efforts to share in the fruits of modern technological
progress. More and more, therefore, the population problems of
these countries are seen in terms of high natality levels.[1] The
recently noted trends toward increasing natality in some underdeveloped countries raise serious questions concerning the prospects for early declines in natality.

It is the purpose of this paper to describe—within the limits
of available data—observed trends in the natality of underdeveloped countries and to examine the factors that may be
influencing these trends. The latter purpose poses a number of

1. The observed levels in underdeveloped countries today are generally higher than
those which characterized Western Europe before industrialization.

analytical problems as well as measurement problems; these problems will be dealt with in the final section of the paper by describing one approach utilizing a stochastic model.

THE DATA

Since the Second World War considerable improvements have been achieved in the adequacy of birth registration systems of a number of countries in the underdeveloped regions of the world. Nevertheless, birth rates based on registered events are reasonably complete for only 23 underdeveloped countries and two segments of the populations of another country.[2] All of the countries included in this study had achieved "relatively good birth registration systems" either prior to 1951 or by 1959 as reported in the United Nations *Demographic Yearbooks: 1951–1959*.[3]

These countries are, however, hardly a representative sample of underdeveloped populations. The achievement of adequate birth registration may in fact be viewed as an indicator of a country's modernization. Thus, as a group, they under-represent the newly developing nations and are atypical of such countries. Notably under-represented are African and Middle Eastern countries, as well as many of the most populous nations of Asia and Latin America. In a few of these other countries, however, special surveys and studies provide some indication of

2. The countries or population segments included are: Mauritius, Reunion, Tunisia, Union of South Africa (Coloured population, Asian population), Ceylon, Taiwan, Federation of Malaya, Singapore, Ryukyu Islands, Costa Rica, El Salvador, Guadeloupe, Guatemala, Jamaica, Martinique, Mexico, Panama, Puerto Rico, Trinidad and Tobago, Argentina, British Guiana, Chile, Surinam, and Venezuela.

3. Countries were deemed to have "relatively good registration systems" on the basis of their reliability as reported in the United Nations, *Demographic Yearbooks* beginning in 1951. The birth registration systems of the countries included in Table 1 were coded as "C" (indicating complete coverage) either in the 1951 or later editions of the United Nations, *Demographic Yearbook* or were indicated to have achieved at least 85 per cent coverage. A few countries, nevertheless, had fairly complete coverage prior to 1951.

For the reliability code of each of the 23 countries and two populations from 1951 to 1963 see Table A of the Appendix. A number of countries were excluded from consideration if their populations were less than 250,000 on the basis of the latest available estimate published in the United Nations, *Demographic Yearbook: 1963* (New York: 1963). In addition, Hong Kong and Israel were excluded because of their heavy immigration since 1945. It seemed reasonable also to exclude Israel on the grounds that its population was predominately of recent European origin and greatly influenced by Western culture.

natality levels and trends; these will also be summarized in the following discussion.

Even in the 25 populations with "relatively good registration systems" the establishment of definite trends is difficult, since only a few of the underdeveloped countries had adequate registration systems as recently as 1945. The island of Mauritius is the only African population, and it is hardly an African population, for which a good set of data exists. In Asia only Taiwan, the Federation of Malaya, Singapore and Ceylon can be included in this group. In the Caribbean and Central and South American only Argentina, Jamaica, British Guiana, Chile, and Trinidad and Tobago possess an adequate time series. It was not until the 1950's and often late in that decade that the other countries included in this review achieved relatively complete registration of births. For instance, Costa Rican data are considered complete only since 1959, while Venezuelan data seem to have varied in their accuracy during the 1950's.[4]

Improvements in the registration of births present difficult problems in the interpretation of natality trends. This is particularly true when the rates tend to be increasing. In many instances it is impossible to assess whether an apparent increase in birth rates is real or due to improvements in registration.[5] The establishment of natality trends depends upon relatively good census data for reliable estimates of the age-sex composition of the population to provide suitable denominators for the calculation of more refined indices. For most countries 1950 is the earliest year for which adequate data are available for such indices.

Both variations in the levels of natality and the existence of trends in natality in the underdeveloped regions of the world require further analysis to identify the correlates of observed changes. After briefly reviewing current natality trends, atten-

4. The 1951 United Nations, *Demographic Yearbook* lists its birth registration as complete, but later editions (1962 and 1963) list the data as unreliable. See Appendix, Table A.

5. The problem is not likely to be as acute in assessing a decline in birth rates. Clearly, if a decline is observed in the period while registration of births is known to be gaining in coverage, the increase in coverage will tend to mask the extent of the actual decline. Birth rates may decline, however, as a consequence of a deteriorating statistical system or by the use of an overestimated population base. The same observations apply to an evaluation of declines in mortality.

tion will be focused upon the many factors—social, economic, and biological—that might give some clues to an understanding of natality trends.

NATALITY TRENDS [6]

Crude Birth Rates

A detailed examination of the crude birth rates in Table 1 indicates that with few exceptions, namely the Ryukyu Islands and Argentina, birth rates have remained above 30. In this sense a certain stability has prevailed. Nevertheless, considerable variation exists in current natality levels, as well as in those immediately following the Second World War. The highest rates are found in the Caribbean and in Central and South America while Asian countries tend to be characterized by more moderate rates. More significant is the fact that the data in Table 1 indicate no clear-cut general trends. On the basis of countries included here, countries in the Caribbean and in Central and South America appear to be experiencing rising natality while Asia would appear to be a region of declining natality.

Very little data exist for Africa other than the Mediterranean littoral and the Union of South Africa. Most certainly the rise in recorded birth rates for Tunisia is due to better registration since complete registration was achieved only in 1957.[7] After some decline in the middle 1950's, the registered rates for the Coloured and Asian populations of the Union of South Africa indicate some increase. The data are, however, complete only since 1956 and likely reflect improved registration. What is striking for these two South African populations is the difference in their natality levels, for they are both mainly urban residents. The level exhibited by the Asians resembles that of other Asian populations and may indicate similar cultural

6. Figures in this section cited from a preliminary draft of Chaps. 3–5, United Nations, *Population Bulletin of the United Nations*, No. 7—1963 (New York, 1965), pp. 15–88. The publication should be consulted for the most recent estimates.

7. *Ibid.*, p. 28. This publication estimates a birth rate of 44 by the census reverse survival method for the period 1946–51. Plans for a national sample survey should give additional information as to the level of natality in Tunisia. See ''Tunisia: Proposed Family Planning Program,'' *Studies in Family Planning*, II (New York: The Population Council, Dec., 1963), pp. 3–4.

Crude Birth Rates for Selected Underdeveloped Countries

Year	Mauritius	Reunion	Tunisia	Union of South Africa Coloured	Union of South Africa Asian	Ceylon	Taiwan	Federation of Malaya	Singapore
				Crude birth rates					
1945	38.4	—	—	—	—	36.7	—	—	—
1946	43.7	—	40.3	—	—	38.4	—	35.0	—
1947	43.1	—	36.8	—	—	39.4	—	43.0	45.9
1948	43.1	42.6	33.1	47.1	39.1	39.7	39.7	40.4	46.2
1949	46.1	43.7	27.1	47.6	36.8	39.1	42.4	43.8	47.1
1950	49.7	48.1	30.6	46.9	37.9	39.7	43.3	42.3	45.4
1951	47.5	46.6	34.3	47.9	35.5	39.8	50.0	44.0	45.0
1952	48.0	51.3	28.6	47.5	34.6	38.8	46.6	45.0	45.4
1953	46.3	51.2	31.0	47.3	34.5	38.7	45.2	44.4	45.8
1954	41.3	49.6	31.3	47.1	34.3	35.7	44.6	44.6	45.7
1955	41.8	49.2	33.5	45.8	34.1	37.3	45.3	44.0	44.3
1956	43.8	47.7	35.6	45.1	30.6	36.4	44.8	46.7	44.4
1957	43.1	47.3	39.4	47.0	30.7	36.5	41.4	46.2	43.4
1958	40.8	45.2	44.7	46.2	30.1	35.8	41.7	43.3	42.0
1959	38.5	44.2	44.9	46.3	32.0	37.0	41.2	42.2	40.3
1960	39.6	44.3	43.7	47.8	35.4	36.6	39.5	40.9	38.7
1961	39.8	43.9	43.5	46.4	40.5	35.8	38.3	41.9	36.5
1962	38.5	—	44.4	47.5	38.6	—	37.4	40.3	35.1
1963	39.9	43.1	—	46.3	—	—	—	—	—
			Five-year averages of crude birth rates						
1945–49	42.0	42.4	33.4	45.9	38.5	38.2	40.2	40.6	46.4
1950–54	46.5	49.4	30.8	47.3	35.3	38.5	45.9	44.1	45.5
1955–59	41.5	46.7	39.7	46.1	31.5	36.0	42.8	44.4	42.8
				Percentage change					
1945–49 to 1950–54	+10.7	+16.5	−7.8	+3.1	−8.3	+0.8	+14.2	+8.6	−1.9
1950–54 to 1955–59	−10.8	−5.5	+28.9	−2.5	−10.8	−6.5	−6.8	+0.7	−5.9

Table 1 (*Continued*)

Year	Ryukyu Islands	Costa Rica	El Salvador	Guadeloupe	Guatemala	Jamaica	Martinique	Mexico
				Crude birth rates				
1945	—	45.9	42.9	—	48.7	30.0	—	44.9
1946	—	45.0	40.8	—	48.2	30.8	—	42.9
1947	—	57.0	47.2	—	52.2	31.9	—	45.3
1948	—	44.5	44.6	37.4	51.9	30.7	35.6	44.6
1949	45.2	44.1	46.2	39.9	51.6	32.3	36.9	44.7
1950	41.1	45.9	48.5	37.3	50.9	33.1	38.0	45.5
1951	38.0	47.6	48.8	39.3	52.3	34.0	38.7	44.6
1952	34.8	48.6	48.7	39.0	50.9	33.6	37.9	43.6
1953	32.5	49.6	47.9	39.1	51.1	34.4	40.2	44.7
1954	31.8	51.3	48.1	39.0	51.5	35.3	40.0	46.0
1955	27.6	50.6	47.9	40.1	48.8	36.2	39.6	45.9
1956	27.9	49.9	47.0	39.5	48.8	37.2	40.1	46.1
1957	24.5	48.2	48.9	37.5	49.4	37.9	40.7	46.6
1958	25.9	46.9	47.3	38.4	48.7	40.3	39.0	44.0
1959	24.9	48.7	45.9	37.2	49.8	41.1	38.5	46.9
1960	23.1	48.1	46.5	38.9	49.5	43.1	38.5	46.0
1961	23.6	46.9	46.1	36.3	49.9	41.0	37.5	45.6
1962	22.1	42.2	48.4	—	47.7	40.8	—	45.8
1963	—	49.9	48.8	36.0	—	39.6	33.1	45.0
			Five-year averages of crude birth rates					
1945–49	36.1	45.6	44.4	37.3	50.6	31.3	35.3	44.4
1950–54	35.5	48.7	48.4	38.8	51.4	34.0	39.0	44.9
1955–59	26.1	48.8	47.4	38.5	49.1	37.7	39.6	45.9
				Percentage change				
1945–49 to 1950–54	−1.7	+6.8	+9.0	+4.0	+1.6	+8.6	+10.5	+1.1
1950–54 to 1955–59	−26.5	+0.2	−2.1	−0.8	−4.5	+10.9	+1.5	+2.2

TABLE 1 (Continued)

Year	Panama	Puerto Rico	Trinidad and Tobago	Argentina	British Guiana	Chile	Surinam	Venezuela
			Crude birth rates					
1945	37.7	41.9	39.5	25.2	36.6	33.3	36.1	36.2
1946	37.0	41.6	38.8	24.7	35.6	36.2	34.7	37.6
1947	37.2	42.2	38.3	25.0	39.4	36.0	33.3	38.2
1948	35.6	40.2	39.9	25.3	42.3	35.3	37.2	39.2
1949	32.8	39.0	37.2	25.1	42.3	34.7	36.4	41.2
1950	33.3	39.0	37.5	25.5	40.4	34.0	37.6	42.6
1951	32.5	37.6	36.7	25.2	42.5	33.9	41.0	43.8
1952	36.1	36.1	34.6	24.9	44.3	32.7	43.5	42.6
1953	37.9	35.3	37.7	25.2	44.1	34.6	44.0	44.3
1954	38.8	35.2	41.9	24.6	42.9	33.5	43.8	44.4
1955	39.2	34.6	41.9	24.3	43.2	35.1	43.7	44.3
1956	39.2	34.8	37.0	24.5	43.1	36.0	44.5	43.5
1957	40.4	33.7	37.7	24.2	44.5	36.9	44.3	42.9
1958	39.2	33.2	37.6	23.7	44.5	36.0	45.9	42.4
1959	40.7	32.3	36.3	23.3	44.5	35.8	45.5	46.1
1960	40.8	32.3	39.1	22.5	42.9	34.9	—	45.9
1961	40.4	31.3	38.1	22.3	42.5	34.0	44.5	45.3
1962	41.1	31.2	37.0	22.1	41.8	34.4	—	42.8
1963	40.1	30.9	—	21.8	—	—	—	—
			Five-year averages of crude birth rates					
1945–49	36.1	40.8	38.7	25.1	40.2	35.7	36.6	38.5
1950–54	37.5	36.6	37.7	25.1	42.9	33.8	42.1	43.5
1955–59	39.8	33.7	38.0	24.0	44.0	35.8	44.8	43.2
			Percentage change					
1945–49 to 1950–54	+3.9	−10.3	−2.6	0.0	+6.7	−5.3	+15.0	+13.0
1950–54 to 1955–59	+6.1	−7.9	+0.8	−4.4	+2.6	+5.9	+6.4	−0.7

Sources: United Nations, *Demographic Yearbooks: 1955, 1958, 1960, 1962, 1963* (New York, 1955, 1958, 1960, 1963).

influences.[8] Another indication of relative stability among a peripheral African population is given by special studies in the United Arab Republic, which seems to have maintained a birth rate of between 43 and 45 over the past 20 years.[9]

Since Mauritius and Reunion are both small islands in the Indian Ocean separated from the continent, their natality trends cannot be considered indicative of future trends on the continent itself. As populations exhibiting high natality, however, they are of intrinsic interest. Further, the data for Mauritius are particularly reliable. After a considerable rise from 1946 through the early 1950's, a decline of almost equal magnitude has now taken place. On the other hand, improved registration likely accounts for part of the rise in Reunion which shows similar trends but at somewhat higher levels.

For other parts of Africa, natality data are totally inadequate to establish trends. All indications are, however, that the populations in this region exhibit extreme variations in natality levels. Recent estimates from demographic surveys range from rates of 30 in Zanzibar to perhaps 57 in Nigeria and 62 in Guinea and Mali. Generally, the rates are above 40.[10] Since a rate of 60 is considered close to the biological limit, this extreme variation raises considerable doubt as to future trends in natality in this area.

While Africa may be said to show relative stability in natality levels, the same may not be stated for the Asian countries represented in Table 1. Ceylon, Taiwan, the Federation of Malaya, and Singapore apparently all experienced some increase in birth rates in the late 1940's or early 1950's. It is likely, however, that in the immediate postwar period the birth

8. Variations in the age-sex composition of these two populations may account for the difference in natality levels. The differences however, are maintained when more refined rates are employed. See Table 2.

9. See M. A. El Badry, "Some Aspects of Fertility in Egypt," *The Milbank Memorial Fund Quarterly*, XXXIV (Jan., 1956), pp. 23–43; H. Rizk, "Social and Psychological Factors Affecting Fertility in the United Arab Republic," *Marriage and Family Living*, XXV (Feb., 1963), pp. 35–43; and United Nations, *Population Bulletin of the United Nations*, No. 7—1963 (New York, 1965).

10. See Table B in Appendix for crude birth rates of selected African countries. See also D. F. Roberts and R. E. S. Tanner, "A Demographic Study in an Area of Low Fertility in North East Tanganyika," *Population Studies*, XIII (July, 1959), pp. 61–80, and J. G. C. Blacker, "Population Growth and Differential Fertility in Zanzibar Protectorate," *Population Studies*, XV (March, 1962), pp. 258–266.

registration systems were still disrupted and a return to more normal procedures may have tended to produce a rise in registered rates. More important is the fact that since the latter part of the 1950's many of these countries have been experiencing declining birth rates. Particularly noticeable is a very large decline in the Ryukyu Islands.[11] In addition, the declines in Singapore and Taiwan, which began in 1957, show every sign of continuing. A decline also appears for the Federation of Malaya while Ceylon's birth rates generally have been quite stable. It should be emphasized though that these countries are all atypical of the massive populations of continental Asia.

In addition to the data cited in Table 1, a basis exists for some estimates of natality in India, Thailand, and the Philippines. No discernible trend can be cited for India. By the census reverse survival method, the United Nations estimates crude births rates of about 40—the average for 1945–54 being 39.9 and the average for 1955–59 being 40.9.[12] From the 1947 census and a demographic survey in 1956, the United Nations estimates that Thailand had an average annual crude birth rate of about 42 in the period 1947–56.[13] The Philippines is estimated to have an average annual crude birth rate between 47 and 53 for the period 1947 to 1957, which is considerably higher than the crude birth rates observed for the larger continental countries. Further, it has been noted that the birth rate may have risen during this period.[14] Perhaps significant is the fact that the Philippines is the only Asian country that has been strongly influenced by a Western religion—namely Roman Catholicism. It is interesting to note that the level of the Philippine birth rate is similar to that of many Latin American countries shown in Table 1.

It would be invaluable to know what is happening in the People's Republic of China. The crude birth rate in the 1950's

11. For an account of population trends in the Ryukyu Islands, see I. B. Taeuber, "The Population of the Ryukyu Islands," *Population Index*, XXI (Oct., 1955), pp. 233–264.

12. United Nations, *Demographic Yearbook: 1963* (New York, 1963).

13. *Ibid.* An estimate for 1950–54 is 46 based on the 1960 census by application of the reverse census survival method.

14. United Nations, Department of Economic and Social Affairs, *Population Growth and Manpower in the Philippines*, Population Studies, No. 32 (New York, 1960), p. 3. A later estimate given in the United Nations, *Demographic Yearbook: 1963*, for 1950–54 is 50 based on the 1960 census.

was officially reported as in the high 30's. Whether or not the reported increase in natality in the Chinese cities during this period is due to better registration, altered age-sex structure, or true increase remains an open question.[15]

Several of the Caribbean and Central and South American countries currently present a puzzle to the demographer. Contrary to demographic theory, birth rates for several countries in this area have been increasing. Table 1 indicates that, with the exceptions of Argentina, Chile, and Puerto Rico, this is an area of high birth rates. Since the end of World War II crude birth rates for the major countries have been above 40, while several countries have rates near 50.

Since 1945 only two countries, Puerto Rico and Argentina, have had any clear decline in their crude birth rates. A minority of other countries in this area exhibited either stability or slight decreases while the majority exhibited increases. While the increases in Panama, El Salvador, and Costa Rica were probably due almost completely to better registration, the same cannot be said for the sizable increases observed in British Guiana and Jamaica. The registration systems in the latter two countries are considered reliable for the entire period under consideration. The increase for Jamaica, which is particularly large, has been fairly continuous since 1945, though it has yet to rise much above the estimates of about 40 made by Roberts for the middle of the nineteenth century.[16] The increase is a significant reversal of a downward trend which began just prior to World War I. The relative stability in Chile's birth rate is of interest; after declining from about 42 in 1940, it has remained at a fairly high level during the 1950's.

Other Indices of Natality

The above is based upon an examination of crude birth rates. Crude birth rates are not generally good indicators for assessing trends—mainly because of changes in age composition over time. In Table 2, therefore, two additional indices of natality,

15. H. Yuan Tien, ''Induced Abortion and Population Control in Mainland China,'' *Marriage and Family Living*, XXV (Feb., 1963), p. 36.
16. G. W. Roberts, *The Population of Jamaica* (Cambridge: Cambridge University Press, 1957), p. 269.

the sex-age adjusted birth rate [17] and the general fertility rate [18] are presented for the years about 1950 and 1960. The decline previously observed for Mauritius is relatively large while the declines in Singapore and the Ryukyu Islands are significant. For Taiwan, the decline is most clearly supported by the general fertility rates. The decline for the Federation of Malaya is very slight—perceptible only in the general fertility rate. The decided decline in Singapore has been observed to be largest among the Chinese, although some declines have been observed among the Indians and Pakistani residing in Singapore, as well as among the Malayans residing there.[19] Apparently, a similar pattern has been observed for the major ethnic groups in the Federation of Malaya.[20] It should be emphasized again that the Asian populations represented here are but a small proportion of Asian populations. Furthermore, with the exception of the Ryukyu Islands which have remained under the residual sovereignty of Japan, all of the populations experiencing declining natality are Chinese.

The increases in crude birth rates previously noted for Jamaica and British Guiana are supported by the indices presented in Table 2. The increase in natality for Jamaica is particularly large—a 38.5 per cent increase in the sex-age adjusted birth rate occurring between 1951 and 1960. In addi-

---

17. The sex-age adjusted birth rate is ''defined as the number of births per 1,000 of a weighted aggregate of numbers of women in the various five-year age groups from 15–44.'' The weights are so chosen not only that they be roughly proportional to the averages of the age-specific birth rates, but also that the sum of the products with the corresponding numbers of women in the various age groups ordinarily be of the same magnitude as the total population. This method is explained in more detail in United Nations, Department of Economic and Social Affairs, *Manual III— Methods of Population Projections by Sex and Age* (New York, 1956), p. 42. The numerators of the rates calculated in Table 2 were arithmetic averages of the number of births occurring in the three-year periods centering upon the date shown in the table. Thus, the rate calculated for 1950 is the arithmetic average of the births occurring in 1949, 1950, and 1951 per 1,000 of the weighted aggregate of numbers of women in the age group 15–44. The three-year average of births was utilized to minimize somewhat the yearly fluctuations in births.

18. The general fertility rate is defined as the number of births per 1,000 women between the ages of 15 and 49.

19. R. F. W. Neville, ''Singapore: Recent Trends in the Sex and Age Composition of a Cosmopolitan Community,'' *Population Studies*, XVII (Nov., 1963), pp. 99–112.

20. J. C. Caldwell, ''Fertility Decline and Female Chances of Marriage in Malaya,'' *Population Studies*, XVII (July, 1963), pp. 20–32.

TABLE 2

Sex-Age Adjusted Birth Rates and General Fertility Rates for Selected Under-developed Countries

Country	Sex-age adjusted birth rates		General fertility rates	
	1950	1960	1950	1960
Tunisia	—	39.2 [b]	—	154.7 [b]
Mauritius	48.8 [a]	44.9 [g]	206.3 [a]	181.1 [g]
Reunion	49.4 [b]	46.6	200.3 [b]	192.4
Union of South Africa				
Coloured	50.0 [c]	50.2	205.0 [c]	211.2
Asian	39.3 [c]	36.7	162.0 [c]	146.6
Ceylon	39.8 [d]	40.5	173.7 [d]	160.2
Taiwan	48.4 [c]	47.6 [g]	210.8 [c]	177.1 [g]
Federation of				
Malaya	43.8 [e]	45.7 *	188.6 [e]	183.8 *
Singapore	49.2 [e]	44.0 *	199.3 [e]	180.6 *
Ryukyu Islands	42.6	24.4	164.3	98.3
Costa Rica	37.8	51.0	192.6	214.8
El Salvador	47.4	58.5 [g]	195.2	213.6
Guadeloupe	42.1 [f]	41.4	164.1 [f]	168.8
Guatemala	52.5	53.6*	210.9	222.5*
Jamaica	31.7 [c]	43.9	127.9 [c]	178.9
Martinique	41.5 [f]	40.1	161.5 [f]	161.6
Mexico	45.1	49.4	185.1	202.0
Panama	33.5	42.9	141.2	170.7
Puerto Rico	40.7	37.2	170.3	143.0
Trinidad and Tobago	37.8 [d]	41.7	159.5 [d]	173.8
Argentina	24.0 *	21.5 [g]	82.9 *	85.6 [g]
British Guiana	45.1 [c]	48.8	179.2 [c]	194.0
Chile	34.7 [a]	38.0	136.4 [a]	146.7
Venezuela	42.8	49.6 [g]	177.9	202.4 [g]
Surinam	45.6	—	172.5	—

[a] 1952 [b] 1956 [c] 1951 [d] 1953 [e] 1947 [f] 1954 [g] 1961

* Figures cited from preliminary draft of United Nations, *Population Bulletin of the United Nations*, No. 7—1963 (New York, 1965).

Sources: United Nations, *Demographic Yearbook: 1960* (New York, 1960); *Demographic Yearbook: 1962* (New York, 1962); and United Nations, *Population Bulletin of the United Nations*, No. 7—1963 (New York, 1965).

tion, the sex-age adjusted birth rates and general fertility rates indicate that Mexico, Trinidad and Tobago, Chile and Venezuela may also have experienced some increase, which was obscured in their crude rates. On the other hand, the decline observed in Puerto Rico's crude birth rate is less marked when sex-age adjusted birth rates or general fertility rates are considered.

The increases in the sex-age adjusted birth and general fertility rates in Chile are difficult to assess. On the one hand, the basic population data may vary differentially in accuracy and in completeness for the two periods under consideration. On the other hand, it has been claimed that Chile is a Latin American country with a continuing decline in natality.[21]

This brief overview of natality trends in a number of underdeveloped populations underscores some important points. While natality is generally high, the differences in natality levels are quite large. To refer to underdeveloped countries as having high natality is indeed correct, but to overlook the great variations in their natality levels is to oversimplify the meaning of high natality. Related to this is the erroneous assumption that since natality is high in underdeveloped countries, it is at, or very near the biological maximum. This has led to the expectation that the only changes that are likely to take place in the natality of such populations are declines. That most, if not all populations, are not reproducing near the biological maximum can be illustrated by the fact that much higher natality has been observed in a few populations. Rates of near 60, implying an average of over 10 children per woman, have been observed.[22] A crude birth rate of about 30 should perhaps be viewed as having a vast potential for increase as well as the possibility of decrease. In the classic demographic transition, three phrases have been delineated: high and stable natality and mortality; high and stable natality and declining mortality; and declining natality and mortality. Another possible phase in this demographic transition should perhaps be inserted: namely, a phase of declining mortality with rising natality.[23] Nevertheless, decreases in natality have been more common than increases if we consider all countries, developed as well as underdeveloped.

21. L. Tabah, ''A Study of Fertility in Santiago, Chile,'' *Marriage and Family Living*, XXV (Feb., 1963), pp. 20–26.

22. T. E. Smith, ''The Cocos-Keeling Islands: A Demographic Laboratory,'' *Population Studies*, XIV (Nov., 1960), pp. 94–130.

23. W. Petersen, ''The Demographic Transition in the Netherlands,'' *American Sociological Review*, XXV (June, 1960), pp. 334–347.

THE CORRELATES OF NATALITY TRENDS

Numerous factors are believed to be contributing to the recently observed natality trends in underdeveloped countries and to the wide variations in observed levels. Declines in natality are attributed to, among other factors, economic development, increasing urbanization, rising levels of education, declines in familism, and rising age at marriage. For increases in natality—better health conditions, better diet, and increasing marital stability—are factors often cited. That these latter factors are likewise related to economic development is often ignored. Economic development may possibly result in a rising birth rate as well as in a falling one. Doubtless, at the minimum, there exists an intricate sequence of events.

Differences in natality levels are generally explained also by varying cultural values and norms governing family formation and growth. These cultural values and norms are deeply embedded in, give support to, and in turn are supported by, the social and economic structure of a society. It is argued that social and economic changes, then, have an impact upon the traditional norms surrounding reproduction, tending to break down familism and increase the involvement of the individual in the larger society and thus to reduce natality.[24]

This, indeed, may be the eventual effect on natality of social and economic changes in all societies; yet in some societies the immediate impact of such changes may be entirely different. While most cultural norms surrounding reproduction are positive and tend to maintain high natality, practically all societies possess cultural practices that depress natality. The net result is a natality level below its biological limit. Changes that break down these traditional norms of natality control can have the immediate consequence of increasing rather than reducing natality. If this occurs, the changes that would act to reduce natality are minimized.[25] Consequently, the period of time be-

24. For a fuller treatment of this view see R. Freedman, ''Norms for Family Size in Underdeveloped Areas,'' *Proceedings of the Royal Society*, Series B, 159 (Dec., 1963), pp. 220–245.

25. L. Henry, ''Analysis and Calculation of the Fertility of Populations of Underdeveloped Countries,'' *Population Bulletin of the United Nations*, No. 5 (New York, 1956), pp. 51–58.

fore a decrease in natality in a particular society occurs may be prolonged.

Social and Economic Factors

Documentation of the extent of economic and social change in underdeveloped countries is relatively difficult. The paucity of data and their deficiencies greatly hinder such an evaluation. Table 3 presents a number of indicators of recent social and economic development for some of the countries previously considered in Tables 1 and 2. Improvements have occurred— almost without exceptions—since about 1950. Yet a case can hardly be made for a strong relationship between these indicators of modernization and the previously discussed natality trends. There is nothing to indicate that a certain degree of modernization automatically reduces natality. Asian countries such as Taiwan and Singapore—both instances of declining natality—underwent in the decade 1950–60 considerable improvements in education, extension of mass communication, and substantial urbanization. The levels of modernization achieved, though, are in some instances below the levels attained by Latin American countries with rising birth rates. The measures of modernization employed, however, are crude bases for drawing definitive conclusions. In addition, it may be the rate of economic development and not the achieved level that is related to changes in natality.[26]

One is tempted to hypothesize that some social structures and cultures are more resistant to change in their natality patterns than are others. On the other hand, as already suggested, another possible hypothesis is that social and economic changes break down the traditional norms that had previously kept natality at a relatively low level, resulting in an increase in natality.

Health Factors

The spectacular decreases in mortality experienced in recent years by many underdeveloped countries are generally attrib-

26. A recent study of the relationship of the rate of economic development to natality levels tends to substantiate this statement. See D. M. Heer and E. S. Turner, ''Areal Difference in Latin American Fertility,'' *Population Studies,* XVIII (March, 1965), pp. 279–292.

TABLE 3

Indicators of Modernization for Selected Underdeveloped Countries

Country	Daily newspaper circulation per 1,000 population		Radio receivers per 1,000 population		Percentage of population living in localities of 100,000 and over		Energy consumption*		Percentage of population aged 15–19 years enrolled in primary and secondary schools	
	1950	1960	1950	1960	1950	1960	1950	1961	1950	1960
Tunisia	—	14	19	41	11.3[a]	10.4[h]	160	172	15	31
Mauritius	43[f]	89	20	62	0.0	0.0	200	115	38	64
Reunion	45[g]	67	7	43	0.0	0.0	—	114	—	60[i]
Ceylon	29	37	4	36	5.4[a]	5.3[a]	80	105	54	60[i]
Taiwan	28	66	2	43[i]	12.5	23.6	—	529	38	59
Federation of Malaya	32	67	10	36	7.4	10.8	—	259	35	50
Singapore	102	140	40	87	72.4	63.1	—	640	42	63
Ryukyu Islands	—	348[h]	1	5	0.0	25.3	—	284	—	93
India	7[g]	11	1	22[i]	6.6[e]	8.1[i]	110	150	19	29[i]
Philippines	3[f]	18	4[d]	7	9.3[c]	9.9	100	154	59	47
Thailand	—	14	—	66	13.3[b]	—	20	67	38	46
Costa Rica	92[f]	92	29	66	17.5	—	240	223	37	56
El Salvador	32	45	6[d]	16	8.7	—	60[d]	121	23	38
Guadeloupe	17	12	5	24	0.0	0.0	100	305	58	70[f]
Guatemala	18	23	10	12	10.2	—	160	174	18	25
Jamaica	39[f]	63	16	91	19.6[a]	23.5	160[d]	602	50	54
Martinique	—	18	11	66	0.0	0.0	120	300	66	81
Mexico	46	83	73	96	15.1	—	610	959	30	42
Panama	—	104	104[d]	159	15.9	25.4	300	520	46	53
Puerto Rico	57[g]	62	—	—	16.2	23.3	480	1,448	66	—
Trinidad and Tobago	78[f]	86	41	75	0.0	0.0	1,610	2,390	—	64[i]
Argentina	100	155	128	167	37.2[b]	—	770	1,178	66	57
British Guiana	42	67	22	65	0.0	0.0	270[d]	576	51	68
Chile	79	134	92[d]	96	28.5[f]	—	760	874	58	58
Surinam	42	67	27	148	82.8	—	420	750	58	64[i]
Venezuela	65	96	44	186	16.6	26.9	850	2,764	30	51[i]

[a] 1946 [b] 1947 [c] 1948 [d] 1949 [e] 1951 [f] 1952 [g] 1953 [h] 1956 [i] 1959 [j] 1961
* Million metric tons equivalent of coal

uted to public health programs. The impact of these programs upon natality, however, has received little attention. A plausible argument may be set forth that declines in mortality may contribute to rises in natality. The most direct effect on natality is likely to be an increase in the number of reproductive years lived by women in the married state due to decreasing female mortality and a decreased incidence of widowhood. The impact of these factors on the birth rate is, nevertheless, believed to be small. Utilizing stable population theory, Basavarajappa estimated only a 2.4 per cent increase in the birth rate when life expectancy at birth rises from 30 to 50 years.[27] Another estimate of the effect of a declining incidence of widowhood among women in the reproductive ages in India indicated a rise of 10 per cent in the birth rate.[28] On the other hand, in societies where males typically marry women considerably younger than themselves, increases in life expectancy may increase the age at marriage of females, and thus bring about a reduction in natality.[29]

The influence of reductions in certain endemic diseases upon natality is more difficult to assess. It has been held that in the case of Ceylon, malaria control has tended to increase natality in certain areas.[30] A number of writers have also suggested that the extremely long periods of postpartum amenorrhea observed in Indian women may be due to poor health and low standards of living.[31] The data to support this view are extremely fragmentary. The Mysore study found that in rural areas women of higher socioeconomic status exhibited higher natality than women of lower status [32]—possibly a result of better health and

27. K. G. Basavarajappa, ''Effect of Declines in Mortality on Birth Rate and Related Measures,'' *Population Studies,* XVI (March, 1963), pp. 237–256.

28. S. N. Agarwala, ''Some Projections of India's Population,'' *India's Population,* ed. S. N. Agarwala (New York: Asia Publishing House, 1960), p. 16.

29. J. C. Caldwell, *op. cit.*

30. See R. Indra, ''Fertility Trends in Ceylon,'' *Proceedings of the World Population Conference, 1954,* Vol. I, pp. 889–898; H. Frederiksen, ''Malaria Control and Population Pressure in Ceylon,'' *Public Health Reports,* LXXV (Oct., 1960), pp. 865–868; and H. Frederiksen, ''Determinants and Consequences of Mortality Trends in Ceylon,'' *Public Health Reports,* LXXVI (Aug., 1961), pp. 659–663.

31. C. Chandrasekaran, ''Physiological Factors Affecting Fertility in India,'' *International Population Conference: New York, 1961* (London, 1963), pp. 89–96.

32. United Nations, Department of Economic and Social Affairs, *The Mysore Population Study,* Population Studies, No. 34 (New York, 1961), p. 124.

diet. In another Indian study, women of higher socioeconomic status resumed menstruation after childbirth earlier than women of lower socioeconomic status.[33] Some low birth rates in Africa are often attributed to the extremely poor health conditions prevailing there.[34] Another indirect indication of the influence of standards of living and health comes from a study of Ceylonese women. In this study women in higher socioeconomic groups have a lower average age at menarche and a higher age at menopause than women in lower socioeconomic groups.[35] Also the number of miscarriages, abortions, and stillbirths may be reduced by improved standards of living, better diet and prenatal care, thus producing higher natality rates.

In addition, the exact relationship of health conditions to primary and secondary sterility is virtually unknown. Available estimates indicate the possibility of some variations within and between populations.[36] Whether such variations are due to inherent biological differences or to the influence of social factors on health is difficult to resolve.[37] Further complicating the picture is the biological influence of lactation upon natality. There is good evidence that lactation prolongs the period of amenorrhea and thus lengthens the intervals between births.[38] It would be helpful if we had more data on the prevalence and length of its practice following childbirth within underdeveloped societies.[39]

Family Structure

The impact of social and economic change on the family depends on the particular position the family occupies within

33. M. Kamat and R. G. Kamat, ''Diet and Fecundity in India,'' *Proceedings of the 6th International Conference on Planned Parenthood,* 1959.

34. It is interesting to note that one hypothesis for the rise in the birth rate among American Negroes since 1945 is the decrease of diseases impairing reproduction in this group.

35. S. Chennatamby, ''Fertility Trends in Ceylonese Women,'' *Journal of Reproduction and Fertility,* III (June, 1962), pp. 342–355.

36. L. Henry, ''Some Data on Natural Fertility,'' *Eugenics Quarterly,* VIII (June, 1961), pp. 81–91.

37. M. A. El Badry, ''Summary of Discussion,'' *International Population Conference: New York, 1961* (London, 1963), p. 137.

38. C. Tietze, ''The Effect of Breastfeeding on the Rate of Conception,'' *International Population Conference: New York, 1961* (London, 1963), pp. 129–136.

39. See R. G. Potter *et al.,* this volume.

the social structure of a society. Since the family is the social unit which translates cultural values and norms pertaining to reproduction into behavior, the types of familial units found within society greatly influence natality.

Demographic research though has largely ignored the question of family structure in underdeveloped countries and its relationship to natality. The literature abounds in generalizations as to the dominance of the extended or joint family system. Yet there are data that contradict this view. In one study of married couples in central India, 52.2 per cent had only one parent living with them.[40] Only 45 per cent of couples aged 25 to 29 interviewed in Taichung, Taiwan lived in a joint or stem family.[41]

Some have argued that the joint family system by spreading the economic and social costs of rearing children encourages high natality; others have taken the view that the joint family system would discourage high natality since within such families married couples have difficulty maintaining a meaningful private life. The available evidence on this point, however, indicates that differences in natality are not large between couples living in joint families and those living in nuclear families. Driver found, for instance, a difference, on the average, of only a child more for couples in joint families who had completed their families.[42]

Marriage

Most underdeveloped societies offer few alternative roles for women beside the familial ones. While early marriage and childbearing preclude alternative roles, it is widely held that this lack of alternative roles contributes to early marriage and to a high proportion of women marrying in underdeveloped countries and thus to high natality. Yet data on the percentage of women ever married and the mean age at marriage do not

40. E. D. Driver, *Differential Fertility in Central India* (Princeton: Princeton University Press, 1963), p. 41. See also pp. 36–38 for a summary of other studies dealing with the prevalence of the joint family system in India. In all of the surveys cited less than two thirds of the families studied were found to be joint.

41. R. Freedman, J. Y. Peng, Y. Takeshita, and T. H. Sun, ''Fertility Trends in Taiwan: Tradition and Change,'' *Population Studies*, XVI (March, 1963), pp. 219–236.

42. E. D. Driver, *op. cit.*

TABLE 4

Percentage of Women Ever Married 15 Years of Age and Over and Mean Age at Marriage for Selected Underdeveloped Countries

Country	Year	Percentage ever married	Mean Age at marriage
Tunisia	1956	84.6	19.3
United Arab Republic	1960	86.9	19.8
Union of South Africa			
Coloured Population	1946	60.6	24.7
Asian Population	1946	75.2	20.9
Mauritius	1962	79.9	19.9
Reunion	1954	58.5 [a]	25.0
Ceylon	1953	78.5	21.2
Taiwan	1956	78.2	21.1
Federation of Malaya	1957	83.7	19.4
Singapore	1957	77.4	20.8
Ryukyu Islands	1960	73.6	24.9
Philippines	1960	68.9	22.3
Thailand	1960	75.4	22.1
India	1961	94.3	16.6
Costa Rica	1950	61.4	21.9
El Salvadore	1961	59.0	18.5
Guadeloupe	1954	45.3 [a]	28.8 [a]
Guatemala	1950	69.2	18.6
Jamaica	1960	56.4	29.3 [a]
Mexico	1960	62.8	21.1
Panama	1960	63.4	18.9
Puerto Rico	1960	74.5	21.6
Trinidad and Tobago	1960	59.6	—
Argentina	1947	57.2	23.8
British Guiana	1946	69.3	19.6
Chile	1952	62.6	24.7
Venezuela	1961	61.4	18.7

[a] Excludes consensually married.

Sources: United Nations, *Demographic Yearbooks: 1958, 1962,* and *1963* (New York: 1958, 1962, and 1963).

generally support this view. Table 4 presents the percentages of ever married women 15 years of age and over and the mean age at marriage [43] for a number of underdeveloped countries. The women classified as ever married include those reported in censuses as legally married, consensually married, widowed, or

43. The mean age at marriage was calculated following a method developed by Hajnal. See J. Hajnal, "Age at Marriage and Proportions Marrying," *Population Studies,* VII (Nov., 1953), pp. 111–113.

divorced. Only India, with 16.6 years as its mean age at marriage and 94.3 per cent of its adult women ever married, exhibits what is considered the typical picture for underdeveloped countries.

Not only though is the listing of countries nonrepresentative but the proportions ever married in the Caribbean and Central and South America are probably understated in view of the prevalence of consensual or visiting unions. This practice would lead to classifying many women as single when in fact they had been partners in some type of union.

Nevertheless, the proportions ever married in Table 4 would lead one to expect Asian countries to exhibit the highest natality and countries in the Caribbean and Central and South America to have somewhat lower levels of natality. As previously noted, however, the contrary is the case. Further, for two countries, one in the Caribbean and the other in South America, it has been shown that the prevalence of unstable marital unions may actually depresss natality below the level it might attain if the unions were stable.[44] Nevertheless, even if we assumed that the true proportions of ever married women in Latin America approach those reported for African and Asian populations, very few of the differences in natality patterns between regions may be explained. In only a few countries do we find a low proportion of ever married and high mean age at marriage together with relatively low natality. This appears true for the Ryukyu Islands and Argentina. In addition, the much higher proportion of ever married women and the lower age at marriage for the South African Asian population as compared with the Coloured population does not explain the direction of the previously observed differences in natality of these two populations.

It is interesting to note also that the data in Table 4 are not unlike the figures for some developed countries. In the 1960 censuses of the United States, Sweden, and Japan, the propor-

---

44. See J. Blake, *Family Structure in Jamaica* (New York: The Free Press of Glencoe, Inc., 1961), pp. 246–250 and J. M. Stycos, "Culture and Differential Fertility in Peru," *Population Studies*, XVI (March, 1963), pp. 257–270. For a more recent article questioning the conclusions of Stycos regarding Peru see D. M. Heer, "Fertility Differences between Indian and Spanish-speaking parts of Andean Countries," *Population Studies*, XVIII (July, 1964), pp. 71–84.

tion of women reported as ever married were 82.7, 73.1, and 81.5 respectively. The mean ages at marriage for these countries were 20.6, 22.5, and 24.7.[45] Underdeveloped countries apparently do not always exhibit higher proportions ever married than do developed countries. For many countries this factor may be acting as a powerful depressant on natality. Yet, contraceptive practices and other forms of birth limitation in developed countries and cultural practices and taboos in underdeveloped countries may be more powerful determinants of reproductive behavior than age at marriage.

The deficiencies of the data and particularly the focus of surveys in underdeveloped countries on currently mated women is unfortunate. The exclusion of women not currently mated is particularly untenable for Latin American countries. Better data are needed on age at first marital union as well as on marital histories of women in underdeveloped countries.

An increase in age at marriage or a decrease in the proportion married, it should be pointed out, is not necessarily followed by a decline in the birth rate, since so much depends upon the pattern of intervals between births within marriage. Any changes that tend to shorten intervals between births, such as better health, might offset the effects upon natality of an increasing age at marriage. In countries where large numbers of women marry in their early teens, increased age at marriage might entail increased fecundity of newly married women since they would have passed the less fecund period associated with adolescence.[46] Nevertheless, the effects of increase in age at marriage can be substantial as demonstrated by Coale and Tye.[47] They show that for India, a shift to a later age of childbearing could bring a sizable reduction in natality as well as in the rate of growth of the population.

Another aspect of marriage that affects natality is the stability of such unions. The more unstable type of marital relation-

45. Calculated from data in United Nations, *Demographic Yearbook: 1962* (New York, 1962), according to method developed by J. Hajnal, *op. cit.*

46. F. Lorimer, *Culture and Human Fertility* (Paris: UNESCO, 1954), pp. 46–49.

47. A. J. Coale and C. Y. Tye, ''The Significance of Age-Patterns of Fertility in High Fertility Population,'' *The Milbank Memorial Fund Quarterly*, XXXIX (Oct., 1961), pp. 631–646.

ships are believed to depress natality levels, since the amount of time spent outside of marital unions greatly reduces the exposure to childbirth. One hypothesis commonly advanced to account for rising birth rates is that marital unions in some countries are becoming more stable. In Table 5 the percentages married and consensually married for about 1950 to 1960 in the few Caribbean and Central and South American countries for which such data are available are compared. In all of the countries shown, the proportions of women reported as legally married have increased, while in El Salvador, Mexico, Panama, and Puerto Rico, the proportions consensually married have decreased somewhat. However, Puerto Rico has had a small decline in its birth rate, while El Salvador, Mexico, and Panama may have had slight increases in their birth rates. It is unfortunate that comparative figures on the number consensually married for Jamaica are not available. The small increase in proportions reported legally married, though, hardly suggests that this has been a major factor in the large increase in natality that occurred in this country.

TABLE 5

Percentage Married and Consensually Married for Women 15 Years of Age and Over in Selected Countries of the Caribbean and Central and South America

Country	Percentage married	Percentage consensually married	Percentage married	Percentage consensually married
	1950		1960	
El Salvador	24.9	26.0	28.1 [a]	24.1 [a]
Jamaica	27.5 [b]	*	29.0	18.8
Mexico	45.3	11.7	48.1	9.4
Panama	25.0	31.6	30.7	26.3
Puerto Rico	44.8	14.6	49.0	8.3
Argentina	47.8 [c]	*	54.2	4.4
British Guiana	45.8 [d]	11.9 [d]	54.3	*
Chile	46.7 [e]	3.4 [e]	48.6	3.3
Venezuela	28.2	20.3	33.6 [a]	20.1 [a]

[a] 1961   [b] 1953   [c] 1947   [d] 1946   [e] 1952

* Not available as consensually married included with single.

Sources: United Nations, *Demographic Yearbooks: 1958, 1962,* and *1963* (New York, 1958, 1962, and 1963).

Other Factors

In addition to the above, a number of other factors impinge on natality in one way or another. The cultural values and norms surrounding natality are not only numerous but complex.[48] For instance, while religion generally places a high valuation on children, there are a number of cultural practices which probably have the effect of reducing natality. It has been estimated that in India upwards of 100 days per year are tabooed for sexual intercourse.[49] The extent of adherence to these taboos remains an open question. The values put on children and especially preferences regarding sex of children are other factors that influence the levels of natality. Further, the degree to which resistance to changes in particular values exists within cultures is likely to affect future trends.

This brief review of some of the many factors influencing natality points not only to the complexity of the phenomena of human reproduction but to the need for better data on many of the variables believed to be affecting natality levels and trends. Disentangling the interaction between these variables presents a difficult analytical problem. The next section discusses this latter problem in more detail.

AN ANALYTICAL APPROACH—A STOCHASTIC MODEL OF REPRODUCTION [50]

The reproductive model which I shall describe here was developed in collaboration with Dr. Mindel C. Sheps.[51] One of

48. See G. W. Skinner, ''Cultural Values, Social Structure and Population Growth,'' *Population Bulletin of the United Nations*, No. 5 (New York, 1956), pp. 5–12.

49. K. K. Mathen, ''Preliminary Lessons Learned From the Rural Population Control Study of Singur,'' *Research in Family Planning*, ed. C. V. Kiser (Princeton: Princeton University Press, 1962), pp. 33–49.

50. For a more recent description of the model including modifications and changes in the computer program see J. C. Ridley and M. C. Sheps, ''An Analytic Simulation Model of Human Reproduction with Demographic and Biological Components,'' in press, and M. C. Sheps and J. C. Ridley, ''Studying determinants of natality: Quantitative estimation through a simulation model,'' paper prepared for the World Population Conference, Belgrade, Yugoslavia, Sept., 1965.

51. The model under discussion drew upon the experience and methods previously developed by Perrin and Sheps. See E. B. Perrin and M. C. Sheps, ''Human Reproduction: A Stochastic Process,'' *Biometrics*, XX (March, 1964), pp. 28–45, and E. B. Perrin and M. C. Sheps, ''A Mathematical Model for Human Fertility Patterns,'' *Archives of Environmental Medicine*, X (May, 1965), pp. 694–698. See also M. C. Sheps' paper, this volume.

the purposes of this model is to aid in the understanding of the trends in birth rates recently observed in underdeveloped countries. Accordingly, we have attempted to construct a model with a certain degree of flexibility, which includes a number of important social and biological factors.

In this model, human reproduction is viewed as a stochastic process. The female survivors of a birth cohort are included in the model population until they have either died or reached age 50. In the intervening period the marital and reproductive experience of each women is simulated by exposing her to the risk of a number of possible events, as a function of time. Whether or not a woman experiences a certain event is randomly determined. We define a number of states into which a woman may pass, passage into a particular state depending upon variable schedules of probabilities.

The model provides for death to occur to a woman in the hypothetical population between the ages 15 to 50 or after the age of 50. Further, a woman may become permanently sterile at any time before age 50. At age 50 we assume all women are sterile and reproduction ends. Until a woman enters the sterile state, she is considered fecundable as long as she is a partner in a marital union and not in a nonsusceptible state.

In Fig. 1 the paths to the possible states that a surviving fecund woman may enter are shown. Not diagrammed in this figure are the additional states of "family planner, sterility, and death." Consider a fecund woman at age 15. To be exposed to the risk of pregnancy, she must enter a marital union. "Marriage" is broadly defined to include any type of sexual union. The model allows for the use of varying probability schedules of age at first sexual union. Once a woman enters a marital union, the marriage may be dissolved by widowhood or divorce. Divorce is defined to include rupture of marriage due to any reasons other than death of the marital partner, thus including dissolution of marital unions due to separation or desertion. The probability of a woman's becoming a widow depends on a constant age differential between spouses and the applicable schedule of male mortality.

As long as a woman is in a marital union, she is subject to the risk of pregnancy. She may become pregnant in a random number of months which is a function of the monthly probability

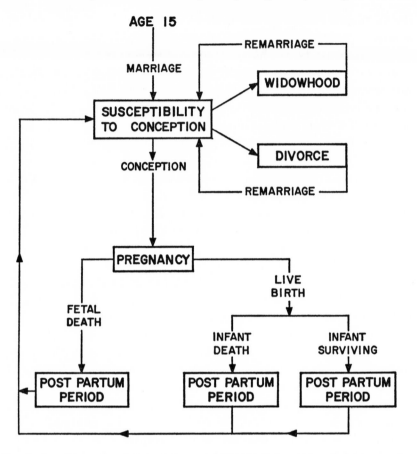

Fig. 1. Possible paths followed by surviving fecund women during reproductive ages, 15 to 50 years.

of conception (fecundability).[52] The duration of pregnancy is a random variable with a specified probability distribution depending upon the randomly selected outcome of pregnancy. The possible outcomes of pregnancy include fetal death, a live birth that dies in the first year of life, and a live birth that survives the first year of life. Fetal deaths include both early and late

---

52. It appeared preferable at this state of investigation not to break fecundability into its many components. Such components as frequency of coitus and of anovulatory cycles are consequently included in our probability of conception.

spontaneous abortions, as well as induced abortions and still-births. Following pregnancy a woman is considered nonsusceptible, the duration of the postpartum period being a random variable which depends on the outcome of pregnancy. Once a woman completes her postpartum period she passes directly into the fecundable state again, and she is then exposed to the sequence of events described above.

In addition to the above states, a woman may become a "family planner" at marriage or after any live birth. Once a woman is a "family planner" she resorts to contraceptive measures after each subsequent birth for a variable period of time. The fecundability of a woman using contraceptives is a fraction (depending on the postulated contraceptive effectiveness) of her natural fecundability at any given age.[53]

This model as outlined should make it possible to investigate directly the influence of a number of important factors on natality. For instance, the effect of changing mortality and marital patterns on age-specific fertility and total fertility may be investigated. It will thus be possible to gain closer estimates of reproductive loss due to each of the factors included in the model.

The lack of or deficiency of data, though, greatly hinders our efforts in utilizing such a model. In many cases we have had to estimate probability distributions and in doing so make rather broad assumptions. For example, the probability distribution of age at first marital union has had to be estimated. While census and survey data do give some indication of ages at marriage, we have had to assume that these data represent the experience of a cohort. In addition, most survey data relate only to women currently mated. Consequently, we have had to assume that the marital experience of women not mated at the time of survey was similar to that of currently mated women. To some extent this type of assumption is probably incorrect. The only check we

53. This approach will provide an opportunity to study the effects of family planning and effectiveness with more adequate provision for realistic assumptions than has been possible in previous studies such as M. C. Sheps and E. B. Perrin, "Changes in Birth Rates as a Function of Contraceptive Effectiveness: Some Applications of a Stochastic Model," *American Journal of Public Health*, LIII (July, 1963), pp. 1031–1046.

can make on the realism of the probability distributions utilized in the simulation program is by the reasonableness of the natality rates and completed natality. It is, however, possible that a number of errors in the probability distributions will compensate for each other and give deceptively plausible results. In this case, the achievement of overall evaluation may be rather tenuous.

The application of such a model should have two results. First, we should be able to gain greater insight into the action and interaction of the many factors bearing upon natality. A second result should be to make us more aware of the specific data that are lacking. Hopefully this may motivate the gathering of more adequate data on relevant factors and the focusing of resources upon those which appear the most important.

CONCLUSIONS

The natality patterns observed in a number of underdeveloped countries throw into question some common assumptions and preconceptions. Not only are wide variations in natality levels exhibited by underdeveloped countries but very few of these countries have experienced significant declines in their birth rates. It would appear on the basis of the apparent increases in natality in a few of these countries that birth rates may move in either direction, upward as well as downward.

The factors influencing natality are many and varied. The interrelationships of these factors are such that plausible arguments may be advanced that their effect would be to either increase or decrease natality. Their relative importance within and between societies is little understood. With the large number of studies currently being carried out in underdeveloped countries it is unfortunate that very little comparable data pertaining to such factors are forthcoming. Agreement among investigators on a number of basic items of information would greatly enhance the value of these studies. A great deal of effort has been put forth toward the discovery of natality attitudes among populations in underdeveloped countries.[54] Yet, very little effort has been expended in collecting the data on the social

---

54. See W. P. Mauldin, this volume.

context in which these attitudes are found. It has been the view of this paper that the social context of reproduction, particularly the family, has been neglected. In addition, analytic efforts to disentangle the interaction of the many variables affecting natality encounter serious difficulties. One approach that may assist in such efforts, namely a simulation model, has been described. The acquisition of more detailed and comparable data would facilitate such analyses and thus further our understanding of human reproduction.

ACKNOWLEDGEMENTS

I am indebted to Dr. Mindel C. Sheps and Dr. Irene B. Taeuber for their helpful suggestions and comments on an earlier version of this paper. I wish to acknowledge also the permission of Dr. John Durand to quote preliminary figures from a study of 'conditions and trends of fertility in the world,' prepared by the Population Branch of the United Nations Bureau of Social Affairs in the *Population Bulletin of the United Nations,* No. 7—1963 (New York, 1965).

APPENDIX

TABLE A

Reliability [a] of Birth Registration Systems in Selected Underdeveloped Countries

Country	1951	1952	1953	1954	1955	1956	1957	1958	1959	1960	1961	1962	1963
Tunisia	U	U	U	U	U	U	U	U	U	C	C	C	C
Mauritius [b]	C	C	C	C	C	C	C	C	C	C	C	C	C
Reunion [c]	–	U	U	U	U	U	U	C	C	C	C	C	C
S.A. Coloured	–	–	–	–	–	C	C	C	C	C	C	C	C
S.A. Asian	–	–	–	–	–	C	C	C	C	C	C	C	C
Ceylon [d]	C	C	C	C	C	U	U	U	U	U	U	U	U
Taiwan [e]	–	–	–	–	C	C	C	C	C	C	C	C	C
Federation of Malaya [f]	C	C	C	C	C	C	C	C	C	C	C	C	C
Singapore	–	–	C	C	C	C	C	C	C	C	C	C	C
Ryukyu Is. [g]	–	–	–	C	C	U	U	U	U	U	U	U	U
Costa Rica [h]	C	U	U	U	U	U	U	U	C	C	C	C	C
El Salvador [i]	–	–	U	U	U	U	U	C	C	C	C	C	C
Guadeloupe [j]	U	U	U	U	U	U	U	C	C	C	C	C	C
Guatemala	–	–	–	–	–	C	C	C	C	C	C	C	C
Jamaica [k]	–	C	C	C	C	C	C	C	C	C	C	C	C
Martinique	U	U	U	U	U	U	U	C	C	C	C	C	C
Mexico [l]	C	C	C	C	C	C	C	C	C	C	C	C	C
Panama [m]	–	–	U	U	U	C	C	C	C	C	C	C	C
Puerto Rico [n]	U	U	U	U	U	C	C	C	C	C	C	C	C
Trinidad and Tobago [o]	–	C	C	C	C	C	C	C	C	C	C	C	C
Argentina [p]	U	U	–	C	C	C	C	C	C	C	C	C	C
British Guiana [q]	C	C	C	C	C	C	C	C	C	C	C	C	C
Chile [r]	C	C	U	U	C	C	C	C	C	C	C	C	C
Surinam	–	–	–	–	–	U	U	U	U	C	C	C	C
Venezuela [s]	C	C	U	C	C	C	C	C	C	U	U	U	U

[a] Data coded "C" are relatively complete; those coded "U" are incomplete or unreliable; "–" indicates no specific information available.

[b] Data tabulated by year of registration rather than occurrence.

[c] Excludes live-born infants dying before registration of birth.

[d] Birth registration estimated to be 88 per cent complete in 1953 according to results of post-censal sample.

[e] Excludes live-born infants dying before registration of birth. Data tabulated by year of registration rather than occurrence.

[f] Prior to 1953, data tabulated by year of registration rather than occurrence.

[g] Estimated to be 88 per cent complete in 1955.

[h] For 1945, data tabulated by year of registration. Beginning 1946, data are births registered during the period 1946–1962 tabulated by year of occurrence. According to a study of births registered 1946–1953, 81 per cent were registered in year of occurrence, 93.5 per cent within two years, and 94.7 per cent within three years.

[i] Prior to 1951, rates are by year of registration rather than by year of occurrences.

[j] Registration estimated 85–90 per cent complete. Rates exclude deaths of infants dying before registration of birth.

[k] Rates for years 1947–1952 are by year of occurrence.

[l] Tabulated by year of registration rather than occurrence.

[m] Registration estimated 90 per cent complete in 1956.

[n] According to test of birth registration, 86.5 per cent complete in 1940 and 95.9 per cent in 1950.

[o] Prior to 1954 by year of registration rather than occurrence.

[p] Registration estimated at 97 per cent complete in 1954.

[q] Excluding Amerindians. Tabulated by year of registration rather than occurrence.

[r] Beginning in 1951, data are births tabulated by year of occurrence.

[s] By year of registration rather than occurrence.

Source: United Nations, *Demographic Yearbooks 1951* through *1963* (New York, 1951–1963).

Crude Birth Rates and General Fertility Rates for Selected African Countries

Country	Year	Crude birth rate	General fertility rate [a]
Basutoland	1955–56 [b]	40	—
Burundi	1957 [b]	46.6	173
Central African Republic	1959–60 [b]	48	144
Congo (Brazzaville)	1960 [b]	42	180
Congo (Leopoldville)	1955–57 [b]	43	167
Dahomey	1961 [b]	54	227
Gabon	1960–61 [b]	36	120
Ghana	1950–55	51	211
Guinea	1955	62	223
Ivory Coast	1961	56.1	248
Mali	1960	62	200
Niger	1959–60	61	239
Nigeria	1952–53	53–57	—
Rhodesia and Nyasaland	1950 [b]	56.8	181
Southern Rhodesia	1954	44.8	—
Rwanda	1957 [b]	52.0	220
Senegal	1960–61	43.3	174
Sudan	1955	51.7	234.3
Tanganyika	1957	46	—
Togo	1961 [b]	55	225
Uganda	1959	42	187
Upper Volta	1960–61 [b]	49.1	197
Zanzibar	1958	30	—
Pemba	1958	40	—

[a] Per 1,000 female population aged 10–49.
[b] Based on demographic sample surveys.
Source: United Nations, Demographic Yearbook: 1963 (New York, 1963).

Ronald Freedman and John Y. Takeshita

STUDIES OF FERTILITY AND FAMILY LIMITATION IN TAIWAN

BACKGROUND

Our population studies in Taiwan are designed to answer in part two sets of questions about that stage of the demographic transition in which mortality has been low for some time and fertility has just begun to decline.

1. Prior to any organized family planning program what changes occur "naturally" in fertility and family planning and what sectors of the population change first and most?

2. Can the process of fertility decline be accelerated in a short period in a large population by a massive program to help married couples have the number of children they want? If such a program is effective, what sectors of the population and what aspects of the program are responsible for the success?

Taiwan is a particularly appropriate place in which to study these questions. For some time it has had low mortality and significant progress in social development, conditions which are probably facilitating, if not essential for, rapid fertility decline.[1] Compared to other developing countries, Taiwan ranks high on such measures as literacy, circulation of mass media, nonagricultural employment, involvement in a market economy, etc. We interpret a high ranking on such measures to indicate increasing involvement of the Taiwanese population in social and economic relations transcending traditional local and familial settings.

Fertility has been falling slowly all over Taiwan since 1958, without benefit of any large-scale organized family planning program. The fertility decline, described in detail elsewhere[2] for the period of 1958–1962, continued in 1963 in every one of the five large cities and the 17 other administrative units of Taiwan. The pattern of fertility decline by age is especially significant:

Age	Per cent change in age-specific fertility, 1958–1962
15–19	+5
20–24	+3
25–29	+3
30–34	−16
35–39	−27
40–44	−28
45–49	−29
Total fertility rate	−11

The declines begin to appear at age 30–34 and then increase sharply with age. This is exactly what we would except if many women want a moderate number of living children, achieve this number by age 30, and then begin to try to limit family size in some way. This is the case, indeed, in the city of Taichung in which we have conducted sample surveys, both to study the existing fertility and family planning patterns and to evaluate

---

1. For a discussion of the theoretical issues involved, see R. Freedman, ''Norms for Family Size in Underdeveloped Areas,'' *Proceedings of the Royal Society*, Series B, CLIX (Dec., 1963), pp. 220–245. For some detail on economic and social development in Taiwan as well as data from the population register on fertility trends, see R. Freedman, J. Y. Peng, Y. Takeshita, and T. H. Sun, ''Fertility Trends in Taiwan: Tradition and Change,'' *Population Studies*, XVI (March, 1963), pp. 219–236.

2. R. Freedman, J. Y. Peng, Y. Takeshita, and T. H. Sun, *op. cit.*

the success of a family planning program which might change fertility.

Taichung, a city of more than 300,000 people, is a provincial capital of Taiwan and its fourth largest city. As in many Asian cities its administrative boundaries include both a densely settled urban core containing about two thirds of the population and a large semi-rural area of farms. A large proportion of those living in the urban core are migrants with a farm background. Apart from variation on the rural-urban dimension, the population is sufficiently heterogeneous with respect to indicators of modernization to permit analysis of their effects on fertility (for example, of education, family type, type of employment).

One of our principal sources of data for Taichung is the intensive interview surveys of a probability sample of 2,432 of the 36,000 married women in the childbearing years (defined as 20–39 years old for this purpose). This sample was first interviewed in November–December of 1962 and reinterviewed in November–December, 1963 after the main part of the family planning actions program was completed.[3]

Some of the important results of the preprogram survey reported in previous publications [4] will be summarized here in outline form as a background for considering new analyses.

1. *There is a strong consensus in the population that a*

3. The preprogram survey was done in two stages. Interviews were taken in November–December, 1962, with a probability sample of 1,367 married women 20–39 years old in Taichung City. Then in January interviews were taken with an additional probability sample of 1,065 married women 20–39 years old with at least two living children. The two samples were combined by weighting, by a factor of two, the interviews from the first survey with wives having less than two living children (a rather small minority). The frequencies shown for the total sample are based on this "inflated" sample of 2,713 cases. We actually interviewed only 2,432 women so frequencies in the total sample should be deflated by approximately 10 per cent. The second set of interviews was shorter than the first, so some of the data presented are based only on the first sample. The response rate for the two samples combined (and unweighted) is 97 per cent. After the action program the same sample was reinterviewed. The response rate for the reinterview was 96 per cent of those still remaining in Taichung. Five per cent of the original sample moved out of Taichung and was not followed. The refusal rate was only one per cent. Most of the noninterviews were for couples who moved to unknown destinations.

4. R. Freedman, J. Y. Peng, Y. Takeshita, and T. H. Sun, *op. cit.*; and R. Freedman, Y. Takeshita, and T. H. Sun, "Fertility and Family Planning in Taiwan: A Case Study of the Demographic Transition," *American Journal of Sociology*, CCX (July, 1964), pp. 29–37.

moderate number of children and sons is what they want for themselves and consider ideal for others.[5]

2. *Under existing mortality conditions most women have the moderate number of children and sons they want early in the childbearing period—by the time they are 30–34 and often earlier.*

3. *Most people know about the decline of mortality and are aware that this means that most of their children will survive to be adults.*

4. *Under these conditions it is not unexpected that a large majority of wives and husbands approve the idea of doing something to limit family size and indicate an interest in learning how to do this.*

5. *A significant minority of couples have begun to practice some form of family limitation, but the practice is often either too ineffective or too late to enable the couples to limit their families to the desired size.*

6. *The strata of the population that are most modern in other ways also have the most modern fertility behavior and lead the way in adopting family planning methods in the period before the organized action program.*

In characterizing such groups as having modern fertility behavior we mean that:

They want the fewest children.

More of the children they have survive.

They are more likely to do something to limit family size and especially to use contraception.

They are less likely to rely exclusively on abortion.

They have the lowest fertility—this is the net result.

Now which groups have the modern fertility characteristics? We have provided detailed evidence elsewhere [6] that they are:

The better educated and those who read the mass media.

Those who own the most modern objects of consumption.

---

5. It is very important in this culture to have at least two children, and at least one son, but there is no desire for large families or unlimited numbers of sons. Three of four children with one or two sons is the modal ideal. Those who have larger numbers are not reluctant to say that they would prefer fewer or, at least, prefer no more.

6. R. Freedman, J. Y. Peng, Y. Takeshita, and T. H. Sun, *op. cit.*; and R. Freedman, Y. Takeshita, and T. H. Sun, *op. cit.*

Those living in nuclear rather than in stem or joint families.

Those who are least favorable to traditional Chinese family values.

Those with no farm experience, especially migrants from large cities.

Those who work in an impersonal setting as employees of nonrelatives.

Those who have received information about family planning from multiple sources.

To illustrate the kind of data on which these sweeping generalizations are based we present in Table 1 for the wives 35–39 years old the relationships between two of these important criteria of modernization (wife's education and number of modern objects owned) and the fertility and family planning variables.

In general the use of *some* form of family limitation is more consistently related to the indices of modernization than any single method of limitation considered or the measures of desired or actual fertility. We interpret this to mean that those with more modern characteristics try various methods to limit family size, but their practice of these methods is frequently either so late or ineffective that it does not limit family size to the desired level, although it does produce a rather consistent fertility differential.

That the practice of family limitation is still ineffective is indicated by the fact that at age 35–39 the average number of children born or alive is higher than desired on the average by the wife for every subcategory considered. This is true despite the fact that the use of some method reaches more than 75 per cent for the advanced categories and includes sterilization for as many as 25 per cent of the wives in some categories.

Data, not previously reported, about the percentage pregnant at the time of the first survey interview (Table 2) indicate that it is likely that the more important specific fertility differentials will be even larger than now when the women have completed their childbearing. Those groups with the lowest fertility at ages over 30 also have the lowest current pregnancy rates. For example, current pregnancy rates are negatively correlated with the couple's education, or the number of objects owned.

TABLE 1

Measures of Actual and Desired Fertility, Survival Rates for Children, Per Cent Using Various Types of Family Limitation, by Wife's Education and by Ownership of Modern Objects of Consumption, for Wives 35–39 Years Old

Characteristics of couple	Number of couples	Mean number of live births	Mean number of living children	Survival rate for children	Mean number of children wife wants	Per Cent Using				Per cent of those with an abortion never using other methods
						Sterilization	Abortion	Contraception	Any of three	
Wife's education										
None	238	5.7	4.9	.86	4.4	10	8	13	26	35
Primary—not graduated	42	5.2	4.7	.90	4.2	26	17	19	48	[a]
Primary—graduated	187	5.3	4.8	.90	4.2	18	18	32	51	9
Jr. level or sr. non-grad.[b]	77	4.5	4.1	.91	3.6	22	17	42	66	5
Grad. sr. level or more[c]	75	3.6	3.4	.94	3.3	21	28	53	76	5
Number of modern consumption items owned[d]										
0 or 1	48	6.4	5.2	.82	4.9	0	10	19	25	[a]
2	72	5.6	4.8	.85	4.4	7	10	14	22	[a]
3	87	5.6	4.7	.85	4.2	10	9	18	31	25
4	84	5.3	4.9	.93	4.2	20	14	14	36	8
5	95	4.6	4.1	.89	4.0	17	14	24	43	15
6	140	4.7	4.4	.92	3.9	21	16	39	63	14
7 or more	93	4.7	4.3	.92	3.9	25	29	48	75	7

[a] Base less than 10.
[b] Equivalent to some high school.
[c] Equivalent to high school graduate or some university training.
[d] The objects are: bicycle, radio with record player, radio, electric fan, sewing machine, electric iron, clock or watch, electric pan, motorcycle.

TABLE 2

*Per Cent Pregnant at the Time of the Preprogram Survey, by Wife's Education and
by Number of Modern Objects Owned, and by Number of Children and Sons, for
Wives 30–39 Years Old*

Characteristics of couple		Per cent currently pregnant	Number of couples in base group
Wife's education			
None		12	465
Primary, non-grad.		8	96
Primary, grad.		8	472
Jr. level school [a]		2	182
Sr. level school or more [b]		4	145
Number of modern objects owned			
0 or 1		18	132
2–4		10	502
5 or more		5	728
Number of living children and sons			
Children	Sons		
0	0	21	38
1	0	15	40
1	1	6	34
2	0	6	18
2	1 or more	4	73
3 or 4	0	17	30
3 or 4	1 or more	7	518
5 or more	any	7	611

[a] Equivalent to some high school.
[b] Equivalent to high school graduate or some university training.

The current pregnancy rates in Table 2 also confirm the
continuing importance of having sons. Comparing women with
similar numbers of children alive, those without a son have
higher pregnancy rates than those with at least one son.

NEW MULTIVARIATE ANALYSES OF THE PREPROGRAM SURVEY

Obviously, many of the modernization variables we have
considered must be overlapping in their content and in their
effect on family planning. Such an important modernization
variable as education, for example, is known to be correlated
rather strongly with such other variables as the number of
modern objects owned or attitudes to traditional familial values.
It is desirable to know how much of the variance in the behavior

is explained by each of these variables alone and how much additional explanation is achieved by considering them in combinations. We can present here only a preliminary report in which the dependent variable is the proportion who have used any form of family limitation (contraception, abortion, or sterilization).[7]

Consider first the education and reading variables. Since husband's education added little to the explanatory effect of wife's education (Table 3), we used a husband-wife education code for the subsequent analyses. This husband-wife education code, together with measures of the frequency of newspaper reading by husband and wife accounts for 16.1 per cent of the total variance. The education-reading variables probably indicate whether the couple has access to specific information about family planning and the small family pattern. Perhaps more important, they may measure roughly the contact of the couple with ideas and systems of interaction beyond local and familial groups. The measures of association for education and reading are in each case somewhat larger for the wife than for the husband. This may indicate the special importance of drawing the wife into the modern sector at least so far as family planning is concerned.

Another important variable is the number of modern consumer objects owned. This is a useful index of a modern standard of living and one way in which the couple is drawn into a modern economic sector. Adding this variable to the education-reading cluster brings the explained variance to 18.7 per cent. It is much more strongly associated with use of family limitation than is husband's income. How income is spent apparently is more important than how much there is. Money can be used to

---

7. The method used here is "multiple classification" analysis. For explanations and examples of use see D. S. Freedman, "The Relation of Economic Status to Fertility," *The American Economic Review*, LIII (June, 1963), pp. 414–426; also J. Morgan *et al.*, *Income and Welfare in the United States* (New York: McGraw-Hill, 1962). Essentially, this is a regression procedure in which each category of each independent variable is a predictor (having the value zero or one). It is unnecessary to consider the categories as having any rank order, and there are no assumptions about the scaling of the variables or linearity of the variables. In the particular case in which we have used family limitation practice as the dependent variable, we have assigned a value of zero to those who have not and of one to those who have practiced family limitation.

TABLE 3

Per Cent of the Total Variance in Use of Family Planning Associated with Various Social Variables, for Wives 30–39 Years Old

Social variables	Per cent of variance in family limitation use explained
Variables considered singly	
Wife's education	13.1
Husband's education	11.3
Wife's frequency of newspaper reading	12.9
Husband's frequency of newspaper reading	10.7
Number of modern objects owned	14.8
Husband's work classification	4.4
Wife's attitude toward traditional family values	6.4
Couple's farm background	3.2
Husband's annual cash income	3.2
Variables considered in clusters	
Husband and wife's education	13.7
Husband and wife's education and newspaper reading by husband and wife (education-reading variables)	16.1
Education-reading variables and number of modern objects owned	18.7
Education-reading variables, number of modern objects owned, and husband's work status	18.8
Education-reading variables, number of modern objects owned, husband's work status and wife's attitudes toward traditional family values	19.2
Education-reading variables and couples' farm background	16.2
Wife-husband's education and husband's income	16.5

achieve traditional rather than new values. Husband's income adds very little to the explained variance associated with the education variables alone.

Very little is gained in explained variance by adding to education-reading and number of modern objects owned such other variables as husband's work status, wife's attitude to traditional familial values, or farm background.

Almost all of the variables considered individually have a reasonable and statistically significant relationship to the use of family planning. Whatever is involved in the other variables is, however, covered by education-reading and the number of modern objects owned, so far as the effect on family limitation practice is concerned.

As a by-product of the multiple-classification procedure, Table 4 shows in detail how the proportion using family limitation differs from the average for each category of each variable: (1) when considered alone and then (2) when various other groups of variables are taken into account. A detailed consideration of these data is not possible here, but the utility of this type of analysis can be illustrated with one example, education. Note that before considering other variables, there is a steady increase from 20 per cent below the average in the lowest educational category to 32 per cent above average in the highest. If we "adjust" these figures to take out the effect of newspaper reading by the husband and wife—a functional test of the meaning of education—the relationship with education persists but is much less steep, the variation (Column A) being from −6 per cent to +18 per cent. If we add an adjustment for number of modern objects the relationship becomes still less steep (Column B). But adjusting for husband's employment status and wife's traditional attitudes makes little additional difference (Column C)—the possible effects of these variables are already taken into account. After adjusting for all these variables the two highest educational groups still stand out as distinctive. The wife's educational level, i.e., junior versus senior level, has a significant residual effect on the use of family limitation, after all the other five variables are taken into account. Adjusting for rural background makes little difference in the effects of education when we allow for the effect of reading (Column D). On the other hand, the small effects of farm background are completely removed when that variable is adjusted for education-reading.

The numbers of living children and of sons influence the use of family limitation independently of the social variables just considered. In another multiple classification analysis, the explained variance was raised to 25.2 per cent by adding a combined code on "number of living children and sons" to the education-reading variables, the number of modern objects owned, farm background and wife's traditional attitudes. Almost none of the influence of the number of children-sons variable overlaps the influence of the social variables, so adding this demographic variable substantially increases the variance explained. It appears that both the demographic and the social

TABLE 4

Per Cent Using Family Limitation Expressed as Deviations from Per Cent for Whole Group (44%), by Various Social Variables in Original Form and Adjusted for Effect of Groups of Other Variables; for Wives 30–39

Social variables	Original deviation from overall average	Deviations from overall average adjusted for effects of variables [a]			
		A	B	C	D
Wife-husband education					
Both none	−20	−6	−3	−2	−6
Wife none, husband more	−21	−13	−10	−9	−13
Both primary non-grad.	−18	−6	−4	−2	−6
Wife primary non-grad., husband more	−2	−1	0	+1	−1
Both primary grad.	−2	−1	−2	−1	−1
Wife primary grad., husband more	+10	+4	+1	+1	+4
Wife jr. level, husband any	+23	+12	+10	+9	+12
Wife sr. level, husband any	+32	+18	+14	+12	+18
Wife's newspaper reading					
Cannot read	−18	−5	−3	−3	
Never reads	−8	−5	−3	−3	
Less than once a week	+12	−6	+5	+5	
1–4 times a week	+9	−2	−3	−5	
Every day	+27	+10	+6	+6	
Husband's newspaper reading					
Cannot read	−24	−13	−8	−8	
Never reads	−22	−9	−5	−5	
Less than once a week	−13	−4	−1	0	
1–4 times a week	−4	+2	+2	+2	
Every day	+15	+6	+3	+3	
Husband's work classification					
Farm occupation	−19			+1	
Other traditional jobs [b]	−4			−2	
Employed by non-relative	+5			+2	
Professional worker	+21			−4	
Wife's attitude toward traditional family values [c]					
Most traditional	−9			−2	
Less traditional	+11			+6	
Least traditional	+19			+2	
Number of modern objects owned					
0 or 1	−23			−13	−12
2 or 3	−22			−13	−13
4	−10			−5	−6
5	+4			+3	+3
6	+16			+10	+9
7 or more	+27			+15	+15

TABLE 4 *(Continued)*

| | Per Cent Ever Using Family Limitation Practice | | | | |
| | | Deviations from overall average adjusted for effects of variables [a] | | | |
Social variables	Original deviation from overall average	A	B	C	D
Couple's farm background					
Farm now	−19				0
Both some farm background	0				0
Husband or wife farm background	+4				−1
No farm background	+10				+1

[a] The variables in group A are: Wife-husband education, newspaper reading of wife and husband.

The variables in group B are: Group A variables plus number of modern objects owned.

The variables in group C are: Group B variables plus husband's work status and wife's attitudes toward traditional values.

The variables in group D are: Group A variables plus couple's farm background.

[b] These include persons employed by relatives or self-employed in nonprofessional business activities (usually small family shops).

[c] This is a classification of wife's attitudes toward living with her children in her old age, being supported by them in her old age, and desirability of sons living together in a large joint family when they marry.

variables have significant and independent influences in the adoption of family limitation prior to a planned program.

THE DESIGN OF THE EXPERIMENTAL ACTION PROGRAM

The preprogram survey, indicating that a large part of the population wanted help in family limitation, encouraged the Provincial Health Department of Taiwan to provide the help. For this purpose an experimental action program was developed that must be one of the largest social science studies ever conducted under controlled conditions.

In most general terms, the objective of the program was to see by how much family planning could be increased by a massive program of short duration. A corollary major objective was to observe whether the birth rate for the city would fall substantially. As far as we know, no population this large has ever had a significant birth rate decline as a consequence of an organized program for dissemination of family planning ideas.

Another major objective was to test the power of indirect diffusion by word-of-mouth in a whole population in which were placed systematically spaced, direct-influence foci from which diffusion could take place. This general objective seems especially important in view of considerable, if unsystematic, evidence that informal word-of-mouth diffusion was principally responsible for the spread of family limitation ideas in Japan and the West. The research question was whether messages about family planning can be placed in this informal network on a massive basis to speed the process of diffusion in a short period.

Apart from these general objectives, the action study was designed to provide partial answers to a number of important basic questions about how best to conduct such a program and what groups would respond most readily.

The more specific objectives were to test the success of the program:

When couples get intensive personal visits by a nurse-midwife.

When both husband and wife rather than wives only receive such personal visits.

When mailings only are used to provide information and support.

When couples not reached directly in any way are surrounded by neighborhoods in which there are intensive direct influence.

In different strata. Do the modernized strata of society lead in acceptance? Is the number of children and of sons important?

The basic unit in the research action design is the *lin*—a neighborhood unit containing an average of about 20 households, of which on the average, about 12 have women aged 20–39 years. Taichung is divided officially into about 2,400 such neighborhood units. Each lin was assigned to one of 12 cells in an overall experimental design for Taichung involving four treatments and three diffusion-intensity sectors, as shown in Table 5. The four treatments range from much to little effort as follows.

TABLE 5

Percentage Distribution of Taichung Lins by "Treatment" and by Density Sectors in the Family Planning Program

Treatment	Density Sectors			
	I Heavy	II Medium	III Light	Total
	Percentage distribution			
Everything: husband and wife	25	17	10	18
Everything: wife only	25	17	10	18
Mail only	25	33	40	32
Nothing	25	33	40	32
Total	100	100	100	100
Number of cases	928	731	730	2,389

1. *Everything—husband and wife:* in these lins all the stimuli of the program are combined; personal visits by trained health workers for information and supporting motivation, mailings of information, and meetings in the neighborhood, mixing entertainment and information about family planning.

2. *Everything—wife only:* this involves all the major stimuli except the personal visit to the husband.

3. *Mailings:* no personal visits (unless requested) or meetings in the neighborhood; instead a series of mailings of letters and pamphlets provide information on methods, rationale, location of clinics, etc., and includes a return-postal device to request more information or a personal visit from a field worker.

4. *Nothing:* no direct effort is made; there are posters in the area and meetings are held at the *li* level (a larger neighborhood unit of about 350 households).

Each lin was assigned to one of these four treatments. It was also located in one of three "density" sectors which differed, so far as possible, only in the proportion of lins getting the more intensive treatments. For this purpose the city was divided into three approximately equal pie-shaped sectors, roughly equated initially on fertility, rural-urban distribution, and educational level. Within each of the three sectors all the lins were distributed randomly among the four treatments in the proportions indicated in Table 5. In Sector I the largest proportion (50 per cent) and in Sector III the smallest proportion (20 per cent) of the lins were assigned to the "everything" treatments. All couples in the lins of a particular treatment type were supposed to get the same direct message regardless of the sector in which they were located. They differed only in the percentage of the surrounding lins getting other treatments. For example, those in the "nothing" lins in Sector I had an environment in which many of the neighboring lins were getting the intensive treatment; "nothing" lins in Sector III had an environment in which relatively few of the surrounding lins were getting intensive treatment.

In addition to the specific treatments, there were some city-wide mass media messages, limited to a very small volume by a local policy decision. In view of the literacy of the population and the excellent mass media available we believe that major supporting use of such media would have increased the success of the program considerably. Several thousand copies of a set of 15 posters also were placed in prominent locations. Some of these carried information about the location of the clinics but mainly they presented the idea of family planning in simple attractive forms. There were also a considerable number of meetings with community leaders and with functional groups, such as the farmers' association and the pedicab drivers association.

Family planning services and supplies were offered at 10 clinics located throughout the city. Information, services, and supplies were offered with respect to the diaphragm, jelly, foam tablets, condom, withdrawal, rhythm, oral contraceptives, and the new intrauterine devices. No effort was made to set up a design that would rigidly test the attractiveness of different methods, but the interest in the intrauterine device was so great, as we shall see presently, that its attraction for this population can hardly be doubted.

The extensive experimental program ran from February to October, 1963. To test the continuing momentum of the program, clinic and informational services continued to be available. As some indication of the scope of the program, nearly 12,000 first home visits and over 500 lin meetings were held by

June, 1963. Follow-up visits of various kinds probably ran to more than 20,000.

The action program was intended to help those who wanted to limit family size rather than to persuade people that they should want to do so. The former is by far the easier task and, in our opinion, it may be the efficient way to begin any large program.

Three sources of data will be available for final evaluation.

1. The official register can be used to determine fertility rates for Taichung as compared with other large cities and other administrative units of Taiwan. Other comparisons will also be made for lins and groups of lins as they are sorted into 12 cells of the experimental design.

2. The before and after panel survey of the 2,432 married women that has already been described.

3. Extensive data can be drawn from short questionnaires for about 4,000 women who came to the clinics and from approximately 12,000 home visits. A major part of our report on results to date is based on these records.

RESULTS OF THE ACTION PROGRAM: A PRELIMINARY REPORT

How successful has the program been? Perhaps the most important test will be the course of the birth rate in the next year or two but a preliminary evaluation of results on other bases is possible.

One criterion is the number of couples who accepted family planning directly from the program clinics or representatives. Acceptance is defined as the actual insertion of an intrauterine contraceptive device (IUCD) or the receipt of instruction and the purchase of supplies for other methods with expressed intention to use them.

A total of 3,968 couples (including 764 from outside Taichung) were registered as acceptors between early February and November 10, 1963. The 3,204 cases from the City of Taichung represent nine per cent of the married women aged 20–39 years. After the formal program for finding acceptors ended in the fall of 1963, women continued to come to the clinics without any formal program of recruitment. By May 2, 1964, the number of acceptors had reached 6,188, of whom 25 per cent were from outside the city, and 78 per cent were IUCD cases.

But many of the wives were really not eligible to accept family planning. For example, this is certainly true of the approximately 10 per cent who had been surgically sterilized and of an additional number who believed themselves to be sterile. By excluding women ineligible by various criteria of this type, we arrive at a range of estimates of the percentage of eligibles who became acceptors. A number of such preliminary estimates have been prepared based on the data up to October 15, 1963 for the approximately 2,400 women in the intensive survey sample. For example, in one estimate we excluded as ineligible the women who were believed to be sterile and also those who already were using a contraceptive method they found acceptable, unless they became acceptors in the program. On this basis, only 71 per cent of the wives were eligible, and the acceptance rate rises from the initial 9 to 13 per cent.

A next step is to exclude as ineligible, in addition, women who wanted more children at the first interview (unless they became acceptors in the program). This additional exclusion decreases the percentage eligible to 42 per cent, and increases the acceptance rate to 21 per cent.

In earlier calculations, we had excluded as ineligible women who were pregnant at the first interview or at the first home visit. However, we found later in the postprogram interviews that the percentage of acceptors among these women was greater than in the sample as a whole, presumably because they were more often in contact with health personnel in prenatal and antenatal services as well as at the time of delivery. The issue of family planning may also have been much more salient for them. A different approach will have to be developed for the pregnant women, providing an adjustment for the number of months of ineligibility by reason of pregnancy.

Not all of the acceptors are new to the practice of family planning. As of October 15, 1963, 37 per cent of the acceptors had previously tried some form of contraception and were dissatisfied with it. Indications are that this group is partly balanced by the couples who adopted some form of family limitation outside of the program itself but in many cases as a consequence of the influence of the program.

As our colleague, Bernard Berelson, has pointed out,[8] these kinds of calculation simply illustrate that in a population of this type at any one time ". . . somewhere between half and three fourths of the target population is simply out of bounds for the purpose. If a program can get as many as a half—or even a third or a fourth—of the remaining group to begin practicing contraception within a few years, it has probably achieved a good deal. In this kind of work, then, having an impact on 10 per cent of the target population in a year or so is not a disappointing failure but a substantial success; one should report 'Fully 10 per cent,' not 'Only 10 per cent!' "

It is clear that we need research criteria for evaluating the "success" of programs in populations with changing panels of eligibles. A significant number of cases classified as ineligible at one or another time during the program became cases in the program before it was concluded because of follow-up visits when a temporary barrier (e.g., pregnancy) was passed. One solution is to cite the results with a range of defined bases, such as the range of 9 to 21 per cent of eligibles already cited. Other criteria and later data raise the percentage to more than 30 per cent.[9]

Diffusion and informal communication channels proved to be as important here as they have been elsewhere where family planning has reached large populations. Perhaps the most striking evidence is that by October 15, 1963, 20 per cent of all the acceptors came from outside the city, although the formal program was limited to the city itself. About 65 per cent of these outside cases came from Taichung Hsien, the administrative unit surrounding the city, but another 25 per cent came from the next two adjacent hsiens. The remaining 10 per cent came from more distant places all over the island.

8. B. Berelson and R. Freedman, "A Study in Fertility Control," *Scientific American*, CCX (May, 1964), pp. 29–37.

9. The higher rates result from adding to the ineligible group some proportion of the pregnant, the lactating, and others in amenorrhea as well as making allowance for the acceptances after October 15, 1963, considerable in number.

Approximately 50 per cent of all the cases from inside the city came without benefit of a home visit, although the "everything" home-visit lins did have a higher acceptance rate than any others. Even in the "everything" home-visit lins, 17 per cent of all acceptors visited the clinics *before* the home visitor could get to them. Word of mouth spread the news faster than the home visitors could make their rounds!

TABLE 6

Per Cent of Acceptors, Who Did Not Have a Home Visit Before Accepting, Reporting Specified Sources of Information About the Program, by Sector [a]

| | Taichung City | | | | |
Source of information	I Heavy	II Medium	III Light	All sectors	Outside Taichung
Friends, relatives, or neighbors	42	51	50	47	66
Regular health station personnel	26	23	31	26	27
Home visitors or MCHI workers	30	21	19	24	5
Letters	14	10	12	12	—
Meetings	16	5	7	10	2
Newspaper	3	2	3	3	2
Posters	1	1	2	1	—
Private midwives or private doctors	—	1	1	1	1
Others	4	4	4	4	2
Total number of cases	631	408	541	1,640	764

[a] Total percentages exceed 100 because some cases gave multiple sources.

The indirect impact of the program has been mediated first of all by word-of-mouth communication of friends, relatives, and neighbors and second by regular health station personnel and the program's home visitors who apparently talked to people on their rounds in addition to home visits (Table 6). It is our impression, so far, that, to an appreciable extent, the indirect diffusion is attributable to the involvement of a considerable number of people scattered over the whole city and moving about in it. Thus, there are multiple sources of possible influence and communication which are mutually and cumulatively reinforcing.

The indirect diffusion effect can also be seen in the percentage of acceptances in each of the 12 cells of the experimental design, as shown in Table 7. Although, as expected, the proportion of acceptors is largest in the "everything" lins, the response in the "nothing" and "mail" lins without any direct contact is not inconsiderable. The acceptance rate was highest in the heavy density sector for each of the four treatments. There was no significant difference between the medium and light sectors.[10]

TABLE 7

Percentage of Acceptors Among Married Women 20–39 Years Old, by Treatment, by Sector in Taichung

Treatment	I Heavy	II Medium	III Light	All sectors
		Percentages		
Everything: husband and wife	18	10	12	15
Everything: wife only	16	13	11	14
Mail only	7	5	6	6
Nothing	7	5	5	5
Total	12	7	7	9

Other preliminary findings shown in Table 7 suggest that mailings were rather ineffective,[11] and that including the husband in home visits made little difference. This latter finding needs to be explored more thoroughly both in the Taichung data and elsewhere in view of its theoretical and practical importance.[12]

The study has clearly demonstrated the overwhelming appeal of the intrauterine devices in this area. Seventy-four per cent of all acceptances up to November 10, 1963 were IUCD cases.[13] It

10. The density variations were related to whether those indicating an intention to become acceptors in the home visits did do so in fact. In the data for the period up to August 10, 1963, the percentage of acceptors among all those indicating a future intention to be acceptors was by Sector: I (Heavy)—60 per cent; II (Medium)—48 per cent; III (Light)—40 per cent. Apparently more reinforcement in the environment helps to move people from intentions to action.

11. The fact that mailings were not more effective may very well be due to the fact that they contained no information about the IUCD which turned out to be almost the only attraction for the nonhome visit cases.

12. It is possible that male workers for the men might have made a difference in the results. However, we have no reason to believe that the female health workers did not have good rapport with the husbands.

13. Among the cases coming after the close of the formal program the overwhelming majority were IUCD cases, so that by May 2, 1964, 78 per cent of the total number of acceptances were IUCD cases.

might be argued that the workers put more emphasis on this method and that this accounts for its popularity. This seems very unlikely since the IUCD was selected by only 49 per cent of acceptors who had had a home visit and by 89 per cent of those who had heard about the program in other ways (Table 8). Further, among those who came from outside the city, a very large majority—97 per cent—were attracted by the intrauterine

TABLE 8

Type of Contraception Adopted by Acceptors, by Treatment, by Whether Acceptance Before or After Home Visit, and by Location Inside or Outside City

	Inside Taichung				
	"Everything" lins		"Mail" and		
	After	Before	"nothing"	Outside	
Method	home visit	home visit	lins	Taichung	Total
	Percentage distribution				
IUCD	49	88	89	97	74
Pills	1	2	3	1	2
Traditional	50	10	8	2	24
Total	100	100	100	100	100
Number of cases	1,572	317	1,315	764	3,968

devices.[14] There seems to be little doubt that the success of the program as a whole depended considerably on the availability of the IUCD with all its advantages. We do not know what would have happened if it had not been available.

We have just begun to assemble the data on acceptance rates for the various demographic and social strata. Again the question of eligibility becomes a problem. In Table 9, for a few of the major variables, we compare the distribution of the acceptors with the distribution of the total survey sample and also with the distribution of the sample cases "eligible" in the sense that they were not sterilized or using a method of contraception that satisfied them at the beginning of the program.

As compared with the "eligible" couples, disproportionate numbers of acceptors are older wives, have three or more (and

---

14. As the program progressed, the proportion having an IUCD removed decreased and the proportion having reinsertion increased. Further, the proportion with complaints steadily decreased.

TABLE 9

Percentage Distribution of the Acceptors in the Program, of All Married Women 20–39 Years Old and of "Eligible" Married Women, by Selected Demographic and Social Characteristics

Characteristic	Acceptors	Married women 20–39 years old [a]	"Eligible" married women, not sterilized and not currently using contraception when program began [a]
Wife's age		*Percentage distribution*	
20–24	15	19	23
25–29	30	31	35
30–34	32	27	24
35–39	23	23	18
Number of living children			
0–2	16	37	46
3	21	19	18
4 or more	63	44	36
Number of living sons			
0	6	20	25
1–2	58	56	56
3 or more	36	24	19
Wife's education			
None	30	29	37
Primary school	49	48	46
More than primary school	21	23	17
Residence			
Rural district	35	71	28
Urban district	65	29	72

[a] Distributions in these two columns are based on the sample survey. The distributions of acceptors are based on the clinic records of acceptances.

especially four or more) living children, and have at least one living son. Contrary to expectation, a larger proportion of acceptors were from rural districts than was the case for the eligible women. Even taking eligibility into account, the demographic characteristics—wife's age and the number of living children and sons—appear to be much more important than the social characteristics considered so far.

We can only speculate now that in this situation where a general interest in family planning exists at all social levels and where desired family size is moderate at all levels, couples at the right demographic stage can be attracted to family limitation by an organized program which moves the undecided and the ill-informed to action. Having the ''modern'' social characteristics may be more important in the natural unplanned development of family planning in which initiative and individual seeking for information and supplies are required.

It is important that significant proportions of acceptors are coming from the demographic and social strata generally considered unpromising. Among the wives who are acceptors, 45 per cent are under 30 years of age; 16 per cent have fewer than three living children; 6 per cent have no sons; and 30 per cent have no education. In part this is a result of the large numbers of women in these categories and the large proportion of them who are eligible by almost any criterion. But such results would not be possible without a rather high acceptance rate even in these unpromising strata. It is a hopeful sign for the long-run success of such programs in Taiwan that they are reaching these large groups that have a long period in the childbearing age group ahead of them.

We have ranged intentionally in this report over various aspects of the research in Taiwan to illustrate both the richness of the material that is becoming available and the rapidity with which significant results can be reported. It has been necessary to treat very lightly many topics that will require the much more intensive analysis that we plan to do.

ACKNOWLEDGEMENTS

The research on which this paper was based involves the cooperation of a large number of people. The research was carried out at the Taiwan Population Studies Center and at the University of Michigan Population Studies Center. The Taiwan Center is associated with the Maternal and Child Health Institute of the Provincial Health Department of Taiwan. Financial support for the basic research activity has come from the Population Council and the Ford Foundation. We are grateful to many people for their assistance, including especially Dr. T. C. Hsu, Commissioner of Health; Dr. C. L. Chen, presently Director of the Maternal and Child Health Institute, and Dr. J.

Y. Peng, formerly Director of the Maternal and Child Health Institute; Dr. C. H. Lee, immediately in charge of the program for providing family planning services under the study plan; Mr. Y. F. Liu, in charge of registration data at the Provincial Civil Affairs Department; and Dr. S. C. Hsu, of the Joint Commission on Rural Reconstruction. Solomon Chu assisted with computations and analysis at the University of Michigan. Dr. Bernard Berelson of the Population Council was the principal advisor to the Taiwan Provincial Health Department in the design of the action program. He has been closely involved in the design of the evaluation work.

Samuel M. Wishik

COMMUNITY PROGRAMS TO MODIFY FAMILY SIZE: INDICATIONS FOR ORGANIZATION AND PLANNING

INTRODUCTION

Efforts to organize community programs in family planning, particularly in developing countries, present many opportunities for experimentation and investigation. Only by exploiting these opportunities can the best answers be found to many of the questions that arise. This paper will present the problems that arise in planning such programs and discuss the questions that need answers. Many of the examples will relate particularly to Pakistan, since the writer has recently been working in that country.

Modification of family size is a family responsibility. In no country in the world is serious thought being given by any government to make family limitation compulsory. Even if there were no other reason for community interest, however, community participation would be justified because it will help families do what they want to do but cannot without help. The community program enables families to carry out their responsibility to determine family size as they wish.

In underdeveloped countries, there is wide spontaneous desire for family planning. Within their present level of wanting

198

family limitation, however, the steps couples must personally take to practice family planning must be made easier for them, if enough of them are to practice it consistently. Toward this end, therefore, community effort must make family planning more *available*. The other feature of family planning programs is *educational effort* to increase the readiness of people to use the services.

There are three possible combinations of these two features of a community family limitation program:

(1) *Education without availability of service.* Obviously, this would be pointless and frustrating, although unfortunately it is not rare for services to lag behind both the spontaneous and the at-times engendered demand for family planning service.

(2) *Availability without education.* All peoples in the world limit births to some extent below the maximum potential. There would seem to be little doubt that if services helping couples to prevent births were readily available, more of them would do so. Whether or not the total effect on birth rates would be sufficient to warrant the effort is an unanswered question, incorporating obvious factors of culture and types of contraceptive methods made available. The information would be spread by way of satisfied "customers." Although it is not possible to demonstrate beyond question that the smaller family is faring better, the woman experiencing a pregnancy annually can see the difference between her state and that of the woman who is successfully spacing her pregnancies.

(3) *Availability and education.* In most cases it seems best to assume that both availability of service and education for family planning are necessary and to proceed on that assumption. At the same time, test programs should be set up for number (2) above—availability without complementary education.

AVAILABILITY OF SERVICES

A. General

The decision on the *what* and the *how* of making methods of family modification available to a population falls into three steps.

1. Delineation of immediate objectives.   Within this category are four possible approaches.

a. Women would start having their first child later in life, either by postponement of marriage or by prolonging the interval between marriage and the first pregnancy. The first is not primarily a "family planning" responsibility. In Pakistan, it is calculated that postponement of marriage until 19 years of age would reduce the average parity by one,[1] but this is not attainable within the culture for a long time to come.

In underdeveloped countries, it does not seem reasonable to invest much effort in an attempt to delay the first pregnancy after marriage. In most of these cultures people wait for the first pregnancy as tangible evidence of consummation of the marriage, with loss of face for both spouses proportionate to the time that elapses.

b. Terminate childbearing earlier in life, for example by seeking to reduce the number of children born to women over 35 years of age. A community program for modifying family size by earlier cessation of parenthood would logically be achieved by sterilization, male or female.

c. Lower the average parity. Here the object would be the acceptance of a ceiling on parity regardless of the age of the mother at the time of the last pregnancy. Again, sterilization, male or female, would be the logical solution for termination of childbearing. It must be recognized, however, that many women would have achieved the desired parity at a relatively early age. Fear of catastrophic loss of children always exists, and the inability to guarantee reversibility seems to warrant delaying surgical sterilization until about age 35. In the intervening period, use would be made of "birth spacing" types of contraceptive methods. In a country with an average completed parity of six or more, it is far from futile to offer surgical sterilization or other birth control service to women who have already had four or five children. Elimination of the many high parity births will reduce the average per woman.

d. Birth spacing. In underdeveloped countries, birth spacing,

1. N. M. Sadiq, "The Economic Effects of Postponement of Marriage for Pakistan," (doctoral dissertation, American University, Washington, D.C., 1963).

or an elective prolongation of the inter-pregnancy interval, would seem beneficial to the health of women who have a high rate of anemia and other nutritional deficiencies, and would also enhance the chances of normal fetal development and better lactation and after-care for the infant. If birth spacing were associated with continued high parity rates, the mothers would, during their later pregnancies, be in the ages of high risk of maternal and infant mortality and morbidity. It is therefore important that birth spacing between pregnancies be followed by a more permanent method of avoiding pregnancy.

The impact on population growth of birth spacing can be considerable, both by reducing the ultimate parity of these women and by its effect on the average interval between generations. More immediately, it is common experience that women who practice contraception successfully may be readier to accept and practice more permanent, less traditional types of birth control after achieving the desired maximum family size.

2. Appropriateness. Obviously, a combination of the above approaches is desirable. In underdeveloped countries, women start having babies early in life, continue having them late in life, and become pregnant many times at close intervals.

Even in a large-scale national family planning program, it should be possible for a staff to individualize their advice on the most appropriate contraceptive method to satisfy the wishes of each family. Each case would fall into one of the following five categories:

a. The woman is not now pregnant and the family want no more children. Treatment of choice would be sterilization, male or female.

b. The woman is now pregnant and the family want no more children after this one. Postpartum tubal ligation could be arranged.

c. The couple want just one more child and the woman is not now pregnant. Here too, plans could be made for postpartum tubal ligation.

d. More children are wanted, but not immediately. An intrauterine device (IUCD) should be inserted, a regimen of oral pills established, or a more traditional contraceptive method made available.

e. More children are wanted with no desire for postponement of the next pregnancy. The parents should be educated on the benefits of family planning and informed where help can be obtained in the future.

3. Readiness. Obviously, national programs are necessarily determined and delimited by the particular country's resources. The programs outlined below are based on the thesis that no country can afford to establish an intensive and extensive network of services, facilities, and personnel devoted exclusively to family planning. Rather, each country must decide how much it can afford and how best to use its resources. When the country is ready, it must also find ways of adapting the program to the needs, customs, and beliefs of its people. In an Islamic society, for example, a woman's daily prayers cannot be said during menstruation or, in the opinion of some, when she is wearing a foreign body in her uterus. The refusal of most Pakistani women to be examined or treated by a male physician presents a tremendous stumbling block in the distribution of medical types of contraception.

B. Medical Family Planning Services

Contraception *per se* is not necessarily a medical matter. In fact, the focus on the medical clinic has been a serious barrier in the way of development of effective family planning programs. By and large, it should not be necessary for a man or woman to go to a doctor, a clinic, or a hospital to discuss contraception or to receive help, unless a specific medical method is under consideration. Medical family planning services should be restricted to methods that require a physician for their administration or immediate supervision.

The question follows, whether or not such medical types of family planning services can be incorporated into general health services, or whether special services should be established. In most, if not all, places there is no choice. The resources are not available for nationwide special services. Usually, they must be built into existing or developing general health services.

Experience has shown, however, that when this is done the family planning activities are neglected in the press of other work. But heretofore, in most places, the medical services have been asked to conduct nonmedical types of family planning work. Subject to varying circumstances, it is suggested that special time set aside for family planning medical work is more logical and feasible than special medical family planning personnel. If one session per week were reserved for family planning work, or an extra session added with extra remuneration for staff, family planning would be less likely to be pushed aside or forgotten.

Medical types of contraception include the diaphragm, the IUCD, oral progestin pills, and sterilization. Although some workers have found success with the use of the diaphragm, it is unlikely that it will be accepted or utilized widely in underdeveloped countries. No further discussion of the diaphragm will be given here, except to say that paramedical personnel should be able to conduct such a service.

1. The Intrauterine Contraceptive Device (IUCD). I shall limit my remarks to questions of mass application of the IUCD in a national community family planning program. Special competence in the use of the IUCD is called for in three respects: (1) selection of women for the device and exclusion of others, (2) technique of insertion, and (3) judgment in follow-up regarding need for removal of the device. It is not desirable that the device be inserted during pregnancy, shortly after pregnancy or in the presence of certain types of pelvic disease. Subject to the reliability of the woman herself, the family planning worker responsible for the IUCD work can reasonably avoid pregnancy and the postpartum period by taking a menstrual history. Similarly, gross pelvic disease can be avoided by a simple history on pain, discharge and bleeding, and by nonforceful insertion.

In a large general program, the objective should not necessarily be to have as many women as possible use this method. On the contrary, criteria of eligibility should be on the conservative side, to minimize the medical hazards. In the same way, surgical procedures should be kept to a minimum. In Pakistan, it has been agreed that a uterine sound will not be passed to assess the length and direction of uterus and that dilatation of the cervix will not be permitted. It is preferable to exclude 25 per cent or more of the women and refer them to another method of contraception than to aim for a higher percentage of IUCD insertions with greater risk of trauma or subsequent difficulties. To launch quickly an IUCD service, an initial intensive effort of home visiting would be useful to bring in a clientele who would then start spreading the word to others.

Physicians can be quickly trained to insert and remove the device. The procedure is a simple one. The logistics, however, of training large numbers of physicians is another story if each has to observe and himself practice a reasonable number of insertions. He has to be at the place where there are enough women coming for this purpose, and it is difficult to train more than one or two physicians at a time in this way. At present, the Population Council is seeking for the manufacture of lifelike manikins of the female pelvis to be used for training large numbers of persons in the use of the device.

Some experience and training in gynecology is desirable for physicians called on to do IUCD work. In countries like Pakistan, however, male physicians have very little opportunity to gain gynecologic experience. In fact, the trained midwife has had more experience and is probably better qualified.

The objective in locating IUCD centers would be to cover as many communities as possible rather than to strive for multiple locations in a single community. In smaller communities, there would not be enough demand to occupy an IUCD center full time. In larger communities, it might be desirable to set up full-time IUCD clinics.

Furthermore, it is unlikely that physicians would be willing to limit themselves to only this type of work. They would quickly become bored. Therefore, it might be better to have a small number of trained paramedical personnel, such as midwives, sometimes called lady health visitors, than to have many physicians working part time. From a number of points of view, it might be preferable to train one midwife for three months rather than a physician for one week. Studies are under way in Pakistan and other places on the use of paramedical personnel under medical supervision.

It should be possible to have IUCD's inserted wherever appropriate medical and paramedical personnel are serving—in clinics, hospitals, and private offices. In most developing countries, this still leaves a gap in the peripheral rural areas. The choices possible in developing a national program are: (1) to omit IUCD work in those areas, (2) to transport professional personnel into the areas on an itinerant mobile basis, and (3) to transport the women to the nearest facility. All three are under trial in different places. If it is decided that itinerant visiting professional personnel will be used, it is here urged that the emphasis be on mobile *teams* rather than on mobile *clinics*. Travel difficulties are compounded if a large, portable, complex clinic has to be pulled from place to place and maintained. Even transporting personnel by jeep with several carrying cases of equipment poses obvious difficulties.

Financial incentives of several kinds are used, such as extra fees for clinic physicians and fees to private physicians. Village midwives, who are a likely source for referring women, might receive a small stipend for each woman referred as a kind of compensation for the possible loss of a midwifery fee. This comment, of course, refers to the untrained local midwife, not to the trained nurse-midwife.

2. Oral Progestin Pills. Previous reports have presented the successes and difficulties in maintaining women on the schedules required for use of the pills. Synchronization of menstrual cycles with the phases of the moon has been tried and is being studied in West Pakistan and elsewhere,[2] but it is still too early for conclusions to be drawn. The possibility, however, of synchronizing a number of women to each other, rather than to the moon or other external guideline, offers an interesting application of methods of group dynamics. In a current study in Pakistan, each group of women (approximately 10 women per group) is held together by a group helper. The latter is a woman of the family or immediate neighborhood who distributes the pills on schedule to the women in her group.

Fig. 1 shows the type of report which she submits once a month to her supervisor. The report, which does not require any ability to read or write, permits detailed information to be obtained on pills taken and not taken, on bleeding, whether

2. N. A. Shah, Sikandar Farhat, and J. C. Cobb, ''A Preliminary Report on the Use of Oral Contraceptive Pills Synchronized With the Phases of the Moon'' (Lahore: March 10, 1964, mimeographed).

spotting or more profuse, on presence or absence of complaints, and grossly on the effect upon lactation. The last item is particularly important, since many women taking pills for birth spacing may be nursing the youngest infant. Incidentally, this study illustrates a principle enunciated by Donald Bogue and others.[3] No pilot project should be initiated unless the method

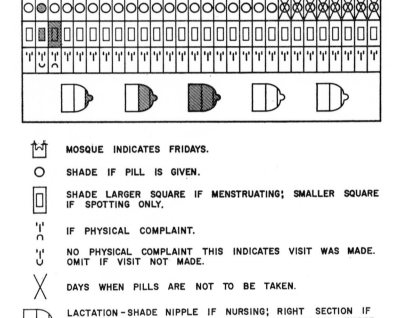

MOSQUE INDICATES FRIDAYS.

SHADE IF PILL IS GIVEN.

SHADE LARGER SQUARE IF MENSTRUATING; SMALLER SQUARE IF SPOTTING ONLY.

IF PHYSICAL COMPLAINT.

NO PHYSICAL COMPLAINT THIS INDICATES VISIT WAS MADE. OMIT IF VISIT NOT MADE.

DAYS WHEN PILLS ARE NOT TO BE TAKEN.

LACTATION – SHADE NIPPLE IF NURSING; RIGHT SECTION IF MILK SUPPLY SMALL, TWO SECTIONS IF MODERATE, THREE IF PROFUSE – AS REPORTED BY MOTHER.

Fig. 1. Sample cycle card for reporting monthly usage of oral contraceptives.

lends itself to wide replication. In this instance, the daily rounds of the group helper would not constitute a chore, because all the women in the group live close to each other and usually see each other practically every day. The method is applicable to the

3. V. S. Heiskanen and D. Bogue, *How to Improve Written Communication for Birth Control* (New York: Community and Family Center, University of Chicago, and National Committee on Maternal Health, 1963).

village or to the urban slum. The group helper would need a very small stipend for her work.

3. Sterilization. Much work has been done in India and elsewhere on sterilization campaigns.[4] The vasectomy camp is a dramatic example. A country that is seriously trying to develop a population control program may be expected to operate vasectomy centers in different parts of the country. Physicians would be trained to perform this simple operation. Equipment would be furnished. Schedules of special sessions would be established and steps taken to reach and encourage men to come. As with the IUCD, referring local midwives or practitioners would receive a small stipend for the referral and physicians would be paid for the surgery. In addition, India, Pakistan, and other countries have given a small remuneration to the man undergoing the operation not as a reward but as a compensation for one or two days' missed work and incidental expenses.

Obstetrical departments of hospitals and medical institutions can be expected to be prepared to perform tubal ligations. Every hospital maternity service should have a routine whereby women could discuss their interest in the possibility of postpartum sterilization, which could be performed before they leave the hospital. Admittedly, however, in underdeveloped countries the large majority of babies are not born in hospitals.

C. Traditional or Conventional Contraceptive Methods

Community programs in the use of traditional contraceptive methods have two components, both nonmedical, namely personal counseling and distribution of contraceptive supplies. Three types of services can exist: (1) counseling, usually without distribution of supplies, (2) counseling and distribution, and (3) distribution, usually without counseling.

1. Counseling, usually without distribution. The medical family planning services will have to take the time necessary to give adequate interpretation to a woman before she consents to having the IUCD, taking the oral pills, or subjecting herself to sterilization. In this process, the choice of nonmedical types of

4. B. L. Raina, "Family Planning Programme—Report for 1962–63," Directorate of Health Services (New Delhi, India: Ministry of Health).

contraception is also given to the woman (or to the man). If the person elects one of the nonmedical methods, an initial supply of contraceptives might be given, while other resources would be used for renewals of supplies. If, perchance, the clinic should be the most convenient place for regular renewal of supply, distribution would be made by nonprofessional personnel without need for the usual clinic procedure or keeping of records.

2. Counseling and distribution. In most places, this would be the heart of the community family planning program.[5] In each village or neighborhood, a local resident would be selected and trained. This person would be an ordinary member of the community, not necessarily literate, but chosen because of intelligence, reliability, motivation, time available, and acceptability to the other members of the community. In India, the last requirement was achieved by quick sociometric questionnaires of a sample of the community.

It is difficult to estimate at present what is an ideal ratio of population to the local family planning worker. In Pakistan, because villages usually consist of about 1,000 or more persons, the initial objective is one worker per 1,000 population. In some situations this ratio may be too low. In a country of one hundred million people, this calls for at least 100,000 family planning workers, and possibly as many as a quarter of a million. In view of the gross underemployment in Pakistan, such an objective is not inconceivable. Unemployment and underemployment are almost constant features of developing countries.

The local worker might serve without any remuneration. He might receive a small regular stipend or earn some money from the sale of contraceptive supplies. In the latter instance, most of the cost would be subsidized by government and the sale price to the consumer controlled. No restriction would be placed upon the amount each person could obtain or the frequency of renewal of supply. The supplies would be so widely available at so low a price that there would be no profit in black-marketing.

A number of possibilities arise regarding possible choices of

---

5. Government of India, ''Procedure for Developing Local Leadership for the Family Planning Program'' (Oct., 1963, mimeographed).

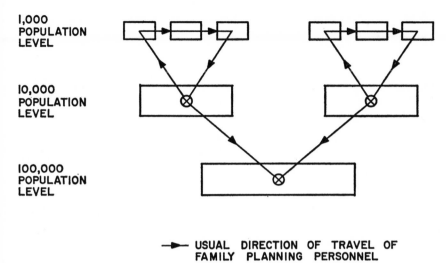

**1,000
POPULATION
LEVEL**

**10,000
POPULATION
LEVEL**

**100,000
POPULATION
LEVEL**

**━━► USUAL DIRECTION OF TRAVEL OF
FAMILY PLANNING PERSONNEL**

Fig. 2. Pattern A of supervision of rural family planning workers: itinerant full-time
workers based at 10,000 population level.

location of work and source of supervision for volunteers.[6]
These problems are especially important in a rural setting. The
same principles apply in neighborhood organization of cities,
but the problems of distance and travel do not exist.

Figs. 2, 3, and 4 show three echelons of community or political
organization radiating from the center out to the periphery.
These can be regarded as logarithmic steps; a village of 1,000
people, a unit of about 10 villages (in Pakistan, called a
Union), and a next larger level of approximately 100,000 population, comparable to an American county (in Pakistan, called a
Thana or *Tehsil*).

In pattern "A" (Fig. 2), a full-time field worker is located at
the 10,000 level and responsible for ten villages. Because of the
constant travel, it would be almost mandatory that each worker
have a full-time transport vehicle, such as a jeep. The cost of
initial purchase and the problems of maintenance would be
enormous. There is also the usual difficulty of recruiting people

6. For a description of the use of volunteers in Puerto Rico see C. Zalduondo,
"Extensive Use of the Volunteer in a Family Planning Program," reprint
distributed by Planned Parenthood Federation of America, N.Y. (April 20, 1961).

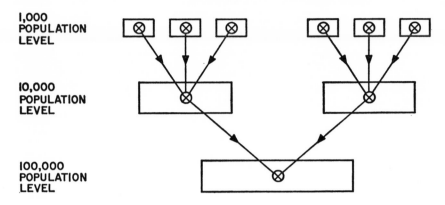

→ USUAL DIRECTION OF TRAVEL OF
FAMILY PLANNING PERSONNEL

Fig. 3. Pattern B of supervision of rural family planning workers: indigenous part-time village workers supervised at 10,000 population level.

to work that calls for constant travel. This problem is increased still further when female workers are required.

Since the home base location of the worker almost always is the largest community in his area, he or she inevitably tends to devote more time to that community and less in travel to the other villages. Assigning two units of 10,000 each to a single worker increases the area covered, reduces the time that can be given to any one community, but psychologically compels the worker to develop "loyalty" beyond his own neighborhood. The small number of workers reporting at the 100,000 level would not occupy more than part time of the supervisor there. In a large country, therefore, this pattern would have a massive core of roving field workers on full-time salary, with no full-time field persons in family planning work above the 10,000 level.

In patterns "B" and "C" (Figs. 3 and 4), the field workers would be indigenous—part-time "volunteers," male and female. They would not need a vehicle for work in their own communities. In pattern "B," they would report periodically at the 10,000 level, and would travel to and fro by commercial or other individualized arrangements. In most countries, it would be necessary for workers to report to group leaders of the same sex. In a large country, therefore, pattern "B" would call for an

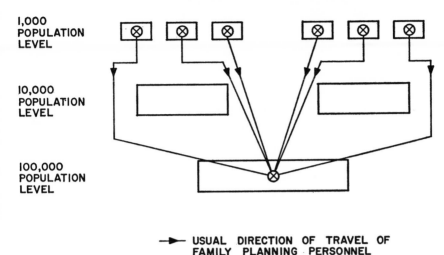

USUAL DIRECTION OF TRAVEL OF FAMILY PLANNING PERSONNEL

Fig. 4. Pattern C of supervision of rural family planning workers: indigenous part-time village workers supervised at 100,000 population level.

army of part-time village workers plus the same large corps of group leaders at the 10,000 level as in pattern "A," though these would now be devoting only part time to family planning work.

In pattern "C," the local village worker reports directly at the 100,000 level. This plan is applicable only where a round-trip visit for such reporting would not be excessively arduous to complete within a single day. It must also be culturally acceptable for female village workers to make such trips. This has been found feasible, for example, in the famous Comilla Academy for Village Development in East Pakistan, despite the severe restrictions on females in this society.[7] In this case, the family planning program is only one of a number of activities in village development that involve the villagers in their own community's uplift.

The justification for bypassing the intermediate level is the

7. See F. E. McCarthy, "Women's Education and Home Development Programme, First Annual Report, January 1962–March 1963" (Comilla, East Pakistan: Pakistan Academy for Rural Development, April, 1963); A. M. Khan, "Rural Pilot Family Planning Action Programme, First Annual Report, March 1961–May 1962" (Comilla, East Pakistan: Pakistan Academy for Rural Development, mimeographed); and A. M. Khan, "Population Control, A Two-Year Rural Action Experience" (mimeographed).

inclusion of family planning in a larger, comprehensive program of village development. Concentration of supervision at the administrative center permits the collection of such supervisors into a training center, organized closely and effectively for implementation of policies, standardization of procedures, coordination, production of training materials, and closer identification with a national movement. The chief advantage of this pattern is the possibility of achieving high-level direct supervision. An army of village workers would be supervised by a staff investing themselves full time in family planning work.

In patterns "A" and "B," the workers at the intermediate level require higher educational qualifications than would be demanded of the village worker. In most emerging countries, schooling is a recent development. Consequently, persons who have had high school education or less are in the younger ages. There is natural resistance on the part of village people to discussing such intimate questions as family planning with young, often unmarried, men and women.

3. Distribution, usually without counseling. In all three patterns described, the village worker distributes contraceptive supplies as well as giving personal counseling. It goes without saying that the village worker must respect the confidentiality of his relationship with the men and women who come to him. It is more difficult, however, for him to protect their privacy. Persons are often embarrassed at being seen visiting the dispenser. It is essential for this and other obvious reasons to establish other channels of ready distribution without counseling. Most of these would be commercial outlets, such as the neighborhood tobacco or tea stands. Some programs have included in the distribution system a requirement that the individual obtaining contraceptive supplies identify himself, and at times produce a referral slip. Such a procedure should not be necessary as a permanent practice. Controls and evaluation are better achieved by sample surveys and spot checks. In at least one large country, international companies engaged in merchandising soaps and related products have offered to take over the entire system of distributing contraceptive supplies at prices stipulated by government. It would be interesting to observe such a system, both alone and together with a program of family planning workers. The postal system of the country is also a logical channel of distribution that reaches all people. In urban industrial areas, the pay-check envelope is a possible vehicle.

D. *General Comments on Availability*

What has been presented thus far offers the individual man or woman a wide array of contraceptive methods from which to choose—what has sometimes been called the "cafeteria approach." There are at least six choices in three major categories: (1) sterilization, male or female, (2) the IUCD or the oral pills, and (3) the male or female type of traditional contraceptive technique. One might well ask whether such a wide choice is more confusing than useful. On the face of it, it seems desirable to recognize differences in individual preference and acceptance. Nevertheless, the program becomes more complex, difficult, and costly as the number of methods is increased. At least, it might be advisable to limit the number of different traditional methods that are recommended and made available. For the male, withdrawal and the condom should be sufficient. For the female, each program might decide to emphasize one particular technique chosen on the basis of pilot projects in the same population. If a more major restriction is imposed so that the program includes only one or two of the three categories above, it is essential that full recognition be given to the gross differences in administrative structure required.

EDUCATION—MOTIVATION

To our best knowledge, it seems correct to say that motivational type of education may be the most important part of a community family planning program. A distinction is being made here between such motivational effort and the personal counseling about contraceptive techniques and services that have been described above. Obviously, there is no sharp demarcation between the two, and the same personnel will at times be doing both. This paper will not attempt to give emphasis to the educational aspects of a community program, but a number of brief comments, in the nature more of questions than of answers, are in order.

1. It is unlikely that a significant reduction in the birth rate

can be achieved in a nation without basic change in certain aspects of the social value system, such as the desire for sons and the large-family ideal. Efforts to change the system of values cannot be limited to family planning workers but must be accepted as a responsibility of the nations's leaders. The implications are far broader than the effect upon birth rate.

2. Social legislation has often been suggested to pave the way for public acceptance of family planning. Laws can be passed on matters of age of marriage, compulsory education, child labor, old age security, income tax, and employment of women. It must be obvious, however, that passage of such laws and general conformity to them would occur only if social change had already taken place.

3. One might appeal to an individual on the basis of his personal benefit, his group loyalty, or his national patriotism. Of these, the first seems to be the most appropriate and could include personal and family health, personal and family welfare, and marital adjustment.

4. We do not yet know to what extent acquisition of knowledge must necessarily precede change of attitude, and to what extent each of these is a prerequisite to the practice of contraception. The three are interdependent, but do not necessarily follow a rigid sequence. Further investigations are needed on this question.

5. The short-term episodic or "campaign" type of educational program can be contrasted with the ongoing indigenous effort. The evident preference in the present paper is for the community organization or community development approach, which builds family planning education and service into the social organization. Nevertheless, studies of the "hit-and-run" method are under way in Pakistan and elsewhere and also merit support.

6. Another distinction needs to be made, i.e., between the generalized and the focused approach. In the latter, the program concentrates upon persons at more "susceptible" points in their reproductive life history, such as marriage, childbirth, and achievement of certain levels of parity.

7. Much attention in family planning education is being given to the concept of "diffusion" of information which makes it

unnecessary for the program itself to attempt to reach 100 per cent of the population affected. Much more study is needed on channels of diffusion and on the utilization of strategic seeding to take advantage of those channels. In Pakistan, a pilot project known as the "ex-villagers" program is being attempted. Although less than 15 per cent of the population of the country is urban, almost every village seems to have sent one or more of its sons to the "city." The ties with the village remain very close, and return visits are made with amazing frequency, despite long distances and limited means. The visitors become respected authorities on all subjects, even to their elders. In the program, ex-villagers are collected, identified as to places of origin and formed into groups for education on family planning. Each trainee then becomes a good-will messenger for family planning in his village. Possibly with an occasional subsidized trip home (on government railway pass), the "messengers" would give support to the local family planning workers, especially in the stages of community organization for local distribution of contraceptive supplies.

8. Much can be done despite illiteracy, not only of the general public but of the family planning workers as well. The oral progestin pill study already described indicates the extent to which measures can be designed for the use of illiterate personnel. The West Pakistan family planning program uses an ingenious system of numbered coupons to keep track of new patients and return visits.[8] Workers in different countries have designed flash cards, tape recordings, films, curriculum guides, and even survey questionnaires for use by illiterate persons.

9. Radio has not been adequately exploited in some countries. Pakistan, for example, has practically no radio system outside the larger cities. Paradoxically, this constitutes an ideal situation for introducing government maintained, community, single-channel, inexpensive radio receiving sets. In the absence of competition, the entire rural population would be a captive audience.

10. Educational programs must be designed for certain key

8. M. S. Mahmood, West Pakistan Family Planning Officer, personal communication to the author (1964).

groups. Of these, perhaps the most important are medical and paramedical personnel, and government officials.

ADMINISTRATION

Community family planning programs in different countries have from the beginning struggled with and are still battling problems of administrative location and structure. A number of the most salient questions are here selected for brief comment.

1. Should the family planning program be placed in a new, special agency, or should it be located in one of the existing governmental agencies, such as health, welfare, or public information? In most countries, the agency has been placed within the public health department. Such location has received and merited considerable criticism, because of the resulting emphasis upon the clinical approach and the failure adequately to involve other governmental units. One compensatory step is to place in each of a number of appropriate agencies, particularly social welfare, education, and public information, "liaison family planning officers." These persons should be located at a very high level in their respective agencies, with considerable status, although without direct line authority. Their function should be to see that their respective agencies carry out as fully as possible the supportive actions that are needed in addition to the health department's program.

2. Should the family planning program be placed in a single agency or divided among several agencies? The answer to question (1) above seems to apply equally well to this question.

3. In India, Pakistan, and some other countries, a greater degree of "autonomy" has been sought for the family planning directorate than is usually given to comparable units of government. This desire for autonomy has an obvious basis in frustration resulting from customary restrictions on recruitment and employment of personnel, expenditure of funds, and administrative channeling. Autonomy is in a sense an evasion of governmental control. Its justification in this case would be the urgency of the problem, that is, the need to achieve quickly effective reduction of the birth rate. At a later date, reintegra-

tion of the program into the ordinary governmental structure could take place. In any event, there is good reason why in some countries at least the evaluation, research, and training activities have been given autonomous or semiautonomous status.

4. Should multipurpose personnel be given family planning duties in addition to other activities? In West Pakistan, an effort is being made to utilize malaria eradication workers.[9] A similar relationship could be considered for social workers engaged in community development work in urban or rural areas. The specifics of this question can only be answered for each situation individually. Personnel might be merged at various levels—centrally, at intermediate supervisory levels, at the peripheral field level, or any combination of these.

5. Because no single formula has yet been devised for the community family planning program, pilot projects are essential, and evaluation should occur concurrently with program development. Other papers in this Symposium discuss the question of evaluative indices more fully. Particular attention may be called to three: (1) M. Freymann in India and others are working on the use of the inter-birth interval. In Pakistan, we are trying to develop a measure of the interval between the most recent and the penultimate pregnancies, with an attempt, for these two most recent pregnancies, to obtain information on all pregnancies, not merely live births. Concurrent with the obvious increase in difficulty, and probably in inaccuracy, is the possible advantage of not having to wait for the end of pregnancy before collecting the data. We hope that it will be possible to base this index on a single, retrospective inquiry after the experimental program has been in operation for a stipulated time. (2) Reports are promising on the development of a simple urine or blood test for pregnancy. With such a test, a pregnancy-prevalence sample survey would constitute a quick and reproducible index. (3) Collection of data might focus on specific "target births." For example, in Pakistan the village family planning worker may be asked to report the high parity (over four) and the short interval (less than three years) births.

9. J. C. Cobb, "Draft for Consideration of Malaria Eradication Board of West Pakistan, February 22, 1964" (Lahore: Feb. 13, 1964, mimeographed).

CONCLUDING REMARKS

This paper has attempted to discuss problems encountered in organizing and planning community programs that attempt to reduce the birth rate through providing services and educational efforts for family planning. These programs address themselves both to the health and welfare needs of individual families and to the country's need to reduce the rate of population growth.

In many ways, the institution of such programs, aimed at covering the population of developing countries, and working with illiterate people under a sense of urgency, presents completely new problems. There are few precedents to guide their development; much pertinent knowledge is lacking. Almost every aspect of such programs, therefore, presents opportunities for experimentation and applied research.

PART III

Measurement and
Evaluation

LaMont C. Cole

DYNAMICS OF ANIMAL POPULATION GROWTH

INTRODUCTION

Probably few persons who study human biology regard the population problem as a general one involving not only the unregulated proliferation of mankind but also the regulation of population growth in pests and game animals and in crop plants and soil organisms. I wish here to examine some of the elementary properties that should be considered in analyzing the population problems of any type of organism.

I belong to a school of ecologists whose special interests are in populations, which we distinguish from other types of aggregations because it is only at the population level that such parameters as rates of birth and death, sex ratios, and age structures assume primary importance. The study of *general demography* has convinced me that a first step in understanding population phenomena in any particular species should be the attempt to understand phenomena that characterize biological populations in general. This position has, however, been challenged [1] on the grounds that "demographic processes in man are

1. F. Lorimer, "Human Populations: Historical Study. Introductory Remarks of the Chairman," *Cold Spring Harbor Symposia on Quantitative Biology,* XXII (1957), p. 17.

largely determined by social conditions, and we must rely largely on the methods of the social sciences in investigating these relations.''

I wish again to argue for the unity of population studies. I am not personally convinced that such fascinating sociological subjects as motivation for reproduction are basic determinants of human population, but there are biologists who will argue such propositions for animals in general. A recent imposing volume,[2] replete with data from throughout the animal kingdom, develops the thesis that many species have evolved patterns of conventional behavior through natural selection operating to limit population size before food resources are actually exhausted. Wynne-Edwards is here extending to animals in general the concepts set forth for man 40 years earlier by Carr-Saunders.[3] If they are correct, modern man's special perils may arise from abandoning such practices as infanticide which enabled primitive man to avoid famine, and from our almost surely unique trait of biasing reproduction in favor of the socially less successful portions of the population.

Some of the data on human populations are superior to those available for any other species. However, the abundant data on populations of forms that are commercially exploited by man have recently been summarized and analyzed in two important books;[4] and, in addition, we have some notable studies of laboratory populations, many field studies, a number of theoretical and analytical approaches to population phenomena, and a wealth of miscellaneous natural history observations on which to draw in attempting to identify the factors that are distinctive of human populations and which, therefore, demand study by the novel techniques of the social scientist. I am hoping to enlist human demographers in support of general demography. Important public policy decisions often hinge upon the acceptance of generalizations about population phenomena. When such

2. V. C. Wynne-Edwards, *Animal Dispersion in Relation to Social Behaviour* (Edinburgh: Oliver and Boyd, 1962).

3. A. M. Carr-Saunders, *The Population Problem, A Study in Human Evolution* (Oxford: Clarendon Press, 1922).

4. R. J. H. Beverton and S. J. Holt, *On The Dynamics of Exploited Fish Populations* (London: Her Majesty's Stationery Office, 1957); E. D. Le Cren and M. W. Holdgate (eds.), *The Exploitation of Natural Animal Populations* (Oxford: Blackwell Scientific Publications, 1962).

generalizations are questionable, all who understand this should unite and be heard whether the immediate problem involves a forest, a fishery, a mosquito breeding ground, or a human population. We should cooperate to correct the present ludicrous situation in which chemists who obviously do not even understand the nature of the problems are presuming to tell a pesticide-conscious public just what it is that controls population size and the composition of biotic communities.

DEFINITIONS

For completeness, and because there is so much popular misunderstanding of even the most elementary properties of populations, it will be well to define a few fundamentals.

The age-specific birth rate, b_x, we define as the mean number of female offspring produced per female aged between x and $x + 1$. For many species age, x, is conveniently measured in years but the time intervals can be made arbitrarily short without loss of generality so it is convenient to regard b_x as the number of daughters born on the mother's xth birthday. For human females, b_x may be taken to assume only the values 0 and 0.5 for different values of x.[5] For armadillos, where a normal litter consists of identical quadruplets, the appropriate values would be 0 or 2. It is simply for convenience in computations that we consider only females. This is justified because the populations of the sexes must ultimately grow at the same rate or the disproportion between them would come to exceed all bounds.

Survivorship, l_x, is the ordinary life table function, and may be defined for our present purpose as the probability at birth that a female will survive to age x. We may introduce three additional symbols which will enable us to characterize the life history of virtually any species.[6] We will employ a to represent

5. The United States sex ratio at birth of 1,054 males per 1,000 females suggests 0.487 as a more precise value. By changing definitions slightly, as by including stillbirths, still other values could be obtained.

6. Some cases require special treatment. See L. C. Cole, "A Note on Population Parameters in Cases of Complex Reproduction," *Ecology*, XLI (April, 1960), pp. 372–375. Asexual reproduction may produce two types of individuals that mature at different rates. Also, the eggs of many Coelenterates, Trematodes, and even some insects develop into larvae that may undergo several generations of asexual reproduction.

the age at which a female first produces female offspring, ω to represent the age at which she produces her last female offspring and λ to represent the extreme age at death.

These life history features vary tremendously among different groups of animals. For some protozoa α is on the order of a few hours. Reproduction is negligible for human females aged less than 15 years,[7] but this is no record among animals. The Sumatran rhinoceros is reported to attain puberty at 20 years[8] and the periodic cicada, *Magicicada septendecim,* is 17 years old when its summer for reproductive activity arrives.

There seems to be a popular impression that age at maturity and adult body size show a strong positive correlation, but I find the relationship so poor that it is more likely to be misleading than helpful. Thus, huge animals like the blue whale, the yak, bison, and Eurasian buffalo may breed when two years old, the same as the pink salmon and many of our common dragonflies, while herring gulls, bullfrogs, and lobsters require three or four years, and various spiders and freshwater turtles do not normally breed before they are 10 years old. In the so-called "coldblooded" forms, rate of maturation is likely to be strongly influenced by environmental temperatures, and there are relatively few that adhere to so rigid a schedule as the cicadas and Pacific salmon.

Probably most animals can be classed as annuals because so many insects, which comprise three quarters of the animal kingdom, mature and reproduce in a single year only. Some mammals, birds, fishes, and amphibians are also annuals. But, of course, all species that produce offspring singly must reproduce at least twice per lifetime or extinction would be certain. This includes all the primates, virtually all the ungulates, the seals, sea-lions, and walruses, the whales, most of the bats, various birds, such as penguins and albatrosses, and even the manta ray.

The human female, normally not reproducing before the age

7. I note that according to the 1958 Annual Report of the National Office of Vital Statistics, U. S. Public Health Service, two white Mississippi girls aged under 15 years each gave birth to her fourth child in that year. Such cases are too rare to affect statistical studies of human population growth.

8. S. A. Asdell, *Patterns of Mammalian Reproduction* (Ithaca: Comstock Press, 1946).

of 15 years, averaging 0.5 female offspring per birth, and with a gestation period of about 280 days, surely is a contender for the record low reproductive potential among animals. I shall not try to designate a champion for high potential reproduction but, for contrast with the human situation, we might note that an amoeba can divide into two offspring and thus double in numbers every couple of days, that under optimum conditions a female housefly can produce 200 eggs and that they can go through 18 generations per year, and that the tapeworm *Taenia* can produce over 100,000 eggs per day and, as a parasite in man, continue this for 30 years or so.

I once heard a social scientist draw important conclusions about the lack of a definite breeding season in primates—man in particular. Clearly he had not been a farm boy associated with cattle and pigs nor had he had much experience with the largest order of mammals, the rodents. I mention this merely as another warning against looking at human biology outside of the context of man's relatives.

It is well known that, in man, individuals of both sexes can live on after they are too old to reproduce and that such postreproductive sterility may persist for about one quarter of the normal life span. Zoologists as well as sociologists have attributed this ability to the value of older individuals in promoting education and survival of the young. Most geneticists seem to be convinced that mutations would eliminate postreproductive life from any species unless the younger individuals benefit from the presence of sterile members of the population, as is so obviously the case in social insects. It is not so widely recognized that Norway rats and certain insects such as the grasshopper *Schistocerca*[9] spend on the average from one third to one half of the life span in postreproductive sterility. It is probable that many additional cases will come to light, and the subject merits additional study. How a population of rats or insects benefits from the presence of superannuated individuals is not clear. It is conceivable that this phenomenon helps retard excessively high population reproduction rates, but it could also be that

9. F. S. Bodenheimer, *Problems of Animal Ecology* (London: Oxford University Press, 1938).

selection for survival at younger ages produced such a vigorous organism that mere "vital momentum" [10] enables it to survive after the gonads are worn out. In any case, man is not unique in this respect, and social scientists should use caution in speculating about the biological value of having living ancestors.

Extreme length of life (λ) is another characteristic that is often considered to show a positive correlation with size, and where popular beliefs are notoriously erroneous. I once watched a television quiz show in which the contestants were expected to know that elephants, whales, and parrots can live for more than a century. Actually, the oldest known bird was a 69 year old crow, the record-holding elephant died in a zoo at 57 as a decrepit old beast that could not have survived nearly so long in nature, and there is no record of a whale living beyond 40 years.[11] There are authentic records of turtles living for 150 years and a questionable record of a sturgeon that old; outside of these, man is probably the only animal capable of living more than a century. In the 50-year capability class, however, we find such diverse forms as clams, sponges, sea-anemones, eels, the horse, and several birds. There is even an authentic record of a beetle larva living for 45 years.[12]

TYPES OF SURVIVORSHIP CURVES

A number of authors, beginning with Pearl and Miner in 1935,[13] have classified survivorship curves into distinct types. Fig. 1 illustrates some of the theoretically most interesting patterns.

The "physiological" type of survivorship is an idealized form for a genetically uniform population living under optimum conditions. In this case all individuals could theoretically live to some maximum age characteristic of the species and all would die at the same age. On the graph this pattern would give a horizontal line at 100 per cent survival out to the age of

10. R. Pearl, *Man the Animal* (Bloomington, Ind: Principia Press, 1946).

11. P. L. Altman and D. S. Dittmer (eds.), *Growth, Including Reproduction and Morphological Development* (Washington, D.C.: Federation of American Societies for Experimental Biology, 1962).

12. E. Korschelt, *Lebensdauer, Altern und Tod* (Jena: G. Fischer, 1922).

13. R. Pearl and J. R. Miner, "Experimental Studies on the Duration of Life, XIV. The Comparative Mortality of Certain Lower Organisms," *Quarterly Review of Biology*, X (1935), pp. 60–79.

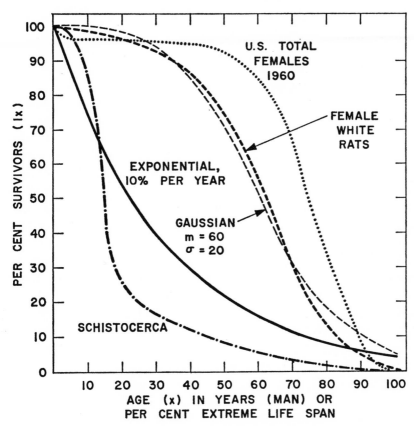

Fig. 1. Some forms of survivorship curves.

physiological longevity and then would show a vertical drop. Fig. 1 shows that man, with modern health facilities, can approach this rectangular form quite closely. The nearly horizontal part of the curve is at something less than 100 per cent survival because of heavy mortality in the first two years of life. And, of course, if we had started the life table at the time of conception rather than the time of birth, there would be a much sharper initial drop in the curve. Alternatively, if we had followed a practice common in fisheries research and started the life table at the time of ''recruitment'' into the population, we could make the curve more nearly rectangular by considering that a human female is only recruited into the population at the time of her second birthday.

It was shown by Pearl [14] that inbred strains of *Drosophila* adults, when starved, show nearly this rectangular type of physiological survivorship. In this case, however, if the life table started at the time eggs were laid, there would be a sharp initial drop as in the case of man.

Fig. 1 also shows a survivorship curve for highly inbred "Wistar" white rats maintained from the time of weaning (30 days old) under the most favorable possible conditions of laboratory care.[15] This curve departs in a definite manner from the physiological type. Survivorship curves of this general shape appear to be common among populations of wild animals, and the shape doubtless reflects genetic heterogeneity and differential impact of environmental factors on different individuals. One might speculate that under these conditions the ages at which individuals die would be normally distributed about the mean age at death. On the figure, I have plotted a curve corresponding to this hypothesis (i.e., the Gaussian curve) where the mean length of life is taken as 60 "years" (actually about 310 days for the rats) and the age at birth is taken as three standard deviations below the mean. The correspondence of the empirical and theoretical curves over much of the life span is close enough to suggest that this type of explanation may sometimes give a useful first approximation to the mortality factors operating on a natural population.

A still more common type of survivorship pattern for natural populations is that in which a constant proportion of the individuals die in each interval of age. Fig. 1 shows the curve that would result from a constant mortality of 10 per cent per year; if survivorship were plotted logarithmically this exponential curve would become a straight line. This type of curve is consistent with empirical data on female fin whales, certain fish such as the brown trout, snowshoe hares, and for wild birds in general for which Deevey [16] postulates a constant mortality rate

14. R. Pearl and S. L. Parker, "Experimental Studies on the Duration of Life, X. The Duration of Life of *Drosophila Melanogaster* in the Complete Absence of Food," *American Naturalist*, LVIII (1924), pp. 193–218.

15. B. P. Wiesner and N. M. Sheard, "The Duration of Life in an Albino Rat Population," *Proceedings of the Royal Society of Edinburgh*, LV (1934), pp. 1–22.

16. E. S. Deevey, Jr., "Life Tables for Natural Populations of Animals," *Quarterly Review of Biology*, XXII (Dec., 1947), pp. 283–314.

of 32 per cent per mean life span. Lack [17] has tabulated the data for various wild birds, and 50 per cent mortality per year emerges as a fairly typical figure.

Exponentially decreasing survivorship means that life expectancy is independent of age, which in turn implies that individuals neither deteriorate with increasing age nor gain experience that promotes survival. If we omit the very youngest animals on which we seldom have empirical data and which, in any case, can be regarded as not yet recruited into the active population, the assumption of constant mortality rates may often be realistic for wild animals. This will be especially true when mortality is heavy so that few individuals reach advanced age and when all individuals are regularly exposed to the risk of accidental death with much of the mortality resulting from such accidents. These criteria appear to apply well to many birds where wild individuals normally live only a fraction of their potential life span. For example, banded American robins have been found to survive an average of less than two years in the wild,[18] although captive individuals have reached an age of about 13 years.

It is noteworthy that the physiological type of survivorship curve can be regarded as a special case of the exponential type in which the mean annual mortality rate is zero out to age ω. It seems reasonable that in primitive man most mortality may have been of the accidental or calamitous type and largely independent of age, thus giving rise to exponentially decreasing survivorship. In fact, Dublin and Lotka commented in 1935 [19] that modern public health programs were changing the survivorship curve for man from a ''concave'' to a ''convex'' type. The wide applicability of the exponential form of survivorship gives this curve special interest for theoretical studies and some of the implications will be explored below.

Fig. 1 shows one additional type of survivorship, illustrated by the grasshopper *Schistocerca gregaria* living in large out-

17. D. Lack, *The Natural Regulation of Animal Numbers* (Oxford: Clarendon Press, 1954).

18. D. S. Farner, ''Age Groups and Longevity in the American Robin,'' *Wilson Bulletin*, LVII (1945), pp. 56–74.

19. L. I. Dublin and A. J. Lotka, *Length of Life. A Study of the Life Table* (New York: Ronald, 1935).

door screened cages in Egypt.[20] The distinctive feature is extremely heavy early mortality (occurring in the first two months of life in *Schistocerca*) followed by a period of very gradual decline which may well approximate the exponential type. Although few examples have been studied quantitatively, it is possible that this is actually the most common type of survivorship curve, and might even apply to man if we constructed our life tables from the moment of conception. Sette [21] estimated the mortality of mackerel (*Scomber scombrus*) eggs and young at 99.9996 per cent in the first 70 days of life, although individual mackerel are known to have lived as long as 15 years. Similarly, a female carp or blue crab or oyster will lay some two million eggs per season, and a tapeworn can produce many times that; but, on the average, only about one of these can survive to maturity. Less extreme, but illustrating the same form of survivorship curve, is the conclusion of Lack that ". . . in song birds less than a quarter of the eggs laid give rise to independent young." [22]

POPULATION GROWTH IN AN UNLIMITED ENVIRONMENT

At least since the late sixteenth century [23] thoughtful students have concluded that a population adhering to constant schedules of survival and reproduction would increase by doubling in successive equal time intervals; that is, it would grow exponentially or by geometric progression. This can be rigorously proved mathematically.[24] Thus any given life history providing fixed values of l_x and b_x for each value of x determines the value of a parameter, r, known as the intrinsic rate of natural

20. F. S. Bodenheimer, *op. cit.*

21. O. E. Sette, "Biology of the Atlantic Mackerel (*Scomber scombrus*) of North America. Part 1. Early Life History, Including the Growth, Drift and Mortality of the Egg and Larval Populations," U.S. Fish and Wildlife Service, *Fishery Bulletin*, L (1943), pp. 149–237.

22. D. Lack, *op. cit.*, p. 79.

23. G. Botero, *A Treatise Concerning the Causes of the Magnificency and Greatness of Cities* (1588, English translation 1606; London: Routledge and Kegan Paul, 1956).

24. A. J. Lotka, "Population Analysis as a Chapter in the Mathematical Theory of Evolution," *Essays on growth and form presented to D'Arcy Wentworth Thompson*, ed. W. E. LeGros Clark and B. P. Medawar (Oxford: Clarendon Press, 1945), pp. 362–363.

increase which represents the rate of true compound interest at which the population would grow.

There are various ways of computing the value of r corresponding to fixed schedules of survival and reproduction [25] but all are essentially modifications of an integral equation originally derived by Lotka [26] which, written in finite form,[27] is

$$(1) \qquad\qquad 1 - \sum_{x=a} l_x b_x e^{-rx} = 0.$$

This an algebraic equation which can be seen from elementary considerations to be satisfied only by a single real positive value of r. Negative and complex roots of the equation are of no interest to us in discussing growing populations. Solutions of this equation for different life history patterns then enable us to evaluate the effects on population growth of changes in birth and survival patterns.

For most animals we can approximate the life history accurately enough by assuming that the average number of females per litter is a constant, b. We may also assume a constant interval between successive litters and measure time, x, in terms of this interval. Because of the wide applicability of the exponential type of survivorship, which includes the physiological type as a special case, we will here consider cases of the type $l_x = h^x$. Thus, $h = 0.9$ would correspond to mortality of 10 per cent per year, and so on.

Because the primary focus of this Symposium is on man, and because the size and spacing of litters in many other animals is like that in man, I shall deal here only with life histories in which births are spaced at one-year intervals and the mean number of female offspring per birth is 0.5 ($b = \frac{1}{2}$). Of course, neither man nor other animals normally reproduce successfully

25. L. C. Cole, ''The Population Consequences of Life History Phenomena,'' *Quarterly Review of Biology*, XXIX (June, 1954), pp. 103–137.

26. A. J. Lotka, ''Relation Between Birth Rates and Death Rates,'' *Science*, XXVI (1907), pp. 21–22.

27. Offspring are not produced continuously but in litters separated by discrete time intervals, and the number of young in a litter is necessarily a discontinuous variable. Accordingly, finite formulas seem more appropriate than forms involving continuous variables.

in each year of reproductive life but we are concerned here with *potential* rates of population growth, and it can be shown that the spacing between births is much less important than other parameters in influencing potential growth.

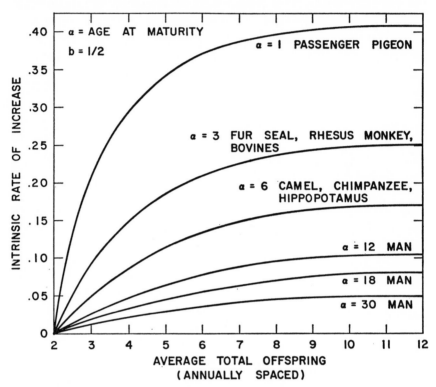

Fig. 2. The effect of progeny number on the intrinsic rate of natural increase when offspring are produced singly and annually and the sex ratio is 1:1.

Fig. 2 shows the intrinsic rates of increase that would result with no mortality before the end of reproductive life ($h = 1$), as age at maturity (a) and total number of offspring vary. Probably the most striking feature of this graph is the demonstration of the drastic changes in potential population growth that accompany changes in the rate of maturation. I feel that this fact still has not been properly appreciated by students of human demography who tend to neglect the age at which reproduction begins and to overemphasize the total number of offspring. Age at marriage is potentially more important in determining contributions to future populations than is total family size.

Fig. 2 reveals some additional points of interest. The three lowest curves represent ages of possible human maturation, and the rapidity with which these curves flatten out is noteworthy. Human populations are not ordinarily capable of sustaining growth rates of more than about three per cent per year ($r = 0.03$), and Fig. 2 shows why; remarkably high average reproductive performance would be necessary to give higher rates. Also, human populations in which families produce an average of five or six children would give nearly as rapid population growth as could be obtained with an unlimited number of children. This is not the case, however, when maturation is more rapid, and it is evident from the figure that a decrease of from five offspring to four for the passenger pigeon or fur seal would detract appreciably from the potential for population growth. The first of these species is extinct and the second was once severely threatened by human exploitation. Consideration of the life histories shows that such species must be very vulnerable to reduction of life expectancy during the reproductive ages.

Let us see, under the conditions we are postulating, how much annual mortality can be sustained by a species before it becomes unable to maintain population size. For this purpose we set $r = 0$ and let each individual reproduce as long as it lives ($\omega = a$). Equation (1) then becomes

$$(2) \qquad\qquad bh^a + h - 1 = 0.$$

With $b = \frac{1}{2}$ and $a = 1$ for the passenger pigeon, a mortality of over 33 per cent per year would be incompatible with population maintenance. I consider it possible that our ancestors, in their zeal to harvest the seemingly inexhaustible supplies of this bird, caused mortality to exceed the critical value of $\frac{1}{3}$ and thereby caused the bird to become extinct.

The fur seal, with $a = 3$, has the critical value $h = 0.77$, so constant mortality rates of over 23 per cent per year would be sufficient to wipe out this species.

I have suggested above that mortality for primitive man may

have resulted mainly from accidents so that survivorship was of the exponential type. On this assumption it is interesting to see how much mortality a human population could tolerate. If we set $a = 12$ years in Equation (2), we obtain $h = 0.89$; a constant mortality rate of over 11 per cent per year would make survival impossible. This is a low mortality rate for a wild animal. Evidently our Pleistocene ancestors must already have evolved very efficient ways of protecting their females before they could afford the luxury of one offspring per litter and even 12 years of prereproductive life.

POPULATION GROWTH IN A FINITE ENVIRONMENT

In actual populations, from bacteria to man, and in the laboratory or in nature, exponential growth does not continue very long. The growth rate falls as some environmental resource begins to be in short supply so that a plot of numbers against time exhibits a sigmoid shape, with population size approaching asymptotically to an upper limit. If I may be forgiven for intruding a population of plants into this Symposium, I can illustrate the points I wish to make with Fig. 3, which comes from a study done several years ago but which I have never published.

This experiment was arranged so that these green algae had an excess of everything they need for growth except fixed nitrogen which was supplied as nitrate ion (NO_3). The lower curve with its dotted extension shows a typical pattern of population growth which, under the experimental conditions, was reproducible in detail time after time.

In this particular experiment I waited until the population was nearly grown and then doubled the effective "carrying capacity" of the habitat by adding another portion of nitrate. The graph shows a brief period of adjustment to the altered environment and then a new cycle of growth heading for a new upper limit twice the height of the original. This pattern is also typical of an animal population limited by food. I think it illustrates nicely the utter futility of proposals we are hearing for dealing with the human population problem by trying to make the food supply keep up with population growth. Unless something else is changed, an increased food supply can be expected merely to stimulate population growth.

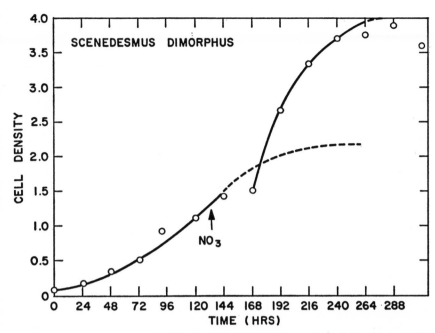

Fig. 3. Growth of an algal population showing the effect of doubling the carrying capacity of the habitat.

The sigmoid form of population growth is the basis for the "optimum yield problem" which is perhaps the most enlightened recent attempt to apply ecology to practical matters. If a population could be maintained at exactly the size corresponding to the inflection point in the growth curve, it could yield a larger sustained harvest than would be obtainable either through "overfishing" or "underfishing." The difficulty of operating so as to obtain just the optimum yield in any particular case provides the inspiration for theoretical studies that are benefiting ecology in general.[28]

The fact that early population growth departs at all from the exponential form shows that there is a negative feedback of numbers on growth.[29] If this were not the case we would expect accelerating growth at least up until the population has very nearly reached carrying capacity.

28. See books listed in footnote 4.
29. I avoid saying that growth regulation is "density dependent" because of the bitter and largely semantic argument about this concept which is current among ecologists.

The mechanisms by which increasing population density reacts to restrain population growth are extremely varied. Direct starvation and disease furthered by malnutrition are less common than cannibalism, interference with mating, and still more subtle processes. Crowded birds may desert their young in the nest, and something about crowding can trigger a migratory behavior pattern for which locusts and lemmings especially have become famous. Many vertebrates and some invertebrates maintain property rights to breeding territories, and those that fail to win a territory do not breed. Thus a breeding population of dragonflies or fur seals is bounded by "bachelor" individuals unless population density is low enough to provide territories for all. Metabolic by-products accumulating in the environment often have fascinating physiological effects; this is what ultimately limits algal growth as in Fig. 3. Crowding of tadpoles inhibits the growth and development of most of them, and a comparable reduction of growth rate in fishes limits population size by exposing the smaller individuals to predation and cannibalism for a longer time. Still more subtle physiological effects of crowding include reduction of litter size through the resorption of embryos and a number of remarkable cases in which the sex ratio is affected, with fewer young developing into fertile females as population density increases.

Man, of course, shows the same basic pattern. Primitive tribes practice abortion and infanticide, but something more subtle appears to operate in civilized surroundings. John Graunt knew in 1662 that something about urbanization limits reproduction, and he considered general unhealthiness of the city environment to underlie this phenomenon. However, he also wrote of changed habits in the city, such as long apprenticeships, as influencing fertility by delaying marriage. Social scientists still seem to be arguing whether cities reduce fertility through slum conditions, or whether it is the increased opportunities for advancement that make urban dwellers reluctant to assume family responsibilities. I could not presume to take sides in such a debate, but I sometimes wonder if it is profitable to seek psychological explanations for a phenomenon that man shares with nearly every other species of animal, and with plants as well.

ERUPTIVE AND "CYCLIC" POPULATIONS

Although in most species and at most times population size is held within bound by feedback mechanisms, we should not leave the subject with mention of some famous exceptions. There are spectacular cases in which a population seems to break away from all restraints and erupt to a size far beyond the permanent carrying capacity of its habitat. In this situation, of course, the population cannot persist so outbreaks are inevitably followed by crashes, mass emigration, or both.

Perhaps the best known population eruptions are the locust plagues and the outbreaks of microtine and murine rodents which may produce population levels such that it is literally impossible for a man to walk without stepping on grasshoppers or mice. Eruptions have also been recorded for squirrels, rabbits, carnivores, certain fishes and birds, various insects, certain ungulates (especially deer and the African springbuck), and in scattered other groups. Machiavelli and, two centuries later, Buffon even attributed the fall of Rome to population eruptions in human tribes beyond the Rhine and Danube. Eruptions are most characteristic of simple biotic communities impoverished in numbers of species and with the eruptive form dependent on one or a very few types of foods. Thus they are most notable in high latitude and high altitude situations, in arid regions, and, unfortunately, on agricultural land where the crop damage may be disastrous.

In some cases the peaks and troughs of population size may succeed each other with what has been interpreted as cyclic regularity, and the subject of "population cycles" has generated a tremendous literature.[30] The numerous explanatory theories, which still have advocates, have sometimes tried to link the cycles to sunspots or other cosmic rhythms, or to find explanations in population and community dynamics, or to discover physiological effects of crowding that bring on a lethal "stress syndrome," or even reverse the selective value of particular genes.

30. E.g., O. H. Hewitt (ed.), "Symposium on Cycles in Animal Populations," *Journal of Wildlife Management*, XVIII (Jan., 1954), pp. 1–112; L. C. Cole, "Population Fluctuations," *Proceedings of the Tenth International Congress of Entomology, 2, 1956* (1958), pp. 639–647.

I fear that I am an extreme heretic on this subject. I have studied the empirical data to see what we actually know about these cycles, and I can only be confident that there are cases in which we know the years when peak populations occurred, and that populations were much greater in those years than in the periods between peaks. I have shown that the spacing of population peaks is no more regular than we would expect from random fluctuations. I have concluded that the multitude of little haphazard and interacting factors that affect population size should produce random fluctuations, just as a multitude of little influences cause the numbers shown on a pair of thrown dice to behave as a random variable. I stand by what I wrote 13 years ago,[31] when we try to construct a theoretical population model that will account for the observed fluctuations in a particular case, ". . . the subject decreases in interest simply because there are too many ways of accounting for the observed facts insofar as their characteristics are definitely known."

Fig. 4 shows an example of a "cyclic" series generated by a digital computer following instructions to play a game analogous to the dynamics of a much oversimplified animal population. It was assumed that a minimum of 100 animals would find shelter and survive any winter. Any excess over 100 present in the autumn would suffer mortality represented by a random number between zero and 100 per cent. In spring the population was assumed to be able to grow by a factor of $az_1(1 - N/Kz_2)$, where $a = 10$ is the assumed maximum possible increase, z_1 is a random number between zero and unity representing random variations in reproductive success, N is the winter minimum population, $K = 10,000$ is the assumed "carrying capacity" of the habitat, and z_2 is another random number between 0.5 and 1.5 allowing for year-to-year variations in the quality of the habitat. The plotted points in Fig. 4 are the peak summer populations attained under these conditions.

If we count every population peak in Fig. 4, we find a mean "cycle" length of slightly over three "years" as predicted from the theory that the cycles are random fluctuations. But, more interestingly, we find five major peaks in the 50 years of

31. L. C. Cole, "Population Cycles and Random Fluctuations," *Journal of Wildlife Management*, XV (July, 1951), pp. 233–252.

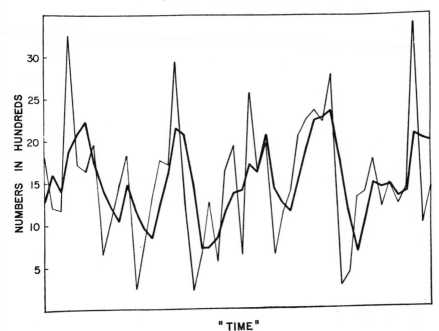

Fig. 4. Synthetic population cycles generated from random numbers by a computer.

observation, thus simulating the "10-year cycle of wildlife." And if we smooth the curve slightly, as with the three-point moving average shown by the heavy line, we obtain an impression of quite orderly fluctuations generated by random environmental fluctuations acting on a very simple population model.

AGE STRUCTURE AND REPRODUCTIVE VALUE

Difficulties arise in interpreting population phenomena for any long-lived species because individuals of different ages have different reproductive potentialities, and the potential of the total population depends on its age structure. In 1958 both France and Fiji had 45 per cent of their human population members aged between 15 and 50, but in France 29 per cent had passed their fiftieth birthday as compared with only nine per cent in Fiji. Clearly the potential for explosive growth is greater in Fiji, and the economies, prevailing health problems, and many other important features would have to differ in these populations for this reason alone.

We encounter comparable problems with populations of wild animals. A predator or disease may appear to be aiding in the control of some noxious species while actually it is increasing the vigor of the prey population by picking off superannuated, reproductively useless, individuals. And a valuable species that is being over-exploited may not reveal this fact for some time except through shifts in its age structure.

R. A. Fisher showed in 1929 [32] that we could avoid these problems by measuring population not in counts of individuals but in terms of "reproductive value" which may be defined as the average remaining expectancy for individuals of a particular age to contribute to the ancestry of future generations. This important approach is still greatly neglected; we almost never collect the data to calculate population values for wild populations and, for man, probably not over one third of the world's nations tabulate annual births by age of mother.

The value of a female aged x may be computed from

$$(3) \qquad \qquad v_x = \frac{e^{rx}}{l_x} \sum_x^{\lambda} e^{-rx} \, l_x b_x,$$

where, by definition, $v_o = 1$, and the total value of the population is the sum of the values for all females: $V = \sum_o n_x v_x$. Postreproductive individuals obviously have zero value, and reproductive value may also be very low for newborn individuals in species where there is an abrupt initial drop in the survivorship curve. My crude calculations for United States females indicate a maximum of v_x at about 17 years, perhaps identical with the 18½ Fisher found for Australian women of 1911.

I am convinced that we should be computing reproductive values for the purpose of following true biological trends in these days when we are worrying about excessive population growth in man and possible inadequate growth in species utilized by man. Total population size can actually change in a

---

32. R. A. Fisher, *The Genetical Theory of Natural Selection* (Oxford: Clarendon Press, 1929).

direction opposite to that of the biological trend. For example, I calculate that between 1930 and 1940, when the number of females in the United States was increasing from 60.6 million to 65.6 million, their reproductive value was dropping from 42.3 million to 35.9 million.

Consideration of reproductive value also suggests possibilities for increasing the optimum yield in cases where we can harvest different age classes selectively.[33] It has long been recognized that postreproductive individuals, and most of the males in species with promiscuous breeding habits, can be harvested without damaging population growth. MacArthur has shown that in general the "selective predator" will obtain maximum sustained yield by adjusting the prey population so that rV is a maximum, and by harvesting individuals with the greatest ratio of worth to predator/reproductive value.

CONCLUSION

The only general conclusion I wish to draw is the postulate with which I started—that all of us who are involved with the intricacies of population problems should join in combating the very superficial views and approaches that are now so prevalent. If policy makers can be persuaded that broadcasting nonselective toxins over the landscape will solve our problems with pest populations, they probably can also be persuaded that environmental pollution will solve the human population problem. It seems to me urgent that we find a way of communicating the great complexity of these phenomena to those who must make decisions about population problems.

33. R. H. MacArthur, ''On the Relation Between Reproductive Value and Optimal Predation,'' *Proceedings of the National Academy of Science of the United States of America*, XLVI (1960), pp. 143–145.

Ansley J. Coale

BIRTH RATES, DEATH RATES, AND RATES OF GROWTH IN HUMAN POPULATION

INTRODUCTION

The relationship between the rate of growth of a closed population—one not subject to gains or losses by migration —and the prevalent birth and death rates is the simple tautology that the rate of increase is the difference between birth and death rates.[1]

Since fertility and mortality rates vary with age, the birth rate depends both on the rates of childbearing at each age, and on the age composition of the population; and the death rate depends on the rates at which persons die at different ages, and on age composition. Two examples illustrate the importance of age composition. First, England and Wales and Japan had the same birth rate in 1960—17.2 per thousand—although the fertility schedule in England and Wales would, if continued, have

---

1. If the equation $r = b - d$ is to hold precisely, it is essential that the denominator of all three rates be the same. Ideally, the rates should be calculated relative to the number of person-years lived by the population in question. This usage is normally followed in calculating birth and death rates, but the annual rate of increase is often related to the population at the beginning of the year, yielding a rate *not* precisely equal to $b - d$.

produced 30 per cent more children per woman than that of Japan. Japan had a birth rate as high as England's only because of what might be called a more fertile age composition: Japan's population had a much higher proportion of women at the ages of greatest fertility. Secondly, Mexico's death rate in 1960 was 11.5 per thousand and Austria's was 12.7; even though the expectation of life in Austria was markedly higher, 68 years compared to 59. Mortality rates at every age were lower in Austria, but the general death rate was higher because such a high proportion of Austria's population was over age 65, a part of life where even under favorable circumstances death rates are high.

The age composition of a population is itself the result of the past history of its fertility and mortality rates. Japan has a higher proportion of women in the childbearing ages than England because a generation ago birth rates in Japan were much higher than in Great Britain. The population of Mexico is much younger than that of Austria because for many years Mexico has had a much higher birth rate.

In this paper the birth and death rates of human female [2] populations will be analyzed in the context of these two equations:

$$(1) \qquad b = \int_0^\omega c(a)m(a)\,da,$$

$$(2) \qquad d = \int_0^\omega c(a)\mu(a)\,da,$$

where $c(a)\,da$ is the proportion of women aged a to $a + da$; $m(a)$ is the proportion of women at age a who bear a female child per year; $\mu(a)$ is the annual death rate of women at age a; and ω is the highest age attained.

Three determinants of each rate will be considered: (1) the age schedules of fertility and mortality, (2) the age composition of the population, and (3) the interaction between the age

2. To analyze fully the two sexes together introduces complications beyond the scope of this discussion. The factors affecting male or female birth and death rates are, with few exceptions, identical; the complications in considering both sexes occur because of logically necessary links between male and female fertility schedules.

distribution and the two schedules. The treatment must be compressed into a few pages, and necessarily consists for the most part of results that are given without detailed supporting evidence or proof.

FERTILITY AND MORTALITY SCHEDULES

Fertility Schedules

Every age schedule of fertility raises from zero in a smooth and continuous fashion to a single maximum and then falls smoothly and continuously to zero. The mean age of recorded fertility schedules falls between 26 years (Hungary, 1958) and a little over 33 years (Sweden, the middle of the nineteenth century).

The shape of the fertility schedule is controlled partly by biological forces. That is to say, the physical capacity to bear children rises from zero at about age 15 (following menarche) to a peak in the early twenties, falls slowly at first and then more rapidly in the late thirties, reaching zero at (or before) menopause, at age 40 to 50. Even in populations where the deliberate limitation of childbearing among women living in a stable union is not customary, the rise and fall of fertility with age is influenced by customs that govern cohabitation and in other ways affect the probability of conception. The importance of marriage as a sanction for sexual union varies. Among societies where marriage is a prerequisite, the average age of marriage differs widely. There are also differences from population to population in the remarriage of widows, toleration of divorce, and so forth.

Schedules of fertility rates as a function of age can describe the performance of women born at the same time and moving through life together, or can describe the performance of women at different ages during a given year. The first kind is of a schedule of "cohort fertility." It is a longitudinal schedule. The second is a measure of "period fertility," and is a cross-sectional schedule. In a population where fertility does not change from year to year, the two schedules are the same. However, when the age pattern of fertility of cohorts is changing, period rates rise above or fall below the fertility rates experienced by any single cohort—rise above when the mean age of childbearing falls, and fall below when the mean age rises.[3]

The area under a fertility schedule is called total fertility. If only female births are counted, i.e., if the reproduction of the female population is considered separately, the area under the fertility schedule is called the gross reproduction rate. Total fertility is the average number of children that would be born per woman who passed through the ages of childbearing experiencing the given fertility rates. The gross reproduction rate is the average number of daughters under these circumstances.

The lowest national gross reproduction rates that I have been able to find recorded were .80 in Austria in 1933 and .81 in Sweden in 1935. (Since the number of males born per 100 females is about 105 to 107 in almost all populations, total fertility is about 2.06 times the gross reproduction rate. Hence, the lowest value of total fertility is about 1.65 births per woman.) At the time that the national gross reproduction rate in Austria was .80, the rate in Vienna was only .30.

The highest gross reproduction rates based on what appear to be complete and reliable records are 4.0 for the Hutterite women of western North America, and 4.17 for the population of the Cocos-Keeling Islands.[4] It is possible that there may have been, or may be today, a population with a gross reproduction rate substantially higher than 4.0. At every age above 20 years, there is well-documented evidence of *marital* fertility rates about one and a half times as high as the fertility rates for each age group found in the Cocos-Keeling Islands. The populations exhibiting these high rates are at some ages the married women among the Hutterites mentioned earlier and at other ages the population of Canada in the eighteenth century. If a synthetic fertility schedule is constructed from the marital fertility rates (at ages over 20 years) of the Hutterites or of the Canadian population of the

3. N. B. Ryder, ''The Structure and Tempo of Current Fertility,'' *Demographic and Economic Change in Developed Countries*, Universities-National Bureau Committee for Economic Research (Princeton: Princeton University Press, 1960), pp. 117–131.

4. T. E. Smith, ''The Cocos-Keeling Islands: A Demographic Laboratory,'' *Population Studies*, XIV (Nov., 1960), pp. 94–130; T. J. Eaton and A. J. Mayer, ''The Social Biology of Very High Fertility Among the Hutterites,'' *Human Biology*, XXV (Sept., 1953), pp. 206–264.

eighteenth century [5] (whichever is higher), the resultant schedule is found to be about 50 per cent higher than that of the Cocos-Keeling Islands' population. If a fertility rate 50 per cent higher than in the Cocos Islands is also ascribed to the age group 15–19, the resulting fertility schedule has a gross reproduction rate of 6.1, or a total fertility of about 12.6.

The range of reliably observed gross reproduction rates thus extends at least from 0.8 to over 4. If urban rather than national fertility is considered, the lower limit becomes about 0.3. If the highest observed rates at different ages are combined, the upper limit is over 6.

It is a curious and perhaps significant fact that national gross reproduction rates below 1.0 have not persisted. Several European countries had rates below 1.0 in the 1930's; all have had a recovery to above 1.0 in the postwar period. Since World War II, the gross reproduction rates of Japan and Hungary have fallen below 1.0 and in 1962 and 1963 the precipitous downtrend that both countries have experienced was arrested. There were three regions in Northern Italy where the gross reproduction rate had fallen below 0.8 in the early 1950's, and in these regions (although in few others of Italy) there was a slight rise in the gross reproduction rate between 1951 and 1956. This fragmentary evidence is at best suggestive, and I would not wish to argue on this mere suggestion that long persistent low fertility will be nonexistent in the future.

It is surprising that there should be such a distance between the gross reproduction rate based on the combination of the highest age specific marital rates reliably observed, and the highest fertility found in populations where voluntary birth control is not the normal custom. The gross reproduction rate of 6.1 that appears feasible is about twice what is commonly found in the underdeveloped areas. In India, for example, the gross reproduction rate appears to be below 3. Limits on cohabitation imposed by age at marriage, taboos, separation of spouses, and the like are a partial explanation. But intervals between the births occurring to fertile women often greatly exceed the

5. L. Henry, ''Some Data on Natural Fertility,'' *Eugenics Quarterly*, VIII (June, 1961), pp. 81–91.

apparent biological minimum. Robert Potter (generalizing on work by Guttmacher, Sheps, Tietze, Henry, and others) suggests that variation in birth intervals among societies practicing little or no birth control occurs mainly because of differences in the length of postpartum amenorrhea.[6] Such differences presumably occur in large part because of differences in lactation.

Mortality Schedules

Although fertility is confined to a definite age interval among human females, mortality can occur at any age from zero to the highest age attained. However, there is a tendency for the age schedule of mortality in different populations to conform more or less closely to a predictable pattern. One way of analyzing the age structure of mortality is to examine the intercorrelations among death rates at different ages in a collection of age schedules of mortality. When mortality data from all over the world are considered together, the intercorrelations involving death rates in infancy and childhood on the one hand, and death rates at higher ages on the other, are moderate. We are uncertain to what degree the low correlations that occur when data from Latin America, Africa, and Asia are combined with nineteenth-century and twentieth-century European data are caused by genuine differences in the age patterns of mortality, and to what degree they result from errors, such as incomplete registration of deaths, especially in infancy, incomplete enumeration in censuses, or inaccurate recording of age on death certificates and in censuses. At the Office of Population Research, we have analyzed the interrelations of mortality rates at different ages in records from areas where both censuses and the registration of vital events appear to have been highly accurate. Among such schedules four slightly different age patterns of mortality emerge. One is the age pattern of mortality characterizing the experience of Norway, Sweden, and Iceland. The second pattern is found among the mortality schedules of Central and Eastern Europe, encompassing Germany, Austria, Northern Italy, Czechoslovakia, Poland, and Hungary. A third

---

6. R. G. Potter, Jr., ''Birth Intervals: Structure and Change,'' *Population Studies*, XVII (Nov., 1963), pp. 155–166.

pattern is found in the experience of Spain, Portugal, and Southern Italy; and the fourth encompasses Western Europe, including Great Britain, and the mortality schedules of Australia, New Zealand, Canada, the United States, Japan, and Taiwan. Within each of these groupings the intercorrelations of mortality rates at one age with those at another are almost always above .90 and usually above .95. These high levels of intercorrelations imply that, for countries whose experience falls within one of these groups, it is possible to estimate with fair accuracy the death rates at every age from knowledge of the death rate at only one age.

The Office of Population Research has calculated (on an electronic computer) a set of model life tables for each sex in each of these four age patterns of mortality, at levels ranging in each instance from an expectation of life at birth of about 20 years to one of about 75 years. These sets of tables express average experience within populations sharing a common pattern of mortality. The four together express some, but almost certainly not all, of the diversity of patterns found in different circumstances.

In almost every age schedule of mortality the death rate is relatively high at age zero, reaches a minimum in the range from 10 to 15, and then begins a gradual increase with increasing age that becomes more marked after age 45 or 50. The lowest expectation of life at birth recorded or reliably estimated for a large population is about 20 years (for example, in India from 1911 to 1921) and the highest is about 75 years (in present-day Sweden and the Netherlands). Most industrialized countries have attained a female expectation of life at birth of 70 years or more. All such countries have age patterns that are remarkably similar in overall outline: an infant mortality rate of 15–35 deaths per thousand live births; death rates below one per thousand in adolescence; and rates which rise rapidly with age above age 60. All very high mortality schedules also have gross features in common. If the expectation of life at birth is less than 30 years, the infant mortality rate is 200 per thousand or higher. Death rates reach a minimum not far from age 10, and follow the same gradual rise to age 50 and the sharp rise thereafter that occurs in low-mortality schedules, but at a higher level. The biggest difference between high mortality and low mortality schedules is always found in infancy and childhood.

AGE DISTRIBUTIONS RESULTING FROM VARIOUS SEQUENCES OF FERTILITY AND MORTALITY

The age composition of any closed population is determined by its past history of fertility and mortality schedules. Using standard methods of population projection, it is possible to calculate the age composition of today's population, on the basis of the age composition at some date in the past and due allowance for the intervening schedules of fertility and mortality. It has recently been proved that if the calculations proceed from a sufficiently remote point in the past, the form of the initial age distribution has no effect.[7] Thus, two arbitrarily different age distributions can be assumed at some date in the remote past and the population projected to the present, using the same sequence of intervening fertility and mortality schedules; the age distributions projected for today's population are then found to be the same. Age composition tends to "forget" the remote past; or, to put the point differently, the age distribution of a population can be considered as the product of the fertility and mortality schedules of the past century or so.

Stable Age Distributions

The fact that an age distribution is determined by the recent sequence of fertility and mortality schedules is the basis for a concept analytically very useful in population theory: Lotka's *stable age distribution* which is the age distribution that would result from the prolonged continuation without change of specified fertility and mortality schedules.[8] The stable age distribution exhibits the influence of fertility and mortality on age composition in pure form. The Office of Population Research has calculated some 2,000 stable age distributions based on mortality schedules that embody the four families of age-pattern of

7. A. Lopez, *Problems in Stable Population Theory* (Princeton: Office of Population Research, 1961), pp. 42–63.
8. A. J. Lotka, *Théorie analytique des associations biologiques* (Paris: Hermann, 1939).

TABLE 1

Parameters of Stable Age Distribution. Proportion Under 15, Proportion Over 65, and Mean Age, in Female Stable Age Distributions with Various Expectations of Life at Birth ("West" Model Life Tables) and Gross Reproduction Rates (Mean Age of Childbearing 29 Years)

Expectation of life	Gross reproduction rate						
	0.80	1.00	1.50	2.00	2.50	3.00	4.00
	Proportion at ages 0–14						
20	.099	.129	.198	.257	.308	.351	.420
30	.117	.152	.230	.294	.348	.393	.464
40	.129	.167	.251	.319	.374	.420	.491
50	.138	.178	.266	.336	.393	.439	.510
60	.144	.186	.277	.349	.407	.453	.524
70	.148	.192	.286	.359	.417	.464	.534
	Proportion at ages 65 and over						
20	.168	.135	.086	.059	.042	.032	.020
30	.180	.143	.088	.058	.041	.031	.018
40	.189	.149	.090	.059	.041	.030	.018
50	.198	.155	.091	.059	.041	.030	.017
60	.206	.160	.093	.060	.041	.029	.017
70	.215	.166	.096	.061	.042	.030	.017
	Mean age						
20	44.6	41.6	35.7	31.6	28.5	26.1	22.7
30	43.9	40.5	34.2	29.9	26.7	24.4	21.0
40	43.5	39.9	33.2	28.8	25.7	23.3	20.0
50	43.4	39.5	32.6	28.1	24.9	22.6	19.4
60	43.4	39.3	32.2	27.6	24.4	22.0	18.9
70	43.6	39.3	32.0	27.2	24.0	21.7	18.5

mortality mentioned earlier, with an expectation of life at birth ranging from 20 years to about 75 years, and on schedules of fertility with mean age that ranges from 27 to 33 years, and gross reproduction rates that vary from 0.8 to 6.0. Table 1 shows the variation in certain parameters of the age distribution at different levels of fertility and mortality in one of the families of stable age distributions.

The age composition of the stable population is given by

$$(3) \qquad c(a) = be^{-ra} p(a),$$

where b is the birth rate, r is the annual rate of increase (the difference between the birth and the death rate) and $p(a)$ is the proportion of women surviving from birth to age a, $c(a)$ is the proportion of the population at age a.

Two stable populations having the same schedule of mortality but different fertility schedules differ in a particularly simple way. The population with higher fertility has a greater rate of increase and differs from the other age distribution by what Lotka called "pivoting" on the mean age. The point of intersection (or pivoting) of the two age distributions is the mean of the mean ages. The ratio of the proportion in the higher fertility distribution to the proportion in the other is a maximum at age zero, falls to 1.0 where the two intersect at the average of the mean ages, and falls progressively further below 1.0 until the highest age attained. The population with higher fertility is unambiguously a younger population, with higher proportions than the other at all ages up to the mean and lower proportions at all ages above the mean.

The effect of differences in mortality schedules on the stable age distribution is more ambiguous and complicated, in spite of the high positive correlation among death rates at different ages, and the usual relation between mortality schedules of higher rates at every age in the schedule with lower life expectancy. The effect of the two schedules on the stable age distribution depends upon the detailed age-pattern of the differences in mortality. In Equation (3), it can be seen that lower mortality rates (implying higher proportions surviving) have two opposing effects on the overall shape of the age distribution. Higher survival means a less steeply sloping $p(a)$, but also implies a greater rate of increase and hence a more steeply sloping negative exponential. In fact, if the difference between the two mortality schedules consisted of the same difference in age specific mortality at every age, the two age distributions would be identical. Lower mortality (higher survival) usually means a stable age distribution with a lower mean age and higher proportion of persons under 15, because a greater difference is usually found between two mortality schedules in infancy and early childhood than at any other age, except possibly the very oldest.

The relationships presented in Table 1 are based upon a set of fertility schedules whose mean age is 29 years, and upon a set of mortality schedules whose age pattern conforms to the experience in 125 mortality schedules of countries of Western Europe, North America, Oceania, and Asia. If a fertility schedule with a younger mean age were employed, the gross reproduction rates at the head of the columns would be somewhat larger for the lowest values and reduced by a progressively larger margin for the higher values.

Age Distributions Resulting from Changing Schedules

When the sequence of mortality and fertility schedules experienced by a population is a sequence of constant change rather than of unchanging values, the resulting age distribution can assume a highly jagged or irregular form. To describe the dependence of the age distribution under these circumstances upon features of the sequence of fertility and mortality schedules is not possible on this occasion. However, it is worth noting that fertility is usually the dominant force in shaping the age distribution. The most prominent exception is the effect of wartime mortality on subsequent male age distributions.

There is one special sequence of fertility that has a predictable effect on age composition, and is of special interest because it has been experienced by many populations in approximate form, at least. This sequence is one of constantly declining fertility over a long period of time. Equation (4) gives an expression for the age distribution resulting from a history of continuously decling fertility at a constant annual rate.[9]

$$(4) \qquad c_d(a) = \frac{b_d}{b_s} c_s(a) e^{-\frac{k}{2}a \frac{k}{2A} a^2}.$$

Thus, $c_d(a)$ is the proportion of the population at age a when fertility has been declining. $c_s(a)$ is the proportion in the stable age distribution with the fertility in the given year. b_d and b_s are the birth rates in the two age distributions. A is the mean age of childbearing. k is the average annual proportion reduction in fertility. Fig. 1 shows the form of the exponential

---

9. A. J. Coale and M. Zelnik, *New Estimates of Fertility and Population in the United States* (Princeton: Princeton University Press, 1963), pp. 82–91.

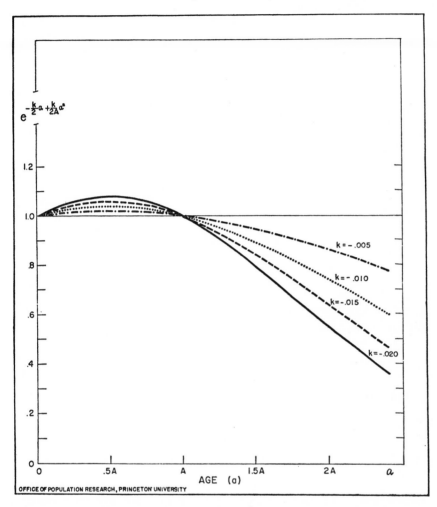

Fig. 1.   The exponential function $e -\frac{k}{2}a +\frac{k}{2A} a^2$. (A is the mean age at childbearing; k is the annual rate of decline of fertility; (a) is age.)

component in Equation (4) and Fig. 2 shows b_d/d_s as a function
of the current level of fertility.

Table 2 shows how various age distribution parameters are
affected by a history of declining fertility at various current
levels of fertility. Note that a population that formerly experienced higher fertility is a younger population than one whose

TABLE 2

Proportions Under 15, Over 65, and Mean Age, in Populations with a History of Declining Fertility (at 1.0 Per Cent per Year), and in Stable Age Distributions for Various Current Gross Reproduction Rates (Mean Age of Childbearing 29 Years, Expectancy of Life at Birth 70 Years)

Current gross reproduction rate	Proportion 0–14		Proportion 65 +		Mean Age	
	History of declining fertility	Stable population	History of declining fertility	Stable population	History of declining fertility	Stable population
.80	.182	.148	.141	.215	38.5	43.6
1.00	.227	.192	.106	.166	34.8	39.3
1.50	.319	.286	.058	.096	28.5	32.0
2.00	.389	.359	.036	.061	24.6	27.2
2.50	.443	.417	.024	.042	21.9	24.0
3.00	.486	.464	.017	.030	20.4	21.7
4.00	.552	.534	.010	.017	17.3	18.5

fertility has always been at current levels. The biggest relative difference is at the older ages.

THE INTERACTION BETWEEN AGE COMPOSITION AND THE FERTILITY SCHEDULE

The birth rate is given by Equation (1) which can be rewritten in the follwing form: [10]

$$(5) \qquad b = \frac{\text{GRR}}{\beta - a} \int_a^\beta c(a)da + \text{cov}_{m \cdot c}(\beta - a)$$

where $\text{cov}_{m \cdot c}$ is the covariance between the age distribution and the fertility schedule in the interval from a to β, the lowest and highest ages of childbearing. The gross reproduction rate (GRR) of course equals $\int_a m(a)da$. Equation (5) follows from the definition of covariance.

$$(6) \qquad \text{cov}_{m \cdot c} = \frac{\int_a^\beta c(a)m(a)da}{\beta - a} - \frac{\int_a^\beta c(a)da \cdot \int_a^\beta m(a)da}{(\beta - a)^2}.$$

10. *Ibid.*, p. 71.

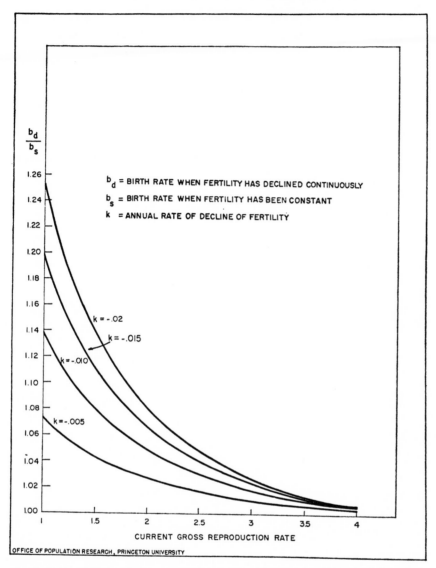

Fig. 2. Ratio of birth rate in a population with a history of fertility declining at an annual rate *k* to the stable population birth rate, for different gross reproduction rates and values of *k*.

If the childbearing interval is taken as from 15 to 45 years, Equation (5) indicates that the birth rate is equal to the gross reproduction rate over 30, times the proportion that women 15 to 45 constitute of the female population, plus 30 times the covariance between the age schedule of fertility and the age distribution in the childbearing interval. The covariance term is negligible whenever the correlation between the age distribution and the fertility schedule is close to zero, or whenever the age distribution itself varies only slightly within the principal ages of childbearing. A uniformly declining age distribution from a to β, combined with a fertility schedule that is symmetrical (with the mean age about midway in the interval) has approximately zero correlation. Equation (5) shows the relationship between

TABLE 3

Proportions of Women 15–44 in Female Stable Age Distributions with Various Expectations of Life at Birth ("West" Model Life Tables) and Gross Reproduction Rates (Mean Age of Childbearing 29 Years)

Expectation of life	Gross reproduction rate						
	0.80	1.00	1.50	2.00	2.50	3.00	4.00
20	.369	.402	.449	.466	.469	.464	.447
30	.371	.404	.445	.457	.455	.447	.424
40	.370	.402	.441	.449	.445	.435	.409
50	.368	.399	.436	.442	.436	.425	.398
60	.365	.396	.432	.437	.429	.417	.389
70	.361	.393	.428	.432	.424	.411	.382

the fertility performance of a population (b) and the fertility performance of the women of childbearing age (GRR). This relationship depends first on the proportion of the population that consists of women in the childbearing age, and secondly, on the degree to which women within the childbearing age are concentrated at ages of exceptionally high fertility. In Table 3, the proportions of females 15 to 45 in stable age distributions are shown as a function of the gross reproduction rate and the expectation of life at birth. Note that the proportion declines with rising expectation of life except when fertility is very low (gross reproduction rate of 1.25 or less) and mortality very high (expectation of life of 20 to 30 years). Such a combination is wholly hypothetical so far as is known. As fertility varies from low to high, the proportion 15 to 45 increases to a maximum at a gross reproduction rate of 2.0 to 2.5 and then declines. The most notable feature of Table 3 is the small range of variation. At central values of fertility (gross reproduction rates of 1.0 to 3.0)

the proportion 15 to 45 varies only within the limits
0.430 ± 0.040.

Thus, in stable age distributions the variation in age distribution has only a limited effect on the birth rate, provided childbearing is centered in the interval from 15 to 45 so that the covariance term in Equation (5) is small. However, when fertility and mortality vary with time, the proportion 15 to 45 may be more strongly affected. Fig. 2 (showing the ratio of the birth rate in the population with a history of declining fertility to the birth rate in the stable population) can equally well be read as the ratio of the proportion 15 to 45 in the declining fertility population to the proportion 15 to 45 in the stable population. For example, if a population with a gross reproduction rate of 1.50 has experienced for many years a fertility decline at a rate of two per cent per year, the proportion of women in the childbearing ages would be about 14 per cent higher, namely 49 per cent instead of 43 per cent (expectation of life at birth 60 years).

Even with the same proportion 15 to 45 and the same gross reproduction rate, two populations may differ in birth rate because one age distribution within the childbearing span is more favorable to reproduction. The most favorable distribution within this span is one that has an unusually high proportion of women at the ages where the fertility rate is the highest. This effect is synonymous with a large positive covariance term in Equation (5).

In stable populations the proportion at each age in the range 15 to 45 declines in a more or less linear manner when the gross reproduction rate is 1.75 or higher, and the expectation of life at birth is 20 years (or 1.04 or higher, when the expectation of life at birth is 70 years). The age distribution is approximately horizontal from 15 to 45 when the GRR is 1.25 and the expectation of life at birth is about 40, and the covariance between the age distribution and the fertility schedule is approximately zero whatever the mean age of childbearing. In the stable age distribution just cited the proportion in each five-year age group within the childbearing span varies only from 7.01 to 7.19 per cent. Consequently, the gross reproduction rates required to give the same birth rate when the mean age of childbearing is 27 years and when it is 33 years are almost identical (1.252 and 1.250).

When the age distribution slopes steeply in the interval from 15 to 45, a large covariance between the age distribution and the fertility schedule is possible. However, even with a steep age distribution, the covariance is approximately zero if the fertility schedule is symmetrical and centered on the middle of the childbearing interval. When the age distribution slopes downward with increasing age, and the mean of the fertility schedule

TABLE 4

The Effect on the Birth Rate in Stable Populations of Covariance Between the Age Distribution and the Fertility Schedule [a]

Expectancy of life	$b = .0100$		$b = .0350$		$b = .0600$	
	$\overline{m} = 27$	$\overline{m} = 33$	$\overline{m} = 27$	$\overline{m} = 33$	$\overline{m} = 27$	$\overline{m} = 33$
20	−.0007	.0007	.0013	−.0010	.0047	−.0062
45	−.0004	.0004	.0021	−.0029	.0063	−.0119
70	−.0002	.0002	.0026	−.0039	.0070	−.0150

[a] The value of

$$\text{cov}_{m.c} \, (\beta - a) = b - \frac{\text{GRR}}{\beta - a} \int_a^\beta c(a) da$$

fertility schedules with mean ages of 27 and 33 years, at various levels of the birth rate, and various expectations of life at birth.

occurs before the middle of the childbearing interval, high fertility rates correspond with above average proportions of women, the resulting covariance in Equation (5) is positive, and the birth rate is elevated. If the mean age of childbearing is above the middle of the childbearing interval the covariance is negative and the birth rate is depressed. The converse effect obtains at low levels of fertility, where the proportions at each successive age within the childbearing span are larger, i.e., where the slope of the age distribution is positive. Under these circumstances early childbearing produces a negative covariance and a lower birth rate; older childbearing produces positive covariance and a higher birth rate. Table 4 shows the effect of the covariance term on the birth rate in the stable population when the mean age of childbearing is 27 and 33 years respectively, at various levels of fertility and mortality.

The entries in Table 4 show the difference between the intrinsic birth rate when the mean age ($\bar{m}$) of the fertility schedule is 27 or 33 years, and its value when the covariance between the age distribution and the fertility schedule is zero, as it is when $\bar{m}$ is approximately 30 years. Thus, if b is .060 and e_0^0 is 70 years, covariance has added .007 to the rate when $\bar{m} = 27$ years, and has subtracted .015 when $\bar{m} = 33$. The GRR producing a birth rate of .060 when $\bar{m} = 27$ would produce a rate of only .053 if covariance were zero; the GRR producing .060 when $\bar{m} = 33$ would produce .075 if covariance were zero. Another implication of covariance is that the gross reproduction rate required to give a birth rate of 60 per 1,000 is 41 per cent higher when the mean age of childbearing is 33 years than when it is 27 years.

A striking instance of interaction between the age distribution and the fertility schedule is seen in the history of fertility in the United States in the 1950's. The gross reproduction rate rose by more than 19 per cent between 1950 and 1959. However, the proportion 15 to 45 was about 91 per cent in 1959 of the proportion in 1950. Hence, general fertility (births per woman 15–44) increased by only 12 per cent. The covariance between fertility and the age distribution within the childbearing span changed from positive to negative because of the entry into the ages of the highest fertility of the small cohorts born in the 1930's, and the increase in the birth rate between 1950 and 1959 was only 1.2 per cent.

THE INTERACTION BETWEEN AGE COMPOSITION AND THE MORTALITY SCHEDULE

Equations (1) and (2) are identical in form, and it is natural to seek a formula for the death rate analogous to Equation (5) for the birth rate. But there is a fundamental difference in the age patterns of fertility and mortality that makes the search useless. Fertility occurs at a central portion of the female age distribution, and because of the limited variation in this central portion found in human populations, the birth rate in a population tends to be closely related to the gross reproduction rate. In fact, an estimate of the birth rate as equal to .430 (a representative value of the proportion of women 15–44) divided by

30 (the number of years in the childbearing span) times the gross reproduction rate is almost always within about 15 per cent of the true value and usually much closer.

It is impossible, however, to develop a similarly valid approximation from Equation (2) for the death rate, especially when mortality rates are very low. The typical age pattern of mortality was described earlier. Fig. 3 shows the age-specific death rates in one of the Office of Population Research sets of model mortality schedules at various expectations of life at birth.

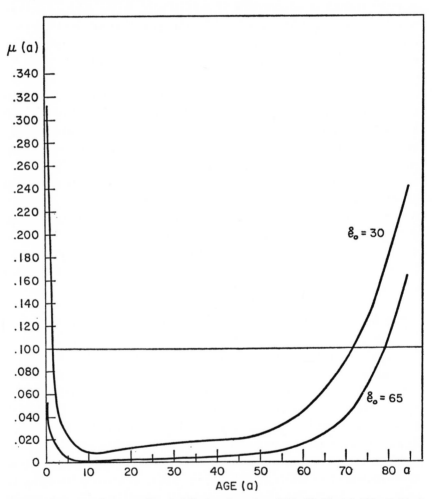

Fig. 3. Age-specific mortality (u(a)) for females ("West" Model Life Tables) at indicated expectations of life at birth.

Above average death rates occur in all schedules at the older ages. In the high mortality schedules there occur very high death rates in the ages of infancy and childhood also. Thus, the over-all death rate is seen to depend on the proportion of the population in the young ages of high death rates, in the ages of 5 to 60 of moderate death rates, and in the ages over 65 of high death rates in the later part of life.

Stable age distributions differ very greatly in the proportions at the extremes of the age distribution. For example, in stable age distributions defined by fertility schedules with a gross reproduction rate between .8 and 4.0 and expectations of life between 20 and 70, the proportion under 5 differs by a factor of 8 and the proportion over 65 differs by a factor of more than 12 (in contrast, the ratio of the highest to the lowest proportions 15 to 44 found in the same populations is only 1.3).

In stable age distributions having the same mortality schedule but differing because of the fertility schedules on which they are based, there is always a level of fertility that produces a minimum death rate. There is a minimum rather than an ever lower death rate the higher the fertility, because all mortality schedules have a higher death rate at age zero than at later childhood ages. At sufficiently high levels of fertility, the proportion of infants is high, and that of persons over 60 is very low. Hence, the rising proportion of children under one as fertility increases ultimately has the effect of raising the intrinsic death rate.

When the expectation of life at birth is low, mortality rates early in life are especially high relative to those at old ages. Therefore, the minimum death rate occurs at moderate levels of fertility. In contrast, when the expectation of life at birth is very great, infant mortality rates (although still above the rates in later childhood) are much lower relative to rates found at the older ages than in a high-mortality schedule. As a consequence the level of fertility has a larger relative effect on the death rate when the expectation of life is 70 years or more. The minimum death rate occurs at very high fertility, when the gross reproduction rate is over 4.0. Table 5 shows the death rate in various stable age distributions differing both as to level of mortality and fertility.

TABLE 5

Intrinsic Death Rates in Female Stable Age Distributions with Various Expectations of Life at Birth ("West" Model Life Tables) and Gross Reproduction Rates (Mean Age of Childbearing 29 Years)

Expectancy of life	Gross reproduction rate						
	0.80	1.00	1.50	2.00	2.50	3.00	4.00
20	.0570	.0532	.0488	.0478	.0483	.0495	.0528
30	.0437	.0398	.0350	.0335	.0333	.0338	.0356
40	.0349	.0309	.0258	.0239	.0233	.0233	.0242
50	.0284	.0244	.0191	.0169	.0160	.0157	.0158
60	.0234	.0194	.0139	.0115	.0103	.0098	.0094
70	.0194	.0154	.0097	.0072	.0058	.0057	.0044

Death Rates in an Age Distribution with a History of Declining Fertility

The effect of a history of declining fertility is to produce a population with higher proportions at ages up to age 35, 40, or 45, and lower proportions above this age, especially lower at the very upper end of the age distribution. The ratio of the age distribution in a population with a history of declining fertility to the stable age distribution with the same current fertility is shown in Fig. 4. The declining fertility age distribution is higher at ages of modern mortality and lower at ages of high mortality (with an exception of infancy). Thus, a history of declining fertility produces an age distribution favorable to a lower death rate. Table 6 shows the death rate in several stable populations

TABLE 6

Death Rates Per Thousand in Populations with a Long History of Declining Fertility at a Rate of 1.0 Per Cent per Year Compared to Stable Death Rates

Gross reproduction rate	Life Expectancy							
	40 years		50 years		60 years		70 years	
	Declining fertility	Stable	Declining fertility	Stable	Declining fertility	Stable	Declining fertility	Stable
	Death rates (per thousand)							
1.00	25.4	30.9	19.1	24.4	14.2	19.4	10.3	15.4
2.50	21.8	23.3	14.5	16.0	8.9	10.3	4.5	5.8
4.00	23.3	24.2	15.1	15.8	8.7	9.4	3.7	4.4

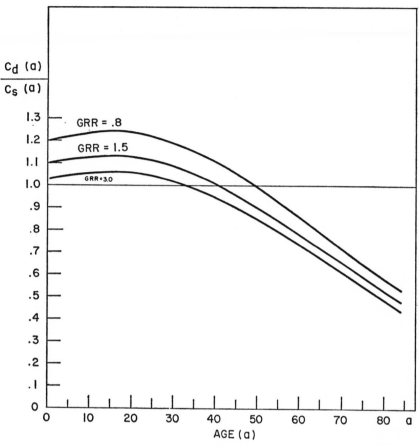

Fig. 4. Declining fertility age distribution relative to stable age distribution. $(\frac{c_d(a)}{c_s(a)}$ is the ratio of the proportion age *a* in the population with declining fertility to the proportion age *a* in the corresponding stable population; rate of decline one per cent per year.)

and in populations with the same mortality, the same current fertility, but a history of fertility that has long been declining at an annual rate of one per cent per year.

THE LIMITS OF THE BIRTH RATE, THE DEATH RATE, AND THE RATE OF NATURAL INCREASE

The highest birth rate that a human population could attain would occur when a schedule of maximum fertility rates would be combined with the most favorable possible age composition.

The fertility schedule would have a high gross reproduction rate, and presumably early childbearing, so that the highest fertility would coincide with high proportions of women within the childbearing span. If the effects of migration are ruled out, the maximum birth rate can be calculated in a stable age distribution because a history of rising fertility would produce a less favorable age distribution, and it is scarcely plausible in calculating the maximum birth rate obtainable to assume that fertility has been declining. The proportion in the childbearing ages is enhanced by high mortality.

If the age specific fertility schedule of the Cocos-Keeling Islands—the highest recorded fertility schedule for a whole population—is combined with the model life tables that the Office of Population Research has calculated, a birth rate of about 63 per 1,000 is found when the expectation of life at birth is 20 years. If the expectation of life at birth were 71 years, the birth rate would be about 53 per 1,000. However, it is at least imaginable that a still higher level of fertility could occur. If the synthetic schedule obtained by combining the highest observed marital fertility rates at each age is employed (gross reproduction rate 6.1), the stable birth rate is 84 when e_0^0 is 20 years and 67 when e_0^0 is 71 years. Even the higher of these two rates is not the maximum birth rate because it occurs in a population growing steadily at about 2.5 per cent per year. If the population were stationary, the birth rate would be over 90—and the expectation of life at birth about 11 years!

The minimum intrinsic death rate consistent with observed mortality and fertility schedules would result from a combination of the fertility of the Cocos-Keeling Islands with a recent Swedish mortality schedule. The death rate of this stable population is about 2.5 per 1,000. The lowest reliably recorded death rate to date is in Hong Kong, 1963: 5.5 per 1,000.

The maximum growth rate would result from a combination of high fertility and low mortality. Cocos-Island fertility combined with Swedish mortality (GRR 4.17, e_0^0 75 years) would produce a rate of increase of about 5.0 per cent per year. A gross reproduction rate of 6.1 (combination of highest observed rates at each age) would lead to a growth of about 6.5 per cent per year. Still lower mortality would, surprisingly enough, add very little to these growth rates. A death rate of zero (immortality for all) would add only about 0.1 per cent to the long-run growth rate.[11] To be sure, the death rate would fall from 2.5 per thousand to zero, but the slight increase in the proportion of older persons would reduce the birth rate by about 1.5 per thousand. Mankind has not closely approached the biologically feasible fertility schedule that would maximize growth, but has come very near to the ultimate in growth-producing mortality schedules.

11. A. J. Coale, ''Increases in Expectation of Life and Population Growth,'' International Union for the Scientific Study of Population, *Proceedings* (Vienna, 1959), pp. 36–41.

C. Chandrasekaran and Moye W. Freymann

EVALUATING COMMUNITY FAMILY PLANNING PROGRAMS

EVALUATION CONCEPTS

General principles of evaluation of community action programs are applicable in the field of family planning as in other fields. These include (1) defining the objectives of the program, (2) selecting the criteria by which achievement can be judged, (3) deciding on the design of the evaluation, (4) collecting and analyzing the data, and (5) providing interpretations of the findings to the program administrators. This paper will identify and discuss some of the special problems to be met when applying this evaluative process to family planning programs, with illustrations from experience in India.

Evaluations might be roughly categorized as relating to *long-term* or *short-term* efforts. A long-term approach might, for example, be used to answer a question about the overall effects of the Indian family planning program since its beginnings some 12 years ago. Such questions imply that the overall "program" may encompass many activities undertaken at various periods, inspired directly or indirectly by the government policy to popularize family planning. It is assumed that the activities

266

need not be very precisely defined, and that rather gross measurements may be involved.

Short-term evaluations are the main focus of the present paper. Ideally, this type of evaluation is built into a program from its outset; its main purpose is to improve a program, through identifying gaps in planning and execution and suggesting appropriate modifications. The evaluative effort may also have important promotional uses, to educate the evaluator and the evaluatee and to maintain official support for the program. This aspect may be particularly important in family planning programs, where the ultimate objectives of fertility change may be achieved only after a considerable time. In addition, the evaluation process is likely to identify fresh problems requiring further research and may enable the use of action situations to test basic research hypotheses.

The theoretical basis for program evaluations has been strengthened in the last few years by the concept developed by Knutson and James that an action program can be analyzed in terms of a "hierarchy of objectives."[1] A program is conceived as having an ultimate objective, from which is derived a descending and branching series of subsidiary objectives. Each of the subobjectives is a means of achieving the objective at the next higher level, and is the goal of an objective (or set of objectives) at the next lower level. Each objective is formulated on the basis of certain assumptions about the best means of achieving the objective above. The ultimate success of a program would depend upon two major factors: the extent to which the objectives in the program network are met, and the validity of the assumptions upon which the various objectives are based.

When this form of analysis is applied to a community action program, the higher-level objectives usually refer to changes that are expected to occur within a target population, as part of the program. These may be termed the *program impact objectives*. They may be subdivided, for convenience, into *ultimate*

1. A. L. Knutson, "Evaluating Program Progress," *Public Health Reports*, LXX (March, 1955), pp. 305–310; G. James, "Evaluation in Public Health Practice," *American Journal of Public Health*, LII (July, 1962), pp. 1145–1154.

impact objectives most directly related to the program goal, and *intermediate impact objectives* of a lower order.

At still lower levels are the *program execution objectives,* referring to development of activities and resources needed to achieve the impact objectives. Program execution objectives may be subdivided for convenience into *performance objectives,* referring to activities which should be carried out, and, at a lower level, *effort objectives,* referring to the mobilization of the personnel, funds, or materials required to perform the activities.

The dimensions of time and area must then be added to this analysis, especially when dealing with a new program. On the basis of certain assumptions, an optimal order of progression of the program elements over time and from area to area, plus the possible need for concentration of resources at certain points, can be proposed. These aspects may be described as a set of *phasing objectives.*[2]

This type of conceptualization makes the program evaluation process more orderly and sensitive. A program is first analyzed in terms of its program impact, execution, and phasing objectives, and their underlying assumptions are identified. Appropriate methods for assessing the achievement of each of the objectives can then be developed and applied, depending upon such factors as the resources and time available and special problems of measurement. Usually the assessment of lower-level, program effort objectives can be done relatively quickly. Among the higher-order objectives the measurement problems often increase, unfortunately, along with the value of such measures for judging the ultimate success of the program.

Quantitative measures of achievement must be accompanied, insofar as possible, by observations on the possible factors influencing the degree of achievement. As a strategy to facilitate this diagnostic process, target groups where there has been differential achievement of an objective may be identified and

---

2. Still other bases for evaluation can of course be used. For example, the concepts of *efficiency* and *adequacy* of achievement have been noted by James; the former refers to the effort-costs for achievement of objectives, the latter to the extent to which an idealized objective is being achieved.

studied for related differences in the characteristics of the groups or in the nature of the activities that reach them.

Obviously, the shape of the set of objectives for a given program will be influenced by the type of ultimate goal, the population, and the available resources. The extent of detailed primary analysis of groups of objectives, as well as the attention given to overcoming measurement problems, would also be influenced by judgments about which aspects of the program are most in need of study. In order to consider the application of evaluation concepts to current family planning programs, therefore, we must pause for a moment to note some of the special features of such programs that may influence their evaluation.

NATURE OF A FAMILY PLANNING PROGRAM

Although the content of family planning programs must of course depend on careful analysis of relevant local situations and resources, new programs in developing countries, at least, may share some general features. These may be illustrated by the official program of the Government of India.[3]

The Director of the Indian program has proposed that its ultimate goal is to accelerate the rate of adoption of family planning so as to reduce the birth rate in India to 25 births per 1,000 population by 1973. Under this ultimate impact objective, three subobjectives are defined, the target groups for these being 90 per cent of the married adult population of India.

(1) *Group acceptance:* Individuals should know that their immediate social group feels that a smaller family size is the normal, desirable behavior for members of the group. The underlying assumption is that without this a couple will hesitate to adopt contraception; with it, most couples will somehow change their behavior in the direction of the norm.

(2) *Knowledge about contraception:* People should acquire information about the feasibility of efficient contraception, about specific methods, and about the salience of family size to the achievement of their various personal values. It is assumed that such information will hasten the adoption of family plan-

3. B. L. Raina, *Family Planning Programme: Report for 1962–63* (New Delhi: Directorate General of Health Services, Ministry of Health, 1964).

ning by innovators in the population, and the diffusion of the small family norm and effective contraceptive practices.

(3) *Availability of supplies:* Any person should feel that he can obtain simple contraceptive supplies with minimal physical, financial, or psychological barriers. It is assumed that this will strongly reinforce the other two objectives, and will foster more efficient contraceptive use.

Under each of these three intermediate impact objectives, the Indian family planning program can be further dissected into increasingly specific program execution objectives. Activities to be undertaken include the training of local leaders in family planning, assistance to them in communicating with their own groups, and establishment of local contraceptive supply channels. A basic pattern of staff and materials for field family planning units is then proposed, which combines such activities into roles for different types of workers, at several organizational levels. Qualifications and relationships of personnel are specified, with the assumption that such workers can effectively perform the needed functions.

Other program execution objectives relate to development of mass communication activities, augmentation of contraceptive production, contraceptive distribution through commercial channels, clinical services for voluntary sterilization and contraceptive consultation, statistical services, basic research activities, a strong training program, and a strong organizational structure to give overall support.

A typical phasing objective adopted in the Indian program has been to concentrate initial resources in "action-research" situations, where, under a set of special conditions, the available knowledge relevant to family planning programs can be further augmented and refined.[4] Such areas are then useful for training and demonstration. A geographic phasing objective is also reflected in an urban-to-rural direction of development of the overall program. Within a given area, an important phasing

---

4. M. W. Freymann, "Observations on Family Planning Action-Research," *India's Population,* ed. S. N. Agarwala (Bombay: Asia Publishing House), pp. 198–208; M. W. Freymann and H. F. Lionberger, "A Model for Family Planning Action-Research," *Research in Family Planning,* ed. C. V. Kiser (Princeton: Princeton University Press, 1962), pp. 443–461.

objective also is the placement of adequate supervisory staff in position before the posting of more junior field personnel.

Now, assuming that for a given program such a pattern of objectives can be worked out, suitable to the local situation, we may turn to the methods of assessing the achievement of these objectives.

ASSESSMENT OF PROGRAM EXECUTION OBJECTIVES

For the assessment of "effort" objectives, as measured in terms of staff placed in position and materials provided, the first principle is to supplement routine administrative reporting by other methods of systematic observation. Program officials sometimes sincerely believe that personnel have been equipped in their training to contribute to the family planning program and are devoting time to it, whereas direct examination of a sample area may reveal that instructions have somehow not been implemented.

For assessment of "performance" objectives, routine reports of number of visits made, talks given, or volunteers enlisted have little use in a careful evaluation. The evaluator can help program officials to differentiate between the possible administrative uses of such reports, on one hand, and the need for reliable, meaningful observations to assess the achievement of performance objectives. Routine reports of activities performed should be checked both by interviews with the field staff and by collecting further evidence directly related to the performance of the activity. For example, the number of contraceptive depotholders developed in an area may be estimated by taking the reported total number and correcting it according to findings from personal visits with the workers and from interviews with a sample of the depot-holders.

There is particular need at the present time for establishment of more precise criteria of *quality* of field educational activities which involve personal and group interaction, and need for adequate methods to measure these criteria. Counting of gross activities or analysis of the content of diaries has not been satisfactory for the purpose.

The detailed assessment of all possible execution objectives in a large program is impractical. Judgments must be made of the objectives that are most critical at the time, in view of the program's phasing-objectives, and whose achievement is most likely to fall short. For each of these, one or more types of observation may be selected that are reasonably precise and feasible. Careful collection of observations even on a few key objectives, in a large program, may still add up to a substantial work load and can provide convincing evidence of the program's current strengths or deficiencies.

ASSESSMENT OF INTERMEDIATE IMPACT OBJECTIVES

The impact objectives of the Indian family planning program involve assumptions that alterations in fertility patterns emerge from a number of underlying psychological and behavioral changes in the population. Measurements of the underlying changes could have great value as early indicators of likely fertility change. Some of the variables to be studied for this purpose will now be considered.

The ideal measure at the intermediate-impact level might be the direct observation of frequency of uncontracepted intercourse among women susceptible to pregnancy, but this is not feasible. It is noted in order to stress the fact that measures available in this field will all be considerably less than perfect. Program evaluations will have to rely on a number of measures which, taken together, can most likely provide sensitive and convincing evidence of program effect.

Use of Contraceptive Methods

With very careful interviewing in certain population groups, fairly good information about contraceptive practices appears to be obtainable. The differential incidence of reported use in various population strata is commonly observed to vary in the expected directions, and to be related to differences in birth rates.[5] Such data provide a valuable means of judging the general extent of acceptance of contraceptive practices and of observing trends in the popularity of certain methods. This is a type of measure which would be useful particularly for the ''long-term'' type of program evaluation referred to earlier.

5. United Nations, *The Mysore Population Study* (New York: United Nations, ST/SOA/Series A/34, 1961).

There is, however, serious doubt whether people's responses to questions about use of contraceptive practices are sufficiently reliable for very *sensitive detection of trends in the total use* of contraceptive practices. Checks on such responses from independent interviews of husbands and wives have revealed significant differences in the reports of total use and of types of methods used. Interviewer bias has been found to be stronger on this type of question than others.[6] Information about coitus interruptus may be especially elusive. Frequency of use and type of methods used may vary from time to time, so that terms such as "acceptor" must be used very cautiously.[7] Changes in total reported use of contraception could also arise from changes in the readiness to respond to such questions, or changes in the extent of use of methods that are more likely to be reported.

In addition, intensive and repeated interviewing of couples regarding their contraceptive practices may contaminate and seriously conflict with educational objectives in a family planning action program, at least with regard to the respondents and those immediately around them. These difficulties all weigh against measures of contraceptive usage serving as sensitive indicators of program impact.

It is possible, on the other hand, to count the numbers of surgical sterilizations done or intrauterine devices inserted, without resort to interview data. The total number of such procedures performed in an area, corrected for residence of the individuals assisted, may serve as a useful index of program impact.

Contraceptive Consumption

The number of condoms or other contraceptive materials fed into a population group may not be closely related to amount of use of contraception, but observation of marked changes in the total consumption can provide evidence of program impact. Data on this subject from official sources and private distribu-

6. *Ibid.*
7. C. Chandrasekaran and K. Kuder, *Family Planning through Clinics: Report of a Survey of Family Planning Clinics in Greater Bombay* (Bombay: Demographic Training and Research Centre, 1965).

tors may be available. Methods can be developed to estimate the proportion of the contraceptives distributed in a population group which might pass outside of the group.

Perceived Availability of Supplies

Little work has been done so far to refine the measurement of this critical variable. In India, women who had visited Bombay clinics were found to have some clear ideas about the difficulties of obtaining supplies from clinic sources.[8] In the course of a current evaluation of the Indian national program, a sample of rural men are asked where a man from their group can obtain condoms if he wants them; they are also asked about difficulties anticipated in obtaining them. Studies in Madras and in Delhi are also approaching this aspect through observations on the patterns of acceptance of supplies through alternative channels in a community.

Knowledge About Contraceptive Methods

Many surveys in India and elsewhere have included questions to ascertain if respondents know that "family planning is possible" and to assess their knowledge about different contraceptive methods. Knowledge of this kind has been shown in India to be related to variables such as education, age, number of children, and urban residence.[9] Such data provide useful impressions about the receptivity of the population to a family planning program. However, relatively little has been done so far to study the reliability and validity of such questions and their applicability to measurement of change in level of knowledge over a period of time.

There appear to be "levels" of knowledge among village women, identified as awareness of the idea of contraception, belief in its efficacy, and knowledge of specific methods.[10] Among higher age groups, the proportion of women at each level increases. The possibility that a scale of knowledge items can be constructed has potential importance for measurement of

8. *Ibid.*

9. S. N. Agarwala, *Attitude Towards Family Planning in India* (Delhi: Institute of Economic Growth, Occasional Papers No. 5, 1962).

10. S. N. Agarwala, "A Family Planning Survey in Four Delhi Villages," *Population Studies*, XV (Nov., 1961), pp. 110–120.

change in knowledge about family planning in a population group.

For the further refinement of measures of knowledge, there is need in any setting to formulate a precise terminology. "Family planning," for example, is a very diffuse term. The various dimensions of knowledge of any particular method must also be considered (whether a device has actually been seen, for example, or whether various aspects of the use of the method are known). Attempts in this direction have been made.[11] For quick assessments, the systematic development of group interviewing methods also merits attention.

Perceived Norms of Family Size, Within a Social Group

Ideally, a measure of social norms would deal with individuals' perceptions of others' views on family size, or their predictions of others' reactions to a large number of children. So far, adequate tools for this purpose are not available. Some studies in India have asked women direct questions about what they would consider the "ideal" number of children. However, the uniformity of response (generally between three and five) has discouraged hopes of gaining from this approach a sensitive measure of change in norms.[12] Questions about ideals should distinguish between number of births and number of survivors to adulthood. There should be further allowance for differential preferences for boys and girls, and for the fact that men and women sometimes differ in their responses.

A satisfactory approach has been to question husbands and wives specifically whether they want another child. Analysis of such responses in the Mysore Study, for example, showed that among rural women having 1–3 children two per cent responded with "no;" among those with 4–6 children, 59 per cent said "no." The responses of urban women were 10 per cent and 72 per cent, respectively. Husbands' "no" responses were fewer than their wives', in both rural and urban groups.[13]

In such questions, allowance must be made, of course, for women who have an obvious impairment of fecundity and for

11. C. Chandrasekaran and K. Kuder, *op. cit.*
12. S. N. Agarwala, *op. cit.*, footnote 9.
13. United Nations, *op. cit.*

those currently pregnant. Reliability of response in the Mysore Study was improved by use of further probes.[14] The response can be made more meaningful by asking questions about how many more children are desired; some studies have also obtained responses to questions whether the last child was desired.[15] It would be worth trying to develop further methods of assessing the intensity of feeling about whether or not another child is wanted.

Norms relating to number of children have behind them the enormous powers of social pressure, and can be presumed to be very closely tied to actual fertility performance. Therefore, the development of sensitive methods for measuring such norms can be considered to have top priority, among the measures needed for assessing ''intermediate impact'' objectives.

ASSESSMENT OF IMPACT ON FERTILITY

For development of sensitive measures of impact on fertility patterns, a number of general considerations would appear to be important.

(1) The index should relate to the changes in fertility behavior of that group in the community which can be most immediately affected by the program. At any particular time not all the women are equally exposed to the risk of a pregnancy. For instance, women who are in amenorrhea following a pregnancy are not at as great a risk as those who have begun menstruating after the termination of a pregnancy.

(2) The data used in the calculation of the index should be such that the events to which they refer can be recorded accurately with the resources available for the program. It is, for instance, a far simpler task to strengthen the regular recording of live births in a community than to try to record all pregnancies, including early and late fetal losses.

(3) The sensitivity of the index should be such that, for the same degree of achievement by a program, the index will show a

14. C. Chandrasekaran, ''Fertility Survey in Mysore State, India,'' *Current Research in Human Fertility* (New York: Milbank Memorial Fund, 1955), pp. 11–23.

15. V. M. Dandekar and K. Dandekar, *Survey of Fertility and Mortality in Poona District* (Poona: Gokhale Institute of Politics and Economics, Publication No. 27, 1953).

greater proportionate change than other possible indices. Since the degree of change that has occurred is likely to be estimated from a sample, the standard error of the estimate of the proportionate change should also be taken into account in judging the sensitivity of the index.

Several measures of fertility based on annual number of live births, such as *crude birth rate, standardized birth rate, general fertility rate,* and *specific fertility rate* are in common use. These indices, discussed elsewhere in the Symposium, are relatively insensitive as indicators of short-term fertility changes.

The use of *parity ratios* (proportion of births of order four and above, say, among all the births registered during a period) have helped to reveal changes in fertility patterns associated with a fall in birth rate. The fertility decline in Western countries from the late nineteenth century up to World War II was associated not only with marked reductions in the age-specific rates of women in the higher age groups but also by decline in the proportion of births of higher order.[16] Model studies substantiate the expectation that increased use of contraception would progressively diminish higher order births in the long run.[17] However, control of fertility mainly by women in lower parity or age groups in the initial stages might actually cause a short-run increase in the proportion of higher order births.

The average number of children born per ever-married woman or currently married woman in the course of her reproductive life is an excellent index of long-term changes in fertility. It is affected not only by fertility control within marriage but also by such institutional factors as age at marriage or remarriage of widows. The value of this index has stimulated attempts to obtain the necessary data during popula-

16. H. S. Shryock, Jr., ''Trends in Age-Specific Fertility Rates,'' *The Milbank Memorial Fund Quarterly*, XVII (July, 1939), pp. 294–307; W. H. Grabill, C. V. Kiser and P. K. Whelpton, *The Fertility of American Women* (New York: John Wiley & Sons, Inc., 1958) ; P. K. Whelpton, *Cohort Fertility* (Princeton: Princeton University Press, 1954).

17. V. C. Chidambaram, ''Use of Birth Order Statistics in the Study of Fertility,'' paper submitted to the Demographic Training and Research Centre, Chembur, Bombay, 1962 (unpublished).

tion censuses.[18] However, for short-term evaluation of a family planning program the index would not be very sensitive, since the total number of children born would, at the early stage, include mostly those born before the program got under way.

The *pregnancy rate* has been used for clinical assessments of contraceptive methods, but as is well-known it is difficult to obtain a complete count of the pregnancies which ended in fetal loss. A number of retrospective surveys on pregnancy histories carried out in India have given estimates of fetal loss which are much lower than that expected from the experience in other countries. For example, abortion rates of 79 and 41 per 1,000 pregnancies were recorded in Bangalore City and a rural area of Mysore. The stillbirth rate was 37 per 1,000 live and still-births in Bangalore City, and 32 per 1,000 live and stillbirths in the rural area.[19] When women were closely followed during pilot studies in India on the rhythm method and the study on the use of metaxylohydroquinone as an oral contraceptive, it was not unusual to find absence of menstruation for periods extending from two to four months. Where such a break in menstruation is not accompanied by clear evidence of the occurrence of fetal loss, it becomes extremely difficult to decide whether or not a conception really occurred. Wrong decisions can markedly affect the pregnancy rate obtained.

Another difficulty encountered in using the pregnancy rate is the establishment of the time at which pregnancy occurred. There may be scanty bleeding at the time of expected menstruation even after the occurrence of pregnancy, and the last menstrual period cannot be entirely relied upon to indicate the time at which pregnancy began.

A PROPOSED INDEX OF FERTILITY CHANGE

An index which is not likely to suffer from the major drawbacks pointed out in the last section could be based on the *occurrence of pregnancies ending in live births among women who are immediately exposed to the risk of conception.* The advantages of this index are (1) that it relates only to the

18. United Nations, *Principles and Recommendations for National Population Censuses* (New York: United Nations, ST/STAT/SERM/27, 1958).
19. United Nations, *op. cit.*, footnote 5.

experience among women who are immediately exposed to the risk of conception and is, therefore, likely to possess high sensitivity, and (2) that it makes use of only conceptions that terminate in a live birth, which are easier to determine both with respect to number and the time of occurrence than conceptions that end in fetal loss.

The concept underlying the index is *the probability for a conception terminating in a live birth to occur in a month among women immediately exposed to the risk of conception.* This probability will decline if attempts are made to increase spacing between children or stop having further births.

In analogy with the well-known *pregnancy rate,* the index to be used can be called the *live birth pregnancy rate* and will give the number of conceptions terminating in a live birth which occur in 100 years of exposure.

Working Definitions

In using the above concept, it will be necessary to have working definitions and assumptions.

(1) *Women immediately exposed to risk of conception:* Currently married women who have resumed menstruation after the last termination of pregnancy and are not pregnant can be considered as immediately exposed to the risk of pregnancy. In keeping with the practice in public health science, such women have been considered by Sheps and Perrin as 'susceptibles.' [20] Theoretically a woman who had not menstruated after the termination of a pregnancy can become pregnant without the restarting of menstruation but from a practical point of view she can be included among the nonsusceptibles. Even among the susceptibles, there would be some who are secondarily sterile but it will not be possible to identify such women without a long follow-up. All susceptible women or only those among them who are not secondarily sterile could be considered as immediately exposed to the risk of conception depending upon the available data and the method of analysis to be used.

(2) *Risk of conception:* The risk of conception will be as-

20. M. C. Sheps and E. B. Perrin, ''Changes in Birth Rates as a Function of Contraceptive Effectiveness: Some Applications of a Stochastic Model,'' *American Journal of Public Health,* LIII (July, 1963), pp. 1031–1046.

sumed to begin immediately after the resumption of menstruation following amenorrhea. It is recognized that a few of the cycles following resumption of menstruation might be anovulatory and that even when ovulation is re-established some cycles might be anovulatory.[21] Under field conditions it will be necessary to assume that risk occurs during all cycles. The risk will be assumed to remain constant from cycle to cycle which for statistical purposes can be considered of fixed duration.

Whether the risk of conception varies with such factors as age of woman or number of pregnancies has been discussed in demographic literature and the evidence indicates that risk continues to be remarkably stable from parity to parity until secondary sterility intervenes.[22] At the same time it is widely recognized that the risk might vary from one woman to another (actually from one couple to another).[23]

(3) *Extent of fetal loss:* Although the index proposed above does not explicitly call for information on fetal loss, the actual formulae developed later will take into account the proportion of conceptions that end in fetal loss. The rate of spontaneous abortion rises slightly with increasing parity and age of mother, but as long as the parity composition of the group of susceptible women under observation is not profoundly changed, the rate of spontaneous fetal loss in the group can be considered to be constant.[24]

Number of Conceptions Terminating in a Live Birth Related to the Probability for Occurrence of Such Conception

The nature of the relationship between the number of conceptions terminating in a live birth and the probability for the

21. C. Tietze, ''The Effect of Breastfeeding on the Rate of Conception,'' *Proceedings of the International Population Conference 1961,* II (London, 1963), pp. 129–136.

22. L. Henry, ''Intervals Between Confinements in the Absence of Birth Control,'' *Eugenics Quarterly,* V (Dec., 1958), pp. 200–211; R. G. Potter, Jr., ''Some Relationships Between Short Range and Long Range Risks of Unwanted Pregnancy,'' *The Milbank Memorial Fund Quarterly,* XXXVIII (July, 1960), pp. 255–263.

23. K. Dandekar, ''Analysis of Birth Intervals of a Set of Indian Women,'' *Eugenics Quarterly,* X (June, 1963), pp. 73–78; C. Tietze and A. F. Guttmacher, ''Time Required for Conception in 1727 Planned Pregnancies,'' *Fertility and Sterility,* I (July, 1950), pp. 338–346.

24. United Nations, *Foetal, Infant and Early Childhood Mortality,* Volume I (New York: United Nations, ST/SOA/Series A/13, 1954).

occurrence of such a conception can be seen from the following illustration. For simplicity of presentation, the formulae have been worked out assuming that all the susceptible women have the same parity and became susceptible at the same instant. Using the symbols

p_b the probability for a susceptible woman not secondarily sterile to have a conception in a month which will terminate in a live birth,

p the probability for a susceptible woman not secondarily sterile to have a conception in a month, assumed to be the same for all women,

N number of susceptible women who are observed for t months following resumption of menstruation after the last termination,

a the proportion of women who are secondarily sterile,

β $= 1 - a$ the proportion of women who are fertile,

θ the proportion of conceptions that end in a live birth,

i the month following the resumption of menstruation $(i = 1, 2 \ldots t)$,

l_i the number of conceptions terminating in live birth which occur in the ith month among the N women,

f_i the number of conceptions terminating in a fetal loss which occur in the ith month among the N women,

it is seen that

$$l_i + f_i \doteq N\beta(1 - p)^{i-1} p \text{ for } i = 1, 2 \ldots t \text{ and}$$

(1)

$$N - \sum_{i=1}^{t} (l_i + f_i) \doteq N\beta(1 - p)^t + Na.$$

If $a = 0$, i.e. the proportion of women who are secondarily sterile is zero, it can be seen from (1) that

(2)
$$p \doteq \frac{\displaystyle\sum_{i=1}^{t} (l_i + f_i)}{\displaystyle\sum_{i=1}^{t} (l_i + f_i)i + Nt - \left[\sum_{i=1}^{t} (l_i + f_i)\right] t}$$

which is the usual formula

(3) $\dfrac{\text{pregnancy rate}}{\text{per month}} = \dfrac{\text{Number of pregnancies which occur}}{\text{Exposure to pregnancy in months}}.$

Under the same condition, i.e. $a = 0$, introducing θ it can be seen from (2) above that

$$(4) \qquad p\theta \doteq \frac{\displaystyle\sum_{i=1}^{t} l_i}{\displaystyle\sum_{i=1}^{t} (l_i + f_i)i + \left[N - \sum_{i=1}^{t} (l_i + f_i) \right] t}$$

$$(5) \qquad p\theta \doteq \frac{\displaystyle\sum_{i=1}^{t} l_i}{\dfrac{1}{\theta} \left[\displaystyle\sum_{i=1}^{t} i \cdot l_i - t \sum_{i=1}^{t} l_i \right] + tN}.$$

Since $p\theta$ is the same as p_b, the relationship (5) shows how p_b can be obtained if N, θ and l_i for $i = 1, 2 \ldots t$ are known. The value $1{,}200 \, p_b$ will give the *live birth pregnancy rate*. *If a is not assumed to be zero but is considered to be known*, the formulae for relating p and p_b to the occurrence of all conceptions and those that terminate in live birth can be obtained respectively from (2) and (5) by substituting $N\beta$ for N.

Although formula (5) for estimation of p_b does not call explicitly for data on the number of conceptions which ended in fetal loss, there is an implicit assumption that the time of the restarting of menstruation after all terminations including those ending in fetal loss will be known. It is only then that an up-to-date list of susceptible women can be maintained. Therefore the degree of error that might arise in recording the conceptions that ended in fetal loss will also affect the value of p_b but the magnitude of its effect on p_b will be less than that on p.

RELATING PROGRAM EXECUTION AND IMPACT

When "program impact" measures show a change, there still remains a question whether this is a result of program activities or not. If the change is due to other factors in the environment, the administrator should know this, so he need not continue unnecessary activities. The researcher who is concerned with testing the assumptions underlying the program objectives must also reassure himself about this question. Possible approaches to the problem are discussed below.

Study of "Whole Program" Impact

The classic experimental situation would call for a control area as similar as possible to the program area, but distant from it. Comparison of "impact" measurements in that area with those in the program area, over a period of time, would provide an estimate of the impact specifically due to the program. This model is attractive especially since social and economic changes not directly related to the program are likely to act in a similar direction as the program. However, it is virtually impossible to find a single, small, completely comparable control area. If the vagaries of changes unrelated to the program are to be properly accounted for, it would be necessary to introduce *replication* and use several control and experimental areas. Another problem is that if the family planning program is a national one, as in India, it will be difficult to find control areas where no family planning program activities are undertaken. A comparison between the experimental and control areas might then amount to comparison of the effect of *a* specific program with the average impact of a number of less intensive programs. Such methodological complexities as these are further compounded by the considerable logistic problems of obtaining high-quality data of the type needed.

Another approach, more suitable for use when time and resources are limited, is to concentrate on obtaining careful measures in the program area before work is started and periodically thereafter, so as to detect any trends which may occur. If marked changes do not appear, the effort to develop external controls is saved. If changes do occur, other internal evidence might then be obtained to test whether the changes are indeed related to the program. As the types of changes which are occurring are identified, specific retrospective studies can also be developed in "control" areas, to check whether such changes are occurring in those areas also.

Study of Effects of Specific Elements of the Program

(1) *Exploiting "natural experiments"*: Family planning programs, as other community action programs, are usually the responsibility of agencies that are sensitive to local political forces, and are operated by individualistic human beings. Even in programs that might be initiated in an experimental framework, it is unrealistic to expect rigid control of many variables over an extended time. The challenge of such programs is to try to encourage an even development towards maximum effectiveness, to record carefully what happens, and to seek to identify and exploit the naturally occurring experimental situations which so often arise. In a program, there usually is differential achievement of various execution objectives in different areas, as a result either of organizational problems or of purposeful phasing. This provides opportunities for observation of resulting differential effects on the achievement of impact objectives (making allowance at the same time for possible differences in the target populations concerned).

When the indicator system used for fertility measurement in an area involves listing of a sample of households and periodic visits to these, such a system can be exploited by adding extra questions from time to time, as required to investigate special situations or test new hypotheses.

(2) *Small experiments*: Whereas long-term, rigid experiments are difficult, hypotheses about specific, internal mechanisms of program action may be tested by small experiments. A short-run, limited-area experiment is more likely to hold the attention of action staff, and to avoid the disruptions which may occur over a longer period.

(3) *Diagnostic studies*: This term is used to refer to investigations that need not be experimental or statistical in nature, but seek a depth of information and insight about a particular facet of the program. If the program appears to be blocked in a given locality, for example, a series of exploratory interviews might be carried out to discover the relevant new factors operating. A useful strategy, also, is to compare a sample of "high response" with a sample of "low response" persons, to seek explanations for the difference. Such studies are also very

useful for testing specific hypotheses about the relationship of certain program activities to the effects being achieved.

SUMMARY

This paper has attempted to outline some major concepts, methods, and problems in the evaluation of community programs to control family size. The primary step in evaluation is a careful mapping of the network of objectives underlying the program. These may be categorized as program impact objectives, execution objectives, and phasing objectives.

Assessment of execution objectives must utilize direct observation and other study methods to supplement administrative reports. In the early phase of a program, emphasis will be on assessment of effort objectives, especially the deployment of staff and their understanding of their roles. Measurement of various performance objectives will gain importance as the program advances.

Assessment of intermediate impact objectives may involve measurement of trends in contraception usage, contraceptive consumption, perceptions of availability of contraceptive supplies, knowledge about contraception, and family size norms. Among these variables, the measurement of contraception usage is beset with so many difficulties as to make it generally impractical as a sensitive indicator of program impact. The possibilities of developing instruments for measuring small changes in the level of knowledge about contraception, and in the family size norms of a population group, are more promising.

The ultimate impact of family planning programs will be measured in terms of changes in natality. For the program administrator a small change in fertility patterns is important, even if this considerably precedes a fall in crude birth rates. Several principles for the development of sensitive indicators of fertility change have been proposed, including the need to focus especially on the women who are "susceptible" to change, and the need to use data likely to be reliable and available. One such index, called the "live birth pregnancy rate," is described for purposes of discussion; testing of this and other possible indices is now in progress.

Judging whether changes in "impact" variables are in fact due to program activities poses some difficult problems. The ideal of an external control for assessing overall program impact may be unachievable. Also, controls for various specific elements of the program may be elusive. The researcher is challenged to identify and exploit the experimental features which may arise in any program. Other evidence about causal relationships can be obtained from "diagnostic" inquiries, small experiments, and retrospective studies.

Norman B. Ryder

THE MEASUREMENT OF FERTILITY PATTERNS

INTRODUCTION

This essay presents a summary of principles and problems in fertility measurement, moving from the simplest to the most complex approaches. The presentation identifies general emphases in the different levels of measurement, and accentuates unresolved difficulties. Thus the summary may be useful to the novitiate as well as to those who are proficient in one or another particular topic.[1]

The most common and elementary fertility measure is the crude birth rate. For any population located merely in time and space, the crude birth rate is the ratio of the number of births experienced by population members within a defined period to the number of person-years of their exposure to the risk of occurrence of birth. The base is two-dimensional because events require both actors and the passage of time. Most of the

---

1. Two previous papers on the same topic may still be useful. N. B. Ryder, ''Fertility,'' *The Study of Population*, ed. P. M. Hauser and O. D. Duncan (Chicago: University of Chicago Press, 1959), pp. 400–436; N. B. Ryder, ''La mesure des variations de la fécondité au cours du temps,'' *Population*, XI (Jan.–March, 1956), pp. 29–46.

measures discussed in this paper consist of such rates, calculated for ever more refined definitions of the exposure base.

AGE SPECIFICITY

The first step toward refined fertility measurement depends on the commonplace observation that, within the total population, only women are childbearers, and only within the age span from menarche to menopause, and differentially by age in that range. Therefore an important increase in knowledge of fertility accrues by computing birth rates, of the same form as the crude birth rate, for women of each age. If the specific fertility rate for women of age a is $f(a)$, then the crude birth rate is the sum of all products $f(a).c(a)$, where $c(a)$ is the proportion of total population exposure contributed by women of age a. The simplest index based on age-specific fertility rates is the total fertility rate, the sum of $f(a)$ for all ages. The crude birth rate is a distorted version of the total fertility rate, the distortion deriving from the age-sex distribution of the population, $c(a)$.

The decomposition of the crude birth rate into two types of element, $f(a)$ and $c(a)$, where $f(a)$ is a more detailed description of reproductive behavior, contributes to the study of changes in fertility through time to the extent that the age distribution, $c(a)$, tends to vary. In general, the age distribution manifests the entire history of the population, but in particular the most relevant influence is usually the movement of the crude birth rate a generation ago, because that is what produces the current stock of potential childbearers. Ordinarily the age distribution changes slowly with time, but it is now worth special attention in the United States because of the rise in the crude birth rate from the 1930's to the 1950's. In the next few years the proportion that women in the principal childbearing ages represent of the total population will increase markedly, and the crude birth rate will respond accordingly relative to the total fertility rate.

It is often said that the total fertility rate represents the fertility of a year, uncontaminated by the influence of the age distribution. The increase in analytic acuity seems certain because the age distribution is the heritage of the past and has merely an arithmetical influence on the current reproductive output. But this neglects the persistent influence of the age distribution on fertility rates themselves, not in a logical sense, but as part of the aggregate environment within which fertility occurs. For example, the fertility of an age group may be expected to respond to the relative shortages of jobs and housing which are a probable consequence of its large size relative to its predecessors. An instance of this will be provided in the next few years, as the entrants into adulthood swell in numbers. This influence of the age distribution on fertility requires nondemographic types of analysis. The proposition that distributional influences, although arithmetically controlled by appropriate specificity, remain potentially important in analysis applies throughout the entire realm of fertility measures presented here.[2]

PERIODS AND COHORTS

The most insistent question about fertility is its changes through time. The data for time series analysis using age-specific birth rates may be visualized as a table of such rates, with years for columns and ages for rows. From this table may be derived two types of time series. If the total fertility rate is used as a summary index, the question arises which particular rates to total when calculating it. One choice is to determine the total for each successive period by adding the birth rates in each column, thus obtaining a series of "period" total fertility rates. The alternative is to compute total fertility rates for birth cohorts—women born in the same year. Thus the set of fertility rates for any cohort, representing consecutive experience, will be found in a diagonal of the table. This provides another time series of total fertility rates—but for successive cohorts—from the same table of rates.

Despite their common source the two time series of period and cohort total fertility rates have been found to differ in various contexts.[3] Clearly any statement about the character of fertility change requires a choice between them whenever they yield

2. Cf. G. J. Stolnitz, "Population Composition and Fertility Trends," *American Sociological Review*, XXI (Dec., 1956), pp. 738–743.
3. N. B. Ryder, "Problems of Trend Determination During a Transition in Fertility," *Milbank Memorial Fund Quarterly*, XXXIV (Jan., 1956), pp. 5–21.

discrepant results. Period series generally fluctuate more than cohort series but may also show long run divergence. The problem of choice is which mode of temporal aggregation gives the most appropriate analytic entity. The same decision applies to any table of measurements for time and some variable of the time-interval type.

Cohort and period total fertility rates diverge whenever the age distribution of childbearing varies from cohort to cohort.[4] For example, when the decline in Western fertility occurred, it was associated with a lower age distribution of fertility from cohort to cohort—partly because of a progressively earlier initiation of childbearing, but principally because of a progressively earlier termination of childbearing. This inflated the fertility rates in each period, because relatively higher birth rates in the younger ages of more recent cohorts were combined with relatively higher birth rates in the older ages of the more distant chorts. Thus the period total was distorted above the actual experience of the participant cohorts. As for the short run, economic depression is known to induce a temporary disturbance of cohort childbearing, typically causing a decrease of fertility for a while, followed by a compensatory increase. Although the period total fertility rate will reflect this fluctuation, the participant cohorts in this experience will show no changes in their total fertility, provided they eventually recover the postponed births. In successive cohort records, the mark of the fluctuation is on the changing age distribution of cohort fertility. Thus, as before, the period total fertility rate varies in response to the changing age distribution of fertility from cohort to cohort.

The criteria for choice between these two time series of fertility indices are the relative contributions in the data of idiosyncratic features of the period-specific environment, on the one hand, and the persistent organic interdependency of the cohort-specific life history, on the other. The assertion that families are getting larger (or smaller) is more likely to be interpreted by demographers in cohort terms than by resort to

---

4. N. B. Ryder, ''The Process of Demographic Translation,'' *Demography*, I (1964), pp. 74–82.

some synthetic summary of the annual performance of the population. Even in so obviously period-oriented an analytic problem as the impact of conditions that affect all cohorts in much the same way, a cohort orientation is recommended because the most likely response is the transfer of births from an earlier to a later time in the cohorts' lives. This may be inferred from a fluctuation in period fertility, but validation of the inference requires cohort records. Moreover, such short-run analysis is most efficient when deviations from trend are identified, and the trend is established by cohort analysis.

The cohort approach is still used reluctantly, perhaps partly because it fails to answer the important question: "What is the current trend in fertility?" In the United States, the period total fertility rate has been declining since 1957. The above presentation makes clear that this may mean a decline in cohort total fertility or a rise in the age distribution of cohort fertility, or a sufficient rise in the latter to mask a rise in the former. Which of these alternatives is true cannot be determined until the cohorts responsible have essentially completed their child-bearing, and the most active ones still have 10 or 15 fertile years. Variations in the timing and amount of fertility from cohort to cohort cannot be separated in incomplete histories. The problem of the current trend in fertility is a problem in forecasting. Increasing methodological sophistication in this area leads to the position that nothing can be said with confidence.

EXPOSURE AND MARRIAGE

Fertility is normatively confined to married couples. Therefore the key fertility component of any age group is the proportion married. As a more refined identification of exposure, the status of married person is a surrogate for that class of experience necessary to fertility, i.e., copulation. Now married status is obviously neither necessary nor sufficient to identify the population exposed to the risk of conception by copulation, and the degree of approximation is an important cross-cultural topic. Premarital conceptions, if not illegitimate births, are frequent in most societies. Nevertheless, the proportions of women married in each age provide an improved approximation of the population really exposed.

Fertility research is deficient in its attention to nuptiality. Age-specific first marriage rates provide a basis for the study of female nuptiality which is methodologically equivalent to mortality measurement. (The single female is regarded as experiencing "death" by the act of marriage.) But the analogy conceals a problem. The exposure of a young women to the risk of marriage is unquestionably conditioned in part by her personal characteristics, like age, but in part also by the kind of spouse she is seeking, and more generally by the availability of unmarried men and the extent of competition from other unmarried women. Marriage is a joint occurrence, and the observed age-specific nuptiality rates for females and males reflect the total state of the marriage market, i.e., the joint distribution of bachelors and spinsters by age and other relevant characteristics. This is a macroanalytic phenomenon which cannot be analyzed by the conventional approach of progressive specification of subgroups. Changing distributions of the population by age and sex are frequent enough to justify more investigation than heretofore. An example of change is probable soon in the United States. Husbands customarily come from a somewhat earlier cohort than their wives, but in the next few years the earlier cohorts of males are going to be far outnumbered by the later cohorts of females, as the babies of the baby boom come of age. This will probably produce some convergence of the ages of bride and groom, and perhaps a decline in the proportions of women marrying. The general process is little understood, either factually or theoretically, and it has consequences for fertility.

The proportion married in any age is determined not only by nuptiality but also by the level and age pattern of termination of marriage by divorce, by widowhood, and by selective mortality of the married and unmarried. Changes in mortality can play an important role in determining the proportions married in each age, and thus the age-specific fertility rates.[5] Complete analysis requires data on dissolution and remarriage by age, sex, and marital status. The proportion of marriages which are remar-

5. N. B. Ryder, "The Influence of Declining Mortality on Swedish Reproductivity," *Current Research in Human Fertility* (Milbank Memorial Fund: 1955), pp. 65–81.

riages is well over one quarter in the United States.[6] The neglect of nuptiality as the foundation of fertility analysis is partly attributable to the sluggish development of adequate marriage statistics for the United States. The importance of the topic is enhanced by its major influence on the time pattern of fertility.

The measurement link between nuptiality research and fertility research is provided by a birth rate specific for marital status, or marital duration, as well as age. Marital duration is an expression of the time interval since entry into marriage just as age is an expression of the time interval since entry into the population. Its utility is dulled by its ambiguity. It may be defined as the length of time since the wife first married or since the husband first married or since this couple married. It may be defined in gross or net terms, the latter excluding intervals between marriages and perhaps also lengthy separations (associated with military service, for example). The practice of defining it as the gross interval since the wife's first marriage is an analytic convenience with deficiencies which can be judged by the extent of remarriage and separation.

BIRTH PARITY AND BIRTH INTERVAL

The most important fertility variable is birth parity, not merely because it influences fertility, but because it is fertility. Valuable analyses of cohort reproduction are feasible with no other information than the parity distribution itself, particularly for women past the menopause. Parity is of particular interest to American statisticians because it is the only variable besides age for which we have data for the whole population.[7] The basis of parity-specific fertility is the fact that the only women who can have a first birth are those with no previous births, the only women who can have a second birth are those with a first birth but no second birth, and so forth. This is a further indication of the importance of parity: the reproduc-

6. N. B. Ryder, "Measures of Recent Nuptiality in the Western World," *International Population Conference New York, 1961* (London: International Union for the Scientific Study of Population, 1963), II, pp. 293–301.

7. P. K. Whelpton and A. A. Campbell, "Fertility Tables for Birth Cohorts of American Women. Part I," *Vital Statistics—Special Reports*, LI (Jan. 29, 1960), pp. 1–129.

tivity of a couple occurs step by step, with each birth signifying a new family structure, and a new set of influences on prospective childbearing. The parity variable shares with marital duration the problem of different meanings assignable to it. Although most sources define it as the total number of live births to a woman, it may also be considered as the number of births to the husband or the couple, or as the number of pregnancies or full-term pregnancies. Each alternative is relevant for some kind of research, and the producers of data face a difficult problem of compromise.

Associated with parity is the variable, time interval since the preceding birth. Fertility data by birth interval are rare despite their value. American data now permit the computation of birth rates specific for age and parity. Although the age distribution of births by order gives an approximate view of the time pattern of fertility, no distinction can be drawn between the times of occurrence of those nth births which are and those which are not followed by an $(n + 1)$th birth. This distinction, which is necessary for the study of varying time patterns of fertility from parity to parity, requires interval data, at least in the form of year of preceding birth.

The set of variables presented here constitutes a systematic program of fertility measurement based on representation of the childbearing process as a series of dated steps. There are six variables in the set: population membership and age; marital status and marital duration; birth parity and birth interval. These are arranged in pairs, each pair consisting of a status acquired by the occurrence of an event, and the length of time since that occurrence. The six variables display the complete skeleton of a procreative history; they are operationally precisely defined; they are major components of (statistical) explanation of fertility variance; they are important variables in the short run and the long run; they are feasible items within a governmental system of registration and enumeration; and they are amenable to demographic analysis in the formal sense of the term.[8] All fertility measures are derivable from the system of birth rates jointly specific for these six variables.

8. N. B. Ryder, ''Notes on the Concept of a Population,'' *American Journal of Sociology*, LXIX (March, 1964), pp. 447–463.

SUCCESSIVE COHORT REDEFINITION

The set of formal variables permits reconstruction of a complete reproductive history for any birth cohort, consisting of a distribution by times (and thus ages) of first marriage (including the never-married as a residual), a distribution of each time-of-first marriage group by time of first birth (including the infertile as a residual), a distribution of each time-of-first birth group by time of second birth, and so on. A multidimensional table like this would obviously place a great strain on the data. The information required to estimate the appropriate person-years of exposure in each category is formidable even if the registration system is sufficiently comprehensive, and particularly if some independent variables are also required. If primary sources are exploited, the size of sample is the inhibiting consideration.

One proposal which makes the problem of analysis less intractable is successive cohort redefinition.[9] The cohort concept, although conventionally signifying persons of common birth year, may be applied to persons of common year of occurrence of any significant event in reproductive (or other) history. The fertility history may be subdivided as follows: the marriage distribution (by age) for a birth cohort, the first birth distribution (by duration) for a marriage cohort, the second birth distribution (by first birth interval) for a parity-one cohort, and so forth. Each segment may be analyzed independently, using the conventional array of demographic measures. Following the life table model, the radix is the number of women constituting the parity-n cohort of a particular year. Occurrence of an $(n+1)$th birth removes a member from this parity. Appropriate measures would include the proportion who depart from the cohort eventually or by any particular time since the cohort-defining event—a measure the writer has termed the "parity progression ratio"—the rate of departure in any time interval, the time distribution of departure, and so forth.

The successive cohort approach is justified because couples in fact form their families one step at a time, and no decision need

9. N. B. Ryder, "La mesure des variations . . ." (see footnote 1).

ever be made about any birth but the next one. Furthermore the members of each type of cohort have a kind of homogeneity, because they share that stage of the family life cycle, and the environment of the period. The members of a marriage cohort face common "newlywed" problems which are specific to their year of marriage, independently of their birth cohort. The next transition (from nonparent to parent) may be even more selective, justifying the use of the parity-one cohort. The process of subdivision is convenient for the analysis of fluctuations, if the impact of the disturbance is confined to the particular interval in which the couples are then located. It also permits the focusing of research on crucial stages in childbearing. For example, the decision whether to stop with two children or to have a third is a kind of threshold for couples which is vital for population growth because it represents the dividing line for replacement.[10]

This orientation is not without pitfalls. The paradox of analysis is that parts which are separated from the whole for detailed scrutiny thereby lose some of their meaning. The events in such small subhistories may depend so closely on temporal idiosyncrasies that the pattern of the totality is lost. The phases of reproductivity may be intelligible only as a complete sequence, or the pattern of fertility age by age may be merely the cumulative consequence of decisions within each segment. One protection against excessive fragmentation is provided by retaining a cross-classification of the members of any cohort by the variable defining the previous cohort types to permit analysis of the interdependencies of successive childbearing phases.

SPECIFICITY AND PERIOD ANALYSIS

The extension of specificity procedures from age to the variables introduced above may be exemplified for parity. In a given age of women, separate birth rates can be calculated for each parity. The age-specific birth rate for these women is a weighted sum of their parity-specific birth rates, the weights

10. The parity-two cohort is the basis for the sample used in C. F. Westoff, R. G. Potter, Jr., P. C. Sagi, and E. G. Mishler, *Family Growth in Metropolitan America* (Princeton: Princeton University Press, 1961); and in C. F. Westoff, R. G. Potter, Jr., and P. C. Sagi, *The Third Child* (Princeton: Princeton University Press, 1963).

being their parity distribution. Since that distribution is the outcome of their past reproductive experiences, the age-specific birth rate can be called crude with respect to the parity distribution in the same sense as the crude birth rate is crude with respect to the age distribution. The same principle applies to all relationships between rates at differing levels of specificity.

Refined measurement of fertility in a period, for the purpose of relating its variations to the nondemographic environment, is achieved by calculating birth rates for higher levels of specificity, and thus separating the rates of the period from those weights which represent the persistent arithmetical influence of the past. For example, since fertility is generally highest in the earliest years of marriage (the lowest durations), a wave of marriages tends to be followed by a (dampened) wave of births, even if duration-specific fertility rates remain fixed. Each new variable increases the discriminability of period perturbations. This is particularly necessary in a context of rapid change like that to be experienced when the large birth cohorts come of age.

Since a multidimensional table of rates for each period is analytically awkward, it is desirable to summarize the rates with an index. This implies the provision of a system of weights for the rates. One popular procedure, standardization, applies —as the weighting system—the observed distribution for some population, to each set of rates being compared. This is convenient but arbitrary, because a different choice of observed distribution might change the comparison. A more elegant procedure, which might be called stabilization, derives the weighting system from the rates themselves by reconstructing for a synthetic cohort the distributions which would result from permanent fixity of those rates at the observed levels. But the situation in which high specificity is most necessary, because of environmental disturbance, is for the same reason one in which the assumption of fixed rates is least tenable. Furthermore, indices for successive periods, no matter what the level of specificity of the rates on which they are based, are subject to the same distributional distortion from intercohort variation explained in the section relating to *Periods and Cohorts*.

In the writer's opinion, the problem of index construction has attracted more attention than it deserves, to the neglect of other features of the rate distribution. Summaries are sufficient for approximate discursive analysis but should not displace detailed appraisal of the components and their particular concomitants.[11]

To conclude the topic of specificity, a distinction may be drawn between the contributions to cohort and period analyses respectively, of the computation of specific rates. For both modes of temporal aggregation, the occurrence-exposure ratio performs the task of controlling exposure for changes in numbers of persons because of mortality or migration. For a cohort, such changes are generally although not necessarily small. A neglected problem concerns not the arithmetical effect so much as the consequences for observed rates of the likely selectivity of mortality and migration *vis à vis* fertility.[12] It is in principle possible to maintain statistical control of those who enter or leave a cohort, if fertility histories can be obtained for such persons, but this has not been done. A similar problem plagues the interpreter of retrospective cohort fertility records, obtained by census questions addressed to women past the menopause, who are a select subset of their cohort by virtue of survival. In summary, the conventional cohort fertility history is a somewhat synthetic construction, and research is required to determine the consequences of implicit selectivity.

For period analysis, the calculation of occurrence-exposure ratios has mandatory rather than subsidiary significance. The components of the synthetic history of a period show the consequences of the differing reproductive experiences of the constituent cohorts, and these experiences have created the varying exposure distributions. Without a stabilization technique, the quasi-history of a period often yields impossible results, and even with it often implausible results.[13] From a cohort record, on the contrary, the results are always plausible because they have in fact occurred—with that one small reservation concerning the possibility of extreme selectivity.

11. R. A. Easterlin, ''The American Baby Boom in Historical Perspective,'' *American Economic Review*, LI (Dec., 1961), pp. 869–911.

12. L. Henry, ''D'un problème fondamental de l'analyse démographique,'' *Population*, XIV (Jan.-March, 1959), pp. 9–32.

13. N. B. Ryder, ''An Appraisal of Fertility Trends in the United States,'' *Thirty Years of Research in Human Fertility* (Milbank Memorial Fund, 1959), pp. 38–49.

FACETS OF FECUNDITY

Fertility measures based on secondary source data are preliminary to causal inquiry. The design of measurements for probabilistic as distinct from deterministic analysis requires the differentiation of intentional and unintentional influences on fertility, to establish the appropriate direction in which to seek understanding. This section and the next represent a bridge between secondary analysis and intensive inquiry.[14]

The necessary but not sufficient condition for exposure is fecund copulation. A preliminary interpolation concerns the relationships between a society's marriage system and its fertility. Married women are selected from all women with respect to fecundity, both directly because of premarital conceptions, and indirectly from association with the desirable characteristics of marriage partners. Married women are also selected by marital dissolution, to the extent that health of wife and husband are related to fecundity. In some cultures, persistent infertility is ground for divorce. The cultural pattern of marriages jointly by ages of husband and wife probably influences average fecundity. Obviously extreme ages at marriage are relevant. Thus, as before, the marriage system is an important topic in fertility research.

One purpose of this section is to define fecundity. Fecundity is the physiological complex comprising, in sequence, viable ovulation and ejaculation, fertilization and nidation. In considering the physiological context within which birth, the focus of fertility measurement, occurs, it is convenient here to include within fecundity the processes of embryonic nurture and the delivery of a living child, even though these are not part of the conventional definition of fecundity. The probability of achievement of each of these steps may vary from zero to one, from person to person, and from time to time for the same person, both with age and with specific or general morbidity. Three facets of fecundity are distinguishable: (1) copulation without ovulation; (2) ovulation without conception; (3) conception without birth. Associated with each are types of unintentional fecundity varia-

14. Drs. Potter, Westoff, and Sagi will recognize the writer's indebtedness to their publications, particularly the works cited in footnote 10.

tion as well as particular modes of fertility regulation, as indicated.

1. Assuming copulation, ovulation may not occur. The preceding discussion considered the woman's life cycle as contiguous phases which have differing relevance for fertility, and thus equated exposure with the passage of time. Actual exposure may be only a small proportion of this total. A woman's reproductive life comprises a set of ovulations at periodic intervals, with these determining conditions: (a) number of years between menarche and menopause; (b) average length of cycle, including the less regular intervals in the initial and terminal stages as well as the abnormal interruption; (c) number and length of anovulatory intervals, beginning with conception and continuing for some period beyond delivery, as a function of pregnancy outcome and lactation behavior; (d) permanent termination of fecundity by processes like tubal ligation and hysterectomy (and, for the couple, vasectomy of the husband); and (e) temporary interruption of ovulation by birth control pills.

2. Assuming ovulation, conception may not occur. Fecundability—the probability that an ovulation will result in conception —is reduced by defective ovulation, or ejaculation, or fertilization, or nidation, or by noncoincidence of copulation with the fertile period. If copulation and ovulation are independent events, the last may be attributed to chance. The time pattern of copulation is influential because a woman can ordinarily conceive only during a small interval during her cycle. The probability system includes normal and abnormal variability in the length of the cycle, in the temporal location and viable duration of ovulation, and in the viable duration of the sperm. Fecundability (except where it is zero) cannot be measured directly. Estimates for a particular couple, based on the number of ovulations required for conception, have a large variance. Some with low physiologic fecundability will wait a short time; some with high physiologic fecundability will wait a long time. Estimates for an aggregate depend on the length of the observation period, because of changing composition through the self-selectivity of conception. Reduction of fecundability, as an aim of fertility regulation, may be achieved by modifying the time pattern of copulation or by adopting practices which inhibit

either fertilization (with mechanical or chemical barriers) or nidation (probably with the intrauterine coil).

3. Assuming conception, birth may not occur. The major distinction here is between unintentional pregnancy wastage and intentional abortion as a mode of fertility regulation. This research area requires expansion beyond its customary limits. In the first place, the distinction between abortion and infanticide is technically a small amount of time, and infanticide is not insignificant in some contemporary cultures and in the history of the West. In the second place, this is a borderland between fertility and mortality. Discussions of mortality generally exclude fetal mortality but include infant mortality. Since a large proportion of infant mortality (in a healthy country) occurs immediately after delivery, as a consequence of reproductive failure, parturition seems to be a meaninglessly precise divide.

The distinction between fertility regulation, as intentional interference, and fecundity limitation, as unintentional interference, is sometimes difficult. Various activities may influence the probability of ovulation (like lactation) or of conception (like the copulatory pattern) without regulatory intent. Sterilization motivated by strong medical indications is a marginal category. Fecundity variation from couple to couple may be normal (comparable with differences in physique) or abnormal, i.e., attributable to morbidity. The extensive areas of inadequate knowledge, verging on ignorance, limit severely the possibility and the sensibility of sophisticated methodology.

REPRODUCTIVE ENDS AND MEANS

Fertility regulation is the effective use of means which may be necessary to achieve reproductive ends. The two obvious measurement questions—"How much use is there?" and "How effective is it?"—are more difficult to answer than they appear.[15] There are three categories of nonuse, each of which requires its own interpretation: (1) Couples who regard reproductive rationality as an illegitimate orientation. This may be elicited by direct questioning, but the answer may change with time and

15. *Ibid.*

circumstance. (2) Couples who want a child at the time. There is now considerable research interest in the correlates of reproductive ends. (3) Couples who may not want a child, but believe themselves (by inference from experience) not to be fecund. The fallibility of the inference may be large if fecundity has been little tested by noncontraceptive exposure.

The active users may in turn be classified according to the means they are employing and the quality of use, as clues to the explanation of achieved efficacy. The means chosen can locate these couples on a rational-irrational continuum, to the extent that some means are intrinsically inferior to others. A semi-rational category is also required, for those who feel morally precluded from using some of the effective means. The quality of employment varies from careful to careless, particularly with respect to persistence of effort.

The measurement of regulatory efficacy begins with the occurrence or nonoccurrence of a birth as the outcome of the activity being appraised. If a couple is infertile in the relevant time interval, this is the (indeterminate) consequence of effective choice and use of means, some type of infecundity, and the chance timing of copulation. Given sources of success other than contraceptive efficacy, it seems to the writer that failures should be restricted to cases of the occurrence of birth, and not to the part of the process, like conception, to which the particular means may have been directed. Separation of the roles of efficacy and infecundity by securing estimates of the latter from the experience of other nonusers encounters the problem that nonusers are selected for infecundity. The previous noncontraceptive experience of the same group is a better source, but the inference is weakened by the necessarily probabilistic nature of the estimate, the prevalence of fecundity variation with time, and the changing location of couples with respect to ultimate reproductive goals. If a couple is fertile in the interval, this may indicate a contraceptive failure or unsuspected fecundity which led to nonuse, or a failure may be denied by retrospective rationalization which leads the couple to declare the birth as wanted.

If the degree of regulatory efficacy is estimated by the length of the infertile interval, then the quality of the estimate is affected by the probabilistic character of the event, by the salience of the end, and by the difficulty of its achievement. Fecund couples who are sure that they want no more children are in a quite different category from semifecund couples who may want to postpone a birth for a few months. The measurement is particularly sensitive to changing age, with the accumulation of fecundity impairments, the decline of copulatory frequency, and the approach of menopause. Parity-specificity is crucial to the evaluation of infecundity and fertility regulation as alternative explanations of infertility because fecundity differentials are obviously selective for fertility, and births may affect fecundity as well as reproductive goals.

In the present state of the art, the lack of an independent measure of fecundity leaves a degree of indeterminacy in the explanation of the proximate sources of fertility differentials from couple to couple that is serious enough to call for an evaluation of research strategy.[16] Although fecundity is very important in the microanalysis of the fertility of particular couples, it is probably of little consequence in the comparison of aggregates defined on sociocultural grounds. Analysis of group behavior is, then, away out of the measurement dilemma. Even at this less demanding analytic level, the research person must pay careful attention to the probabilistic selectivity implications of high fecundity and the accident-proneness at different points in a time interval, and particularly if the interval is truncated at time of interview.

FERTILITY AND REGULATORY EFFICACY

The writer has attempted in this paper to consider in one methodological survey the entire range of measurement problems from the most primitive secondary-source procedures to the complexities facing the analyst on the frontier of inquiry into fecundity and contraceptive efficacy. Encouragement in this expansive task has come from three recent publications which consider the consequences of varying types and degrees of fecundity and fertility regulation for reproductive output.

16. P. C. Sagi and C. F. Westoff, ''An Exercise in Partitioning Some Components of the Variance of Family Size,'' *Emerging Techniques in Population Research* (Milbank Memorial Fund, 1963) pp. 130–140.

Tietze compares the reductions in fecundability which may be achieved by contraception with the consequent reductions in the birth rate, in populations which have the structure by age and marital status that are generally associated with high fertility.[17] Potter solves some similar problems by considering the changing lengths of the ovulatory and anovulatory proportions of a birth interval.[18] This mode of conceptualization permits him to estimate the interdependency of regulation and fetal mortality, particularly induced abortions. Sheps and Perrin develop a stochastic model which permits them to intrude probability distributions in place of average estimates of the relevant variables, and derive a surface of results for variant combinations of input.[19]

The most striking result, expressed variously in all three papers, is that 80 per cent efficacy (a reduction of fecundability to one fifth its noncontracepted value) yields only a 50 per cent reduction of the birth rate. This is one approximate example of the array of relationships. The discouraging result stems from the circumstance that a contraceptive failure eliminates much exposure, but a contraceptive success must be repeated at the next ovulation. The recurrence of the problem in a short time is also characteristic of abortion as a solution. In terms of policy design, a higher level of efficacy for some is more desirable than a lower level of efficacy for many. As Robert Osborn put it, ''A little contraception is a nugatory thing.''

Extension of these important contributions requires the determination of the kinds of interdependence which exist between various inputs of the model. These inputs are now regarded, *faute de mieux,* as independent: the marriage system, fecundity of various types, reproductive ends, fertility regulation of various types, and mortality. Second, a place must be found for the relationship between reproductive delays and birth rate movements from year to year. For a couple, lengthening of the

17. C. Tietze, ''Pregnancy Rates and Birth Rates,'' *Population Studies,* XVI (July, 1962), pp. 31–37.

18. R. G. Potter, Jr., ''Birth Intervals: Structure and Change,'' *Population Studies,* XVII (Nov., 1963), pp. 155–166.

19. M. C. Sheps and E. B. Perrin, ''Changes in Birth Rates as a Function of Contraceptive Effectiveness: Some Applications of a Stochastic Model,'' *American Journal of Public Health,* LIII (July, 1963), pp. 1031–1046.

interval until the next unwanted birth may represent a failure (perhaps worse than no lengthening), but for the population any delay is a contribution to the reduction of population growth, because a decelerating time pattern of fertility lengthens the intergenerational interval and promotes a downward distortion of period fertility.[20]

A third enlargement of the scope of research seems appropriate. Although the focus of fertility measurement is almost exclusively the live birth, much socioeconomic theory and research are concerned implicitly or explicitly with a closely related but different phenomenon—the number of children per family. With no change in mean parental parity, the number of children present in the home (as claims on the domestic budget, for example) may vary greatly, depending on the extent of child survivorship and the (culturally determined) age of departure from child status.[21] The demographer's responsibility ought not to be limited by convenience or convention.

CONCLUDING OBSERVATIONS

In this survey of the methodology of fertility measurement, one pervasive problem has gone unmentioned—the quality of information of requisite detail. Accurate data are difficult to obtain for any phenomenon so fraught with technical complexity, and particularly if that phenomenon is, like fertility, normatively circumscribed. Furthermore, the participants in the marriage and childbearing sequence are by definition transforming their statuses. It is well established that such persons are the most likely to be misenumerated as they change their family affiliation, their labor force status, and their residence. A case in point is the statistical importance and annoyance created by higher education and military participation.

A second persistent and cumulative difficulty involves the various problematic types of exposure which, for practical reasons, tend to be excluded from surveys. These include, *inter alia,* the migratory population; the marriages broken by death,

20. N. B. Ryder, "Nuptiality as a Variable in the Demographic Transition," paper delivered at the annual meeting of the American Sociological Association, New York, 1960.

21. N. B. Ryder, "The Influence of Declining Mortality . . ." (see footnote 5).

divorce and separation; and premarital exposure, premarital conceptions, and extramarital births. The convenient type may turn out to be a minority.

Although the array of problems of data and method facing the fertility researcher is disturbing, there is a small consolation. The analysis of fertility requires good measurements not only of its dependent variables but also of the independent variables with which they be interrelated. The sophistication of measurement of the former is clearly far in advance of that achieved in those fields which have major definitional responsibility for the latter.

The task of the formal demographer is to establish necessary interdependencies of a deterministic or probabilistic character among reproductive phenomena which are diversly related to the various facets of the substantive environment. The purpose of the writer here has been to provide a cursory but comprehensive survey of problems and solutions in the measurement of fertility patterns.

Mindel C. Sheps

APPLICATIONS OF PROBABILITY MODELS TO THE STUDY OF PATTERNS OF HUMAN REPRODUCTION

INTRODUCTION

This paper is concerned with models for the number and timing of a sequence of births to women living in a sexual union, i.e., for what is known as "couple fertility" patterns. Among approaches to the study of human reproduction, demographic analysis of population data may be placed at one extreme and detailed clinical and laboratory investigations of individual men and women at the other extreme. Between them is the statistical study of the numbers, sequence, and timing of births to couples. The reproductive performance of human populations results from births to couples marrying (or cohabiting) at different ages, of different innate fecundity, different rates of fetal loss, and different practices of family planning, breastfeeding, etc. The study of couple reproduction is in part an effort to evaluate the effects of such variables on natality rates. Although utilizing information from other approaches to natality, students of the reproductive patterns of couples have had to devise new methods of analyzing data and to assess critically the possible role of these methods in systematizing and illuminating the study of this major component of population change.

Again and again in this field of study, the obvious idea, the common sense approach, have turned out to be inadequate. For example, it seems reasonable to suppose that in the absence of birth control the innate fecundity of couples in some quantitative sense is proportional to their birth rates. Analysis shows that such proportionality is not to be expected. At first thought, moreover, one might expect that if 30 per cent of reproducing couples adopt a contraceptive method that is 50 per cent effective, the annual birth rate would fall by 15 per cent. After more thought, this idea is seen to be erroneous.[1]

How many births should a fecund couple expect if they live together for 20 years of the woman's reproductive life, making no deliberate effort to limit family size? How much variation should be expected in the family size of couples with identical fecundity? The answers are not obvious.

Clinical situations, too, raise questions related to the topic of this paper. For example, whether a fecund woman living in a sexual union conceives in any month can obviously be considered a matter of chance, or a random event. How many months of trial without conception should prompt medical investigation? If artificial insemination is attempted, how long should it be maintained before giving up?[2] Answers to such questions must be based not only on orthodox biological studies but also on statistical data and the study of probability models.

Considerations exemplified above have led investigators to formulate models that would assist in the understanding of the reproductive process and of its response to changes in specified variables. The models range from numerical illustrations through computer simulation to mathematical theory. This paper is a review of approaches that have been made to the

---

1. The lack of proportionality stems from the fact that the probability of conceiving in any month depends on what has occurred in previous months, each pregnancy eliminating the possibility of another pregnancy for a time. M. C. Sheps and E. B. Perrin, "Changes in Birth Rates as a Function of Contraceptive Effectiveness: Some Applications of a Stochastic Model," *American Journal of Public Health*, LIII (July, 1963), pp. 1031–1046.

2. The probability of a conception delay of *x* months is a function of the monthly chance of conception. See P. Vincent, *Recherches sur la fécondité biologique* (Paris: Presses Universitaires de France, 1961), and the discussion of fecundability below.

construction of such models. The order of presentation will be: (1) a description of models and their uses, (2) a brief consideration of the reproductive process and the problems of measurement relevant to studying the reproduction of couples, (3) model construction as exemplified by approaches to fecundability, and (4) approaches to more general aspects of the problem. Since space limitations prohibit comprehensive coverage, I shall vary the detail of the exposition, giving fuller references.

MODEL BUILDING

Nature of Models

Any abstraction of an object may be considered a model of the object. We create a model of a billiard ball if, disregarding its color, its surface qualities, and its hardness, we consider only its shape and call it a sphere. In this respect it is equivalent to a class of inflated balloons, to a class of rubber balls, and even to some oranges. For some purposes this description of a billiard ball is useless; for others it suffices completely.

Mathematical models attempt to express and investigate relationships. Deterministic models describe average relationships or results. The statement that an unbiased coin will fall with its head uppermost half the time is a description of expected or average behavior. A more detailed study will lead to probabilistic statements such as: if ten such coins were tossed simultaneously, the chance of observing at least two heads is $1013/1024$, while the chance of exactly five heads is $63/256$.

A sequence of events occurring over time in a probabilistic manner is known as a stochastic (probabilistic) process. A given model may be more or less probabilistic than another. Thus a series of statements about the behavior of tossed coins can be made so that each is more probabilistic (or stochastic) than the preceding one.

While mean or expected values given by probabilistic models agree with those of deterministic models based on sufficiently similar assumptions, stochastic models offer insight into the effects of chance and into the variations that occur naturally in a biological system. The presence and effects of natural variation are otherwise difficult to appreciate in complicated systems.

Stochastic models may thus be more powerful and informative tools for study of a process.

Uses of Models [3]

Models of the reproductive process can contribute to the interpretation of empirical data and to the evaluation of action programs. They facilitate the development of appropriate methods of measurement. The choice of suitable indices of natality among the wide variety of possibilities, the interpretation of the indices and an appreciation of their interrelationships are enhanced by prior analysis of the process such as is involved in model building.

A familiar use of models is to "fit" them to data. A good fit implies that the data are compatible with the model, without negating the possibility that they would be compatible with other models as well. If the data are not well fitted, the inadequacy of the model is clear, and comprehension of the process may be enhanced by the effort to discover how the model falls short.

Inadequacies in a specific approach may be discovered even without fitting data. Formulation of a model and analysis of its implications alone may reveal inconsistencies. Apparently reasonable assumptions may turn out to be unwarranted or contradictory when combined. On the other hand, the formulation may lead to logical deductions that suggest new ideas for theoretical and empirical study.

A suitable model provides insight into the importance of the variables included, their modes of action, and their quantitative effects.[4] Thus even quite unrealistic models advance us some distance toward understanding possible reasons for observed differences in natality levels.

Insights gained from models may facilitate efforts at predicting changes in natality patterns. Social, economic, and psycho-

3. The uses of models in this and allied fields are discussed in references cited below. See also J. Hajnal, "Mathematical Models in Demography," *Symposia on Quantitative Biology*, XXII (1957), pp. 97–103 and L. Henry, "Theoretical Research and Demography," *ibid.*, pp. 105–108.

4. The use of models in elucidating the interaction of several variables is exemplified in applications of stable population theory as in A. J. Coale, this volume.

logical considerations which will not even enter the present discussion must dominate such efforts. Yet, as Davis and Blake showed, factors that affect natality must act through intermediate variables, such as the formation and stability of sexual unions, the monthly chance of conception, or the incidence of fetal wastage.[5] It is some of these intermediate variables that form the basis of the models to be discussed.

THE REPRODUCTIVE PROCESS

Major Variables

The variables included in reproductive models are discussed in a number of papers in this volume [6] and the major ones only will be mentioned briefly here. While primarily biological, they are subject to modification by the behavior of the couple and by environmental influences. Although the maximum duration of a woman's reproductive span, for example, is determined biologically, its effective duration may be shortened by late entry into sexual union or by early termination of the union.

During each menstrual cycle (usually treated as equal to one month) a fecund woman susceptible to conception and living in a sexual union is at risk of conceiving. The probability that she will do so within a given cycle, known as "fecundability," is a result of the physiological status of both sexual partners and may be affected by the use of contraceptives.

If conception occurs, the pregnancy may end in a spontaneous fetal death, in an induced abortion, in a stillbirth, or in a live birth. It seems reasonable to consider that in a given context each of these outcomes has a numerical probability. After conceiving, a woman cannot conceive again while she is pregnant or during the postpartum interval until ovulation or cohabitation is resumed, whichever comes later. The durations of both pregnancy and postpartum nonsusceptibility to conception are variables related to the outcome of pregnancy.

All of the functions in question may vary from couple to

5. K. Davis and J. Blake, "Social Structure and Fertility: An Analytic Framework," *Economic Development and Cultural Change*, IV (April, 1956), pp. 211–235.
6. See, for example, N. B. Ryder and L. Henry, this volume.

couple in a population. For any one couple, they may vary over time and be affected by age, duration of marriage, number of pregnancies or live births already experienced, and many other factors.

Problems of Measurement

Attempts to analyze reproductive patterns seek answers to such questions as: How often? How many? When? Difficulties of measurement arise in part because the process involves the occurrence of repeated events during a limited time. The events are relatively easily defined, though not always easily ascertainable: a conception, a confinement at which at least one child is born alive, or another type of pregnancy termination. It is more difficult to settle on the manner of expressing the relation of these events to the time during which they can occur.

The element of time plays many roles, some rather obvious and others more subtle. The relevance of maternal age both to individual natality patterns and to rates of population growth keep this factor to the fore. The length of the effective reproductive span of each woman has already been mentioned. Whether it is truncated by death or lasts until secondary sterility supervenes, its termination limits the possible number of births. Since the time during which any woman can reproduce is limited, a few long intervals between successive births, even if they occur by chance, tend to decrease the possible size of her completed family. Thus there arises a negative correlation between completed parity and intervals between births. The evaluation of an observed correlation requires a quantitative estimate of the relationship that is inevitable by nature of the process. This phenomenon differs from the usual concept of chance variation and it can be studied only through suitable models.

Determining how to express the time during which a woman is exposed to the risk of conceiving or of a confinement can be troublesome. A woman married for two months has a greater chance of conceiving than she would in one month, though less than twice the chance.[7] How should the duration of marriage enter into the indices? In relation to a woman's total parity,

7. Logically, this follows because she cannot conceive twice in those two months. For a more general proof, see Appendix, section 1.

what allowance should be made for nonsusceptibility to conception during pregnancies?

The concept of marriage duration relevant to reproductive measures is also unclear for a woman who has been married more than once. Assume for example that her first marriage lasted two months and her second 10 months, giving a total of 12 months in the married state. Assuming no premarital conceptions and nine months of pregnancy, this woman could have had a confinement in the interval after the dissolution of her first marriage (provided the interval was long enough) and a second confinement in her second marriage. On the same assumptions, a woman with a single marriage lasting 12 months could not have had more than one confinement.

Appropriate answers to these problems of measurement depend in part on the purpose of the analysis. In relation to detailed studies of the reproduction of couples, they call for specific definition and conceptualization of the process. All the difficulties have not by any means been resolved. The description, to be given now, of efforts to formalize such concepts through probability models will attempt to exemplify the relations between the problems of measurement and the underlying nature of the process.

APPROACHES TO FECUNDABILITY

Estimates of the Distribution

In addition to reasons mentioned earlier, estimation of the fecundability of couples in a population is an important component of any study of couple reproduction. It is basic to the investigation of differences in the childbearing patterns in different societies, and essential for evaluating the efficacy of contraceptive methods. Since it cannot be measured directly, statistical methods of estimation are necessary.

The Italian statistician Corrado Gini, who first defined the concept of fecundability, sought a method of estimating this probability that would be unaffected by the duration of exposure to risk of pregnancy.[8] On the assumption that (except perhaps

8. C. Gini, ''Premières recherches sur la fécondabilité de la femme,'' *Proceedings of the International Mathematics Congress* (1924), pp. 889–892; C. Gini, ''Decline in the Birth Rate and Fecundability of Women,'' *Eugenics Review*, XVII (Jan., 1926), pp. 258–274; C. Gini, ''Sur la mesure de la fécondité naturelle de la femme

for the first month of marriage) the fecundability of a married woman remains constant from month to month before her first conception, he derived an estimate of the mean fecundability of those women who conceive for the first time in months x to $x + y$ of marriage. Assuming further that the duration of gestation and the frequency of fetal deaths in these months remained constant, he concluded that the number of women first conceiving in a given month would be proportional to the number of first live births nine months later. His estimate of fecundability was accordingly based on the numbers of first births by the month following marriage. Although he did not discuss the possibility that some of the first births represented second or later conceptions, this eventuality would probably not affect his estimates greatly.

Louis Henry [9] extended Gini's results, showing that on the assumption of constant fecundability per woman, the values of the mean fecundability of a population and its coefficient of variation could be estimated from data on the proportions of women conceiving during the first and second months of exposure to risk.

The relation between the distribution of the time to the first conception and that of fecundability has been considered by various workers. In a hypothetical homogeneous population, with constant fecundability ρ, observed for a sufficiently long time, the month of first conception is distributed geometrically with a mean value of $1/\rho$. In a heterogeneous population, with fecundability varying from couple to couple but remaining constant for each couple, the expected value of the month of first conception is the reciprocal of the *harmonic* mean of ρ in the population,[10] and may therefore be a good deal longer than the reciprocal of the *arithmetic* mean fecundability. For this reason, Vincent,[11] who formulated a detailed model for the estimation of fecundability from data on first births, suggested that the

mariée,'' *Revue de l'Institut International de Statistique*, IX (1941), pp. 1–20. A modified derivation of his method is given in the Appendix, section 2.

9. L. Henry, ''Fondements théoriques des mesures de la fécondité naturelle,'' *Revue de l'Institut International de Statistique*, XXI (1953), pp. 135–151, and see Appendix, Eq. (6).

10. L. Henry, *ibid.*

11. P. Vincent, *op. cit.*; L. Henry, this volume.

difference between the proportion of a group conceiving in the first month of marriage and the estimated harmonic mean could serve as a measure of the heterogeneity of the group.[12]

Pregnancy Rate

Raymond Pearl developed another approach to the estimation of fecundability. The estimate, known as a "pregnancy rate," is defined as the number of conceptions occurring per estimated woman-month of exposure. From the time elapsed since marriage, Pearl subtracted any periods during which the couple were apart, plus the estimated duration of all pregnancies and a few weeks for each puerperium.[13] Pearl calculated pregnancy rates in two quite different ways. One method, yielding what might be termed a global pregnancy rate, consists of summing all the pregnancies of a group of women and dividing this sum by the total estimated exposure time of the women included. In the other method, Pearl divided the pregnancies of each woman by her estimated exposure time and then averaged the resulting rates. Calculations with a few sets of numbers will easily demonstrate that the two methods are not equivalent and may give very different values.[14]

Modifications of the global pregnancy rate were used by Pearl and others [15] to study differential natality and to estimate the effect of birth control on reproductive performance. In critical

12. Further investigations of fecundability and its distribution are reported in R. G. Potter and M. P. Parker, "Predicting the Time Required to Conceive," *Population Studies*, XVIII (July, 1964), pp. 99–116; M. C. Sheps, "On the Time Required for Conception," *ibid.*, pp. 85–97.

13. R. Pearl, "Factors in Human Fertility and Their Statistical Evaluation," *Lancet*, CCXXV (Sept. 9, 1933), pp. 607–611; R. Pearl, *The Natural History of Population* (New York: Oxford University Press, 1939). In different publications, the details of Pearl's calculations varied. In later work he used the estimated number of ovulations in the denominator multiplying the number of years by 13. Other users of the rate allowed for longer postpartum nonsusceptible periods related to lactation amenorrhea. Not all writers who calculated pregnancy rates identified them as estimators of fecundability, but the inference that this was their intent seems justified by their descriptive statements.

14. L. Henry, "Fondements théoriques des mesures . . ." and Appendix, sections 3 and 4.

15. See, for example, G. W. Beebe, *Contraception and Fertility in the Southern Appalachians* (Baltimore: Williams and Wilkins, 1942), pp. 223–229; R. K. Stix and F. W. Notestein, *Controlled Fertility: An Evaluation of Clinic Service* (Baltimore: Williams and Wilkins, 1940).

analyses of these measures and their interpretation, Gini [16] pointed out that ignoring lactation amenorrhea or inserting an arbitrary value for its duration might lead to taking differences in the breastfeeding practices of two groups for differences in fecundability. In other instances real differences in fecundability might be masked. He contended also that rates calculated for groups of women who had been at risk for different lengths of time were not comparable, since values obtained either for pregnancy rates or for mean intervals between births depend on the duration of observation. Gini stated that if his objections were met, the pregnancy rate would be identical with fecundability as estimated by him. The basis for this statement is unclear. This and other difficulties attending the pregnancy rate will be indicated in the Appendix and in the next section.

Conception Rate

In the late two decades, use of the global pregnancy rate has declined except with respect to a simpler modified version, which may be referred to as a conception rate. Under the term "contraceptive failure rate," it has been widely used to measure the effectiveness of contraceptives in clinical situations.[17] A group of women, all susceptible to conception, are followed from a starting date until they first conceive or withdraw from observation for some reason, or until the reporting date is reached. The conception rate is the number of conceptions divided by the number of woman-months of exposure. Each woman contributes at most one pregnancy to the numerator. The denominator is the total months of observation for all women, up to and including the month of conception for those who conceive.

16. C. Gini, "Sur la mesure de la fécondité naturelle . . ." and C. Gini, "Sur la mesure de l'efficacité des pratiques anticonceptionelles," *Revue de l'Institut International de Statistique*, X (1942), pp. 1–35. Gini also discussed the importance and difficulty of making comparisons only between groups that are comparable in other respects; this question is taken up by L. Lasagna in this volume.

17. C. Tietze, "The Clinical Effectiveness of Contraceptive Methods," *American Journal of Obstetrics and Gynecology*, LXXVIII (Sept., 1959), pp. 650–656; C. Tietze and S. Lewit, "Recommended Procedures for the Study of Use-Effectiveness of Contraceptive Methods," *International Planned Parenthood Federation Handbook, Part I* (London: International Planned Parenthood Federation, 1962), pp. 59–72.

This definition eliminates some of the problems encountered by the more general pregnancy rate, since postpartum insusceptibility does not enter. More generally, it avoids the questions of how best to handle recurrent pregnancies, periods of separation, or pregnancies that end in fetal deaths. The simplification does not, however, eliminate all the logical difficulties inherent in this rate.[18]

If n women with mean fecundability 0.2 were observed for one month, they would on the average have $0.2n$ conceptions, with an expected conception rate of 0.2. When a group is observed for more than one month, the expected value of the conception rate for small samples is more difficult to arrive at. If a large number (n) of fecund women were followed until they all conceived and each woman's fecundability remained constant over time, the expected exposure time would be n times the reciprocal of the harmonic mean fecundability. In this case, the conception rate might be expected to approximate the harmonic mean rather than the arithmetic mean fecundability. When the period of observation is limited, though longer than one month, it can be shown [19] that, for a theoretical homogeneous population, the expected value of the index changes with the duration of maximum observation as well as with the size of the sample.

Since, however, the groups observed usually consist of women with unequal fecundability who are followed for unequal maximum periods, the problem becomes much more complicated. Observations on groups of women frequently show a decreasing rate of conception with the passage of time,[20] whether the index used is the conception rate per exposure month, the proportion of still eligible women who conceive each month, or the esti-

18. In a discussion of this index at the Symposium (see p. 494), there was widespread agreement that the rate should be discarded in favor of a life table estimate, such as is presented in R. G. Potter, "Additional Measures of Use-Effectiveness of Contraception," *Milbank Memorial Fund Quarterly*, XLI (Oct., 1963), pp. 400–418.

19. M. C. Sheps, "On the Person Years Concept in Epidemiology and Demography," *Milbank Memorial Fund Quarterly*, XLIV (Jan., 1966), pp. 61–91. See Appendix, section 4.

20. R. K. Stix, "Birth Control in a Midwestern City," *Milbank Memorial Fund Quarterly*, XVII (Oct., 1939), pp. 413–423; C. Tietze, A. F. Guttmacher, and S. Rubin, "Time Required for Conception in 1,727 Planned Pregnancies," *Fertility and Sterility*, I (July-Aug., 1950), pp. 338–346.

mated mean fecundability of those conceiving. The phenomenon is to be expected in heterogeneous groups, even when the fecundability of any woman remains constant.[21] Accordingly, the value of the index is affected both by the length of follow up and by the heterogeneity of the population. The apparent effects of contraceptive use on conception rates may also change with the length of observation even without real changes during this time, as is indicated by hypothetical calculations in a recent paper.[22]

One further point deserves mention. In reality, the fecundability of women who are participating in a trial of contraceptives is likely to change with time—it may be reduced if they become more efficient contraceptors with experience or it may rise if their desire to avoid a pregnancy becomes less marked. Therefore the monthly risk of first conception to a group of women followed for a time may be expected to change, both because the more fecund women tend to be removed from the sample by earlier conception and because the fecundability of individuals may change. These changes with time, which are lost in a single index, may be studied in a life table curve.[23]

Probabilistic Interrelationships

Space limitations preclude discussion of other applications of probability models relating to fecundability and the risk of pregnancy. These include studies of the relation between the level of fecundability and the probability of avoiding conception during a period of 10 or 15 years, efforts to estimate the probability of conception per coital exposure, and probability models for estimating the duration of the fertile period during a

21. C. Tietze, ''Differential Fecundity and Effectiveness of Contraception,'' *Eugenics Review*, L (Jan., 1959), pp. 230–237; R. G. Potter, ''Contraceptive Practice and Birth Intervals Among Two-Child White Couples in Metropolitan America,'' *Thirty Years of Research in Human Fertility: Retrospect and Prospect* (New York: Milbank Memorial Fund, 1959), pp. 74–92; R. G. Potter, ''Length of the Observation Period as a Factor Affecting the Contraceptive Failure Rate,'' *Milbank Memorial Fund Quarterly*, XXXVIII (April, 1960), pp. 140–152. See also papers cited in footnote 12.

22. M. Seklani, ''Efficacité de la contraception,'' *Population*, XVIII (April–June, 1963), pp. 329–346.

23. For an example of such a life table curve in a presumably noncontracepting population, see paper by Potter *et al.*, this volume.

cycle.[24] Such reports exemplify the possible ramifications of this approach and lead to important insights as well as to some surprising results.

THE SEQUENTIAL PROCESS

Fecundability is subsumed under more general models of the reproductive process. The pattern of a recurrent sequence of pregnancies or confinements experienced by a woman during a specified period is an example of the class of processes known as renewal processes,[25] where the probability that a second event (e.g., a confinement) will occur at a given time depends on the prior occurrence of a first event and on the time elapsed since the first event occurred. Analogous statements hold for the 3rd, 4th, . . . , *n*th events. The stochastic theory of renewal processes is concerned with the probability distributions of intervals between recurrences of an event. These distributions determine the probability distribution of the number of recurrences during a specified period after the start of the process as, for example, the number of confinements in *y* years of marriage, and also determine the probability that the event will occur during a time unit, e.g., a birth rate.

Since all fecund women are susceptible to conception at the beginning of a sexual union, the distribution of intervals to a first birth is different from that of intervals between subsequent births. Renewal processes with this characteristic are known as

24. R. Pearl, ''Pregnancy Rates and Coitus Rates,'' *Human Biology,* XII (Dec., 1940), pp. 545–558; D. V. Glass and E. Grebenik, ''The Trend and Pattern of Fertility in Great Britain,'' *Papers of the Royal Commission on Population,* VI (1954), p. 255; R. G. Potter, ''Some Problems in Predicting a Couple's Contraceptive Future,'' *Eugenics Quarterly,* VI (Dec., 1959), pp. 254–259; R. G. Potter, ''Length of the Fertile Period,'' *Milbank Memorial Fund Quarterly,* XXXIX (Jan., 1961), pp. 1–31; R. G. Potter and C. Tietze, ''A Statistical Model of the Rhythm Method,'' *Emerging Techniques in Population Research* (New York: Milbank Memorial Fund, 1963), pp. 141–158; C. Tietze, ''Probability of Pregnancy Resulting from a Single Unprotected Coitus,'' *Fertility and Sterility,* II (Sept.–Oct., 1960), pp. 485–488; C. Tietze and R. G. Potter, ''Statistical Evaluation of the Rhythm Method,'' *American Journal of Obstetrics and Gynecology,* LXXXIV (Sept., 1962), pp. 692–698; A. J. de Bethune, ''Child Spacing: The Mathematical Probabilities,'' *Science,* CXLII (Dec. 27, 1963), pp. 1629–1634.

25. One form of renewal process well known in demography is the basis of stable population theory discussed in this volume by A. J. Coale and L. C. Cole. Stochastic approaches to renewal theory are given in W. L. Smith, ''Renewal Theory and its Ramifications,'' *Journal of the Royal Statistical Society,* XX, Series B, 2(1958), pp. 243–302 and D. R. Cox, *Renewal Theory* (New York: John Wiley, 1962).

general, modified, or delayed renewal processes. An extension of the theory of renewal processes called Markov Renewal Processes permits simultaneous consideration of the occurrence of different events such as conceptions, confinements, miscarriages, or stillbirths, and even affords an opportunity to distinguish between premature and full term births.[26]

A number of workers have, more or less explicitly, viewed the reproductive process as a renewal process. Explicit mathematical results are available only if the process is treated as though the parameters involved, such as fecundability, did not depend on the number of events already experienced (e.g., on the number of previous births), and as though these parameters were constant and did not change with age or duration of marriage. Despite these limitations, informative results have been obtained. The restrictions on the models can be lifted by simulation procedures, as will be indicated below.

The Study of Intervals Between Confinements [27]

Corresponding to the inherent relationship, in a renewal process, between the distribution of the number of events in a specified period of time and that of intervals between recurrences of the events, the distribution of the number of births in a defined period is the obverse of the distribution of intervals between births. Efforts to study these intervals are, however, confronted by an important objection. For any group of women, the longest interval that can be recorded between marriage and any birth is not greater than the duration of their marriages at the time the observations are made. The resultant possibility of selection against long intervals is fairly obvious with respect to first births. It can be dealt with more or less satisfactorily by limiting the data to women who have been married for a sufficiently long time, say for at least 10 years.

26. E. B. Perrin and M. C. Sheps, ''Human Reproduction: A Stochastic Process,'' *Biometrics*, XX (March, 1964), pp. 28–45. The relevant theory is given, for example, in R. Pyke, ''Markov Renewal Processes of Zero Order and Their Applications to Counter Theory,'' *Studies in Applied Probability*, ed. K. J. Arrow, S. Karlin, and H. Scarf (Stanford: Stanford University Press, 1962), pp. 173–183; R. Pyke, ''Markov Renewal Processes,'' *The Annals of Mathematical Statistics*, XXXII (Dec., 1961), pp. 1231–42 and 1243–59.

27. The study of birth intervals is also discussed in the papers by Henry, Ryder, and Potter *et al.*, this volume.

It is less obvious, however, that, with respect to births of higher order, the difficulty remains even if all the women in a sample live with their husbands beyond the age of 50. As a simple example, assume that a fifth child is born to some women three years before they become sterile. Then for those women the interval between the fifth and sixth child, to exist at all, must be shorter than three years. Selection against long intervals may thus occur again. To a degree, this effect could be removed by life table analyses of successive intervals.[28] This solution is, however, imperfect since we cannot know when an individual woman becomes sterile and should be withdrawn from the population considered at risk. On the other hand, we do not really eliminate these problems by turning from the analysis of intervals to the analysis of parity-specific birth rates; the same considerations remain since the analysis is essentially identical and the same variation remains in the number of women at risk during any given period following the last confinement.

The theoretical approaches, to be described next, to the distribution of numbers of births at a specified time after marriage have the distribution of intervals between births embedded within them. For this, among other reasons, the study of intervals remains a subject of interest.

DISTRIBUTION OF THE NUMBER OF CONFINEMENTS

In studying the distribution of the number of births to women in a period of time, investigators have defined the time period in two principal ways. The first disregards marital duration, defining the period by calendar dates or an age interval. The second approach dates events from marriage. Obviously, different results would be expected from the two types of time classification.

Calendar Period Observations

For practical reasons, available data often show how many married women of a given group had 0, 1, . . . , n confinements

28. M. C. Sheps, ''Couple Fertility Data from an American Isolate,'' *Population Index*, XXX (July, 1964), pp. 310–311 and M. C. Sheps, ''An Analysis of Reproduction Patterns in an American Isolate,'' *Population Studies*, XIX (July, 1965) pp. 65–80. See also Ryder, this volume.

during a specified five-year calendar period. At the beginning of the period, these women had some unknown distributions of duration of marriage, interval since last delivery, or month of a current pregnancy. It is therefore difficult to estimate how many women were susceptible to conception at any particular time, a variable that may well affect the final distribution of confinements.

Wishing to fit such data, Henry assumed that the probability of a live birth to a woman in any year was zero if she had had a birth in the preceding year and constant otherwise. From these assumptions, he developed an "expected" distribution of the number of births per woman over a five-year period, which fitted his data better than an ordinary binomial had done.[29]

Facing a similar problem, V. M. Dandekar[30] developed a model with a constant value of effective fecundability, i.e., of the monthly probability of a conception leading to a live birth. Assuming a fixed period of postpartum nonsuceptibility, he derived expressions for the probability of at least x births in y years of marriage, as well as for the long term, asymptotic distribution of births in a period starting at an indefinitely long time after marriage. He then passed from the discrete monthly probability of conception to a continuous form, and obtained an approximation to the long term probability distribution of births in a specified period. He found, however, that this approximation failed to give a satisfactory fit to observed distributions of births occurring in a five-year period. There are many possible explanations for such failure, since the model is obviously unrealistic in a number of respects.

Subsequently, Singh[31] modified the original discrete model,

---

29. L. Henry, *Anciennes familles genevoises—étude démographique XVIᵉ–XXᵉ siècle* (Paris: Presses Universitaires de France, 1956), pp. 227–229. In later work, Henry made another approach to average fertility rates during such a period. See L. Henry, "Fécondité et famille, modèles mathématiques," *Population*, XII (July–Aug., 1957), pp. 413–444; XVI (Jan.–March, 1961), pp. 27–48; and XVI (April–June, 1961), pp. 261–282.

30. V. M. Dandekar, "Certain Modified Forms of Binomial and Poisson Distributions," *Sankhya*, XV (Jan., 1955), pp. 237–250; D. Basu, "A Note on the Structure of a Stochastic Model Considered by V. M. Dandekar," *ibid.*, pp. 251–252.

31. S. N. Singh, "Probability Models for the Variation in the Number of Births Per Couple," *Journal of the American Statistical Association*, LVIII (Sept., 1963), pp. 721–727.

which treated all women as susceptible to conception at the beginning of the period of observation. He added an assumption that a proportion $(1 - f)$ of the women in the sample had a fecundability of zero throughout the period of observation. Putting the mean duration of gestation plus postpartum infecundability at 12 months and estimating the proportion fecund (f) and fecundability from Dandekar's data, he obtained a better fit than Dandekar had done. For a population of Indian women, an estimate of three months of postpartum infecundability seems very low.[32] Examination of Singh's model together with the data shows, however, that a higher value would produce inadmissible estimates for the other parameters.

It is difficult to evaluate the fit obtained by Singh. Such data usually divide the women into at most five categories, since few women have four or more confinements in five years. Consequently, a large variety of models with several parameters might produce an acceptable fit. With five categories, four parameters would assure a perfect fit. Both Henry and Singh, though their definitions were dissimilar, in effect assumed a value for one parameter and estimated two additional parameters. A numerical "fit" to this type of data would perhaps have more meaning if the model had previously been validated on considerably more detailed long term data.

Dating From the Onset of Exposure

Brass, seeking methods to characterize the natality of populations, assumed a distribution of the "expectation of bearing children per unit time." Incorporating Dandekar's results, he derived descriptive parameters based on completed family size or on the number of births achieved at specified ages.[33]

The important contributions made by workers at the Demographic Institute of Paris to the subject matter of this paper and particularly of this section are summarized in this volume

32. See Potter *et al.*, this volume.

33. W. Brass, "The Distribution of Births in Human Populations," *Population Studies*, XII (July, 1958), pp. 51–72. Applications of this model have been made in: R. G. Potter, P. C. Sagi, and C. F. Westoff, "Improvement of Contraception During the Course of Marriage," *Population Studies*, XVI (Nov., 1962), pp. 160–174; and W. H. James, "Estimates of Fecundability," *Population Studies*, XVII (July, 1963), pp. 57–65.

by Louis Henry. His own work, focusing on the "natural" reproduction of couples who make no conscious effort to control births, has included mathematical analysis and some numerical simulation. It has yielded numerous insights into the patterns that may be expected, and has provided a rational basis for the interpretation of empirical data.

Using renewal theory more explicitly, Perrin and I [34] obtained results which in a number of instances parallel those of Henry. For example, investigation of the effect of fetal mortality on birth rates and birth intervals indicates that models that do not explicitly include this parameter but use effective fecundability may give misleading results. Further, since the expected incidence of conception is highest at the beginning of a sexual union and subsequently varies with the changing patterns of susceptibility to conception, the expected birth rate shows dampened oscillations with increasing duration of marriage, even if the parameters involved do not change with age or marriage duration. Consequently, expected age-specific birth rates would be higher in the age group when most marriages occur than in subsequent age groups, despite constancy of the underlying biological parameters. Approximate results for the expected number of births in the first y years of marriage and the variance of these numbers may be derived from renewal theory.

More generally, Perrin and I have presented flexible models providing for distributions of fecundability, for a variety of outcomes of pregnancy, and for different distributions of the durations of pregnancy and of the postpartum insusceptible periods according to the outcome of pregnancy. These models enable the effects of the different parameters on measures of reproduction to be studied more easily. For these models, all moments of the intervals between events were derived. The probability distribution of women in the various states of the model (state of pregnancy, of puerperium, etc.) at a specified time since marriage may be calculated, as well as the cumulative

34. M. C. Sheps and E. B. Perrin, "Changes in Birth Rates as a Function . . . ;" E. B. Perrin and M. C. Sheps, "Human Reproduction . . . ;" M. C. Sheps and E. B. Perrin, "The Distribution of Birth Intervals Under a Class of Stochastic Fertility Models," *Population Studies*, XVII (March, 1964), pp. 321–331; M. C. Sheps, "Pregnancy Wastage as a Factor in the Analysis of Fertility Data," *Demography*, I (1964), pp. 111–118.

probability distribution of the number of pregnancies, confinements, conceptions, or fetal losses in that time. With a restricted version, which treats the duration of nonsusceptible periods as fixed, expressions were derived that enable numerical results to be obtained more easily than heretofore for the cumulative distribution of births in a specified interval after marriage, or after the adoption of contraceptive measures. The mean and variance of the number of births of course follow. According to these models, in the absence of contraceptive practices the durations of the nonsusceptible periods associated with pregnancy are major determinants of natality rates and affect the variance of the number of live births.[35]

Effects of Antinatal Practices

Studies of the possible effects of antinatal practices on birth rates agree that a contraceptive of a given per cent effectiveness will reduce birth rates by less than this per cent. Potter, adding a provision for fetal death to Dandekar's discrete model, derived the probability distribution of the number of births in a 10- or 15-year period, given the use of relatively effective contraceptive measures.[36] Tietze postulated universal practice of birth control after a couple had achieved a modest number of children and concluded that, to bring birth rates into equilibrium with death rates, a comparatively high level of contraceptive effectiveness would be required.[37] The relations between the parameters determining birth rates, the effectiveness of a

35. The conclusion with respect to natality rates was also reached by L. Henry, this volume, and by R. G. Potter, ''Birth Intervals: Structure and Change,'' *Population Studies*, XVII (Nov., 1963), pp. 155–166. P. Vincent, *op. cit.*, L. Henry and K. Dandekar have attempted, for different populations, to estimate the duration of nonsusceptibility following live births. See L. Henry, ''Intervals Between Confinements in the Absence of Birth Control,'' *Eugenics Quarterly*, V (Dec., 1958), pp. 200–211; K. Dandekar, ''Intervals Between Confinements,'' *Eugenics Quarterly*, VI (Sept., 1959), pp. 180–186; K. Dandekar, ''Analysis of Birth Intervals of a Set of Indian Women,'' *Eugenics Quarterly*, X (June, 1963), pp. 73–78.

36. R. G. Potter, ''Some Relationships Between Short Range and Long Range Risks of Unwanted Pregnancy,'' *Milbank Memorial Fund Quarterly*, XXXVIII (July, 1960), pp. 255–263; R. G. Potter, ''Some Physical Correlates of Fertility Control in the United States,'' *International Population Conference New York 1961* (International Union for the Scientific Study of Population: London, 1963) I, pp. 106–116.

37. C. Tietze, ''Pregnancy Rates and Birth Rates,'' *Population Studies*, XVI (July, 1962), pp. 31–37.

contraceptive, the prevalence of its use, and the expected effect on birth rates were studied by Perrin and me.[38] If all other factors could be assumed equal, more effective methods used by smaller fractions of a population would produce a greater decline in birth rates than would less effective methods used by a large part of the population. From a different viewpoint, Potter investigated the relations among birth intervals, the "ovulatory ratio," (namely that fraction of the mean interval between births that is attributable to the mean time taken for conception) abortions, contraceptive use, and natality rates.[39]

SIMULATION EFFORTS

Even when only a limited few of the factors affecting patterns of reproduction are considered, the effects of a change in any one parameter depend on its original value and on the values of the other parameters. To understand the implications of specific models, it is consequently necessary to insert numerical values into general mathematical solutions. The process of reproduction, moreover, is subject to variation that is not yet amenable to explicit mathematical solutions. Thus, the probability distribution of live births to a couple in five or ten years of marriage cannot be explicitly expressed in fully general models even assuming parameters that are constant over time. It is of interest also to study more realistic models that permit fecundability and the other parameters to vary with maternal age and parity. For these purposes, electronic computers offer opportunities for relatively elaborate simulation programs that lead an imaginary group of women through their reproductive lives, subjecting them to the effects of a postulated stochastic process.

A number of the references cited utilized numerical simulation on desk calculators. The use of electronic computers to extend simulation programs in this area of study is apparently just starting.[40] A simulation program to study stochastic varia-

38. M. C. Sheps and E. B. Perrin, "Changes in Birth Rates . . . ," (see footnote 34).
39. R. G. Potter, "Birth Intervals . . ." (see footnote 35).
40. The few published reports refer to the even more complex problems of population growth. G. Orcutt, M. Greenberger, J. Korbel, and A. Rivlin, *Microanalysis of Socioeconomic Systems; a Simulation Study* (New York: Harper, 1961); H.

tion and to evaluate proposed analytic methods has been devised.[41] This program permits a number of the variables, including marriage, to depend on age. The occurrence of conception, the duration of pregnancy, and all other events in each individual case are subject to the play of chance. A more elaborate simulation model for other purposes is described by Ridley in this Symposium. It is hoped that these models will permit wider investigations of short term and long term effects on natality of changes in mortality, marriage patterns, and the use of contraceptive methods.

CONCLUDING REMARKS

The numbers and the complexity of the variables affecting patterns of reproduction of couples, though still considerable, represent an appreciable simplification of those involved in general population natality. This is even truer when the focus is on reproductive patterns under restricted conditions. Concentration on a relatively restricted aspect of a process permits more detailed and specific consideration of the factors included, even though other factors are ignored for the time being. The relative simplicity of the study of the reproduction of couples as compared with that of populations has permitted the degree of model building described above. On the other hand, this process itself is sufficiently complex both to create an enduring need for models and to engender dissatisfaction with the models available as yet.

As I have attempted to show, the models constructed to date, though limited, have proven useful and instructive. Even disagreements about the validity of a model help to further our understanding of the process. Although the foregoing does not include examples of direct applications to empirical data, I hope that the interplay between theory and data is implicit in the

Hyrenius, ''New Technique for Studying Demographic-Economic-Social Interrelations,'' paper presented at UN Conference of the Application of Science and Technology for the Benefit of the Less Developed Areas, February, 1963; J. M. Beshers, ''Birth Projections with Cohort Models,'' *Demography,* II (1965) pp. 593–599.

41. A preliminary report of the results was made in E. B. Perrin and M. C. Sheps, ''A Monte Carlo Investigation of a Human Fertility Model,'' presented before the Statistics Section, American Public Health Association, November, 1963, processed.

description. It can be seen clearly in many of the references.

Unsolved problems remain, as has been indicated. The literature cited in this report reveals inconsistencies in terminology and a lack of standardization in definitions. More inconsistencies become apparent when analyses of actual data are also considered. Standardization of definitions and terminology in this area of study seems highly desirable.

Attempts to work with theoretical or simulation models are hampered by the lack of data on variables that should obviously be included in the models. In addition to uncertainty about the distributions of such parameters as the probability of fetal death or the duration of postpartum nonsusceptibility to conception, difficulties are encountered in obtaining usable information even on such characteristics as age at first marriage. Continued development of models and exploitation of their potentialities would be favored by specification of needed data and successful efforts to obtain them.

Further developments in model building and the application of their results will probably extend in many directions. Some of the questions that may now be amenable to solution are: How should we relate the dimension of time to the measurements we make? Since in reality the parameters involved most likely change with the passage of time and with parity, how can these changes be estimated independently of the other complications that the time dimension introduces? What kinds of data would be most useful not only to provide parameters for models but to test models and to indicate the variables that need to be included? What are valid and appropriate criteria for the usefulness and acceptability of a model? Along what lines should simulation programs best be developed? How should simulation of couple reproduction be extended to the study of population growth?

The literature does not contain, to my knowledge, any example of a set of data completely "explained" by a probability model. It is, indeed, doubtful whether this will be achieved. Models have, however, contributed to efforts: (1) to derive indices that are well understood and are valid reflections of the variables governing the process of reproduction; (2) to achieve greater insight into the sources of differences in the natality patterns of different groups; and (3) to enhance our understanding of changes in natality that may be expected to follow changes in specified variables. The prospects for continuing progress toward these goals are good.

ACKNOWLEDGEMENTS

This investigation was supported in part by Public Health Service Research Grant GM 11134 from the National Institute of General Medical Sciences.

APPENDIX

1. *Relation between exposure time and the probability of a first conception*

Assume that a woman has a constant monthly fecundability ρ where $0 < \rho < 1$ and $\rho = 1 - q$. The probability of first conceiving in the first month is $1 - q$, the probability of first conceiving in the first two months is $1 - q^2$ and the probability of first conceiving during the first m months is $1 - q^m$. Now,

$$(1) \qquad 1 - q^m = (1 - q)(1 + q + q^2 + \cdots + q^{m-1}).$$

Since $1 + q + q^2 + \ldots + q^{m-1}$ is unity plus the sum of $m - 1$ terms, each of which is less than unity,

$$(2) \quad 1 + q + q^2 + \cdots + q^{m-1} < m \text{ and } 1 - q^m < m(1 - q).$$

Consequently, it has been proved that the probability that a woman who is at risk of conceiving during m months conceives in that time is less than m times as great as her chance of conceiving in the first month.

2. *Estimates of fecundability*

The probability that a woman with constant fecundability ρ conceives for the first time in month m of her sexual union is $\rho(1 - \rho)^{m-1}$. Assume that we have data on a number of couples, the unknown distribution of whose fecundability is some function $f(\rho)$ where $0 \leq \rho \leq 1$. Then the proportion expected to conceive for the first time in month m is

$$(3) \qquad\qquad C_m = \int_0^1 \rho(1 - \rho)^{m-1} f(\rho) \, d\rho.$$

and the proportion expected to conceive the following month is

$$(4) \quad C_{m+1} = \int_0^1 \rho(1-\rho)^m f(\rho) \, d\rho = C_m - \int_0^1 \rho\left\{\rho(1-\rho)^{m-1}\right\} f(\rho) \, d\rho.$$

Accordingly, the ratio C_{m+1}/C_m may be considered as an estimate of 1 minus the mean fecundability of those included in C_m. By an extension of the above reasoning, Gini concluded that the mean fecundability of those conceiving in the course of months $x, x+1, \ldots, x+y$ is the weighted mean of the series of such monthly estimates.[42] This latter estimator, incidentally, reduces to

$$(5) \qquad \bar{\rho}(x+y) = \frac{C_x - C_{x+y+1}}{C_x + C_{x+1} + \cdots + C_{x+y}}.$$

It should be noted that Equation (5) is the ratio of two expected values. The expected value of this ratio for samples of limited size may be quite different from the ratio of the expected values and, accordingly, from the desired mean.

From Equation (3), the expected value of C_1 is $\bar{\rho}$, the mean fecundability of the total group. Similarly, Henry showed,[43] an estimator of σ^2, the variance of ρ, may be obtained from the equation

$$(6) \qquad 1 - C_2/C_1 = \bar{\rho}(1 + \sigma^2/\bar{\rho}^2) \, .$$

Reservations regarding the expected value of a ratio hold here as well as for Equation (5).

3. *Means of individual conception rates*

The expected value (mean) of individual rates for first conceptions in a homogeneous population observed for m months is

$$(7) \qquad \rho + \frac{\rho(1-\rho)}{2} + \frac{\rho(1-\rho)^2}{3} + \cdots + \frac{\rho(1-\rho)^{m-1}}{m}$$

42. C. Gini, ''Premières Recherches . . .'' (see footnote 8).
43. L. Henry, ''Fondements théoriques des mesures . . .'' (see footnote 9).

which is obviously $> \rho$ if $\rho < 1$. As m approaches infinity, the value of Equation (7) approaches

$$(8) \qquad \frac{\rho}{1-\rho} \sum_{m=1}^{\infty} \frac{(1-\rho)^m}{m} = \frac{\rho}{1-\rho} \ln \frac{1}{\rho} \, .$$

For a group of women with unequal fecundability, the expected value of the mean of individual conception rates is a weighted mean of Equation (7). [44]

4. *Expected value of a global conception rate in a homogeneous population*

If a conception rate is calculated as the sum of all first conceptions divided by the sum of all months of exposure, in a homogeneous population (with equal fecundability ρ) where all n couples are followed for at least m months, the expected value of the rate may be shown [45] to be approximately

$$(9) \qquad E(R_m) \doteq \rho \left[1 + \frac{q}{n(1-q^m)} - \frac{m\rho q^m}{n(1-q^m)^2} \right].$$

Equation (9) generally has a lower value than Equation (7). It also, however, increases with increasing m (duration of observation).

5. *Estimates of Gini and Pearl*

For simplicity, assume that we follow a heterogeneous group of women from month 1 to m. Then Gini's estimate of the mean fecundability of those conceiving in this time is, from Equation (5)

$$(10) \qquad F_m = \frac{N_1 - N_{m+1}}{N_1 + N_2 + \cdots N_m}$$

44. *Ibid.*
45. M. C. Sheps, article in preparation.

where N_k is the observed proportion of women conceiving in month k. As shown elsewhere,[46] the expected value of N_k is $q_{k-1} - q_k$ where q_k is the kth moment of $q = 1 - \rho$. Therefore, when the number of women is very large, the value of F_m may be expected to approach

$$(11) \qquad F'_m = \frac{1 - q_1 - q_m + q_{m+1}}{1 - q_m} = 1 - \frac{\bar{q} - q_{m+1}}{1 - q_m}$$

and as $m \to \infty$ Equation (11) $\to 1 - \bar{q}$, or the mean fecundability of the original sample. Assuming there are no dropouts before month m, Pearl's estimate, i.e., the conception rate, is, according to the definition commonly used and given earlier

$$(12) \quad R_m = \frac{N_1 + N_2 + \cdots + N_m}{N_1 + 2N_2 + \cdots + (m-1)N_{m-1} + m\left(1 - \sum_{x=1}^{m-1} N_x\right)}.$$

When the sample is very large, R_m might be expected to approach the value

$$(13) \qquad R'_m = \frac{1 - q_m}{1 + q_1 + q_2 + \cdots + q_{m-1}},$$

which is not equal to (11) in a heterogeneous group. As $m \to \infty$, the numerator of $R'_m \to 1$ and the denominator approaches the reciprocal of the harmonic mean of ρ, so that $R'_m \to$ the harmonic mean of ρ.

46. M. C. Sheps, "On the Time Required for Conception . . ." (see footnote 12).

Louis Henry

FRENCH STATISTICAL RESEARCH
IN NATURAL FERTILITY

This article will report statistical investigations of natural fertility conducted in France. The title needs some explanation. The term "statistical" is used to specify from the beginning that the research in question is not at all biological or medical, but rather consists of observations of an essentially demographic nature treated by current statistical methods. Nevertheless, a special effort has been made to provide a solid theoretical foundation for these studies.

These investigations can be classified into two groups: (1) those devoted to physiological sterility, which were initiated earlier than those of group two, and (2) those directed toward the definition, the study, and the measurement of fundamental factors in natural fertility and toward the study of the natural growth of families from the beginning of marriage.

PHYSIOLOGICAL STERILITY

Primary or secondary sterility can be attributed to the husband, to the wife, or to both of them as a couple. The wife's age is, however, a very important factor in the onset of sterility, since all women are sterile beyond the age of 50. Consequently, in studying the effect of age, it is more convenient to speak of female sterility rather than of couple sterility. This is what we shall do, with the understanding that the discussion refers to married women and that the sterility ascribed to them is in fact the sterility of the couples of which they constitute only one half.

P. Vincent [1] made the first study of the incidence of physiological sterility, using parity progression ratios in populations which do not as yet practice birth control extensively. This method was developed by me [2] and subsequently applied to data from rural Japan. [3]

In the absence of birth control and premarital conception, the proportion, $1 - a_0(x_0)$, of women married at age x_0 who are childless equals the proportion of women sterile at age x_0 plus the proportion that become sterile before having conceived a child that will be born alive. [4] During younger ages, the cumulative incidence of sterility by age rises slowly and the increase may be considered linear; $1 - a_0(x_0)$ is therefore equal to the proportion $s_0(x_0 + c_0)$ of women sterile at age $x_0 + c_0$, where c_0 is the mean interval between marriage and the first conception, and $s_0(x)$ is the proportion of women sterile at age x. The equation

$$(1) \qquad t_0(x) = \frac{s_0(x + 1) - s_0(x)}{1 - s_0(x)}$$

represents the quotient of sterility acquired extramaritally during age x. [5] Similarly, the proportion $1 - a_n$ of mothers of n

1. P. Vincent, "La stérilité physiologique des populations," *Population*, V (Jan.–March, 1950), pp. 45–46.

2. L. Henry, *Fécondité des mariages. Nouvelle méthode de mesure* (Paris: Presses Universitaires de France, 1953).

3. L. Henry, "La fécondité des mariages au Japon," *Population*, VIII (Oct.–Dec., 1953), pp. 711–730.

4. $a_0(x_0)$ is the parity progression ratio of families without children in marriages occurring at age x_0. a_n is, similarly, the parity progression ratio of families with n children.

5. P. Vincent, who introduced this quotient, specified that it is concerned with sterility acquired extramaritally, *in part*, since in part it is acquired after marriage but before the first conception. It is, nevertheless, simpler and hardly erroneous to omit this reservation.

children who have not had an $(n + 1)$th child equals the proportion that become sterile after the conception of the nth child and before having had time to conceive the $(n + 1)$th-born child.

At the conception of the nth child these women are of average age $x_{0n} = x_0 + c_0 + (n - 1)i_n$, where i_n is the mean interval between conceptions of ranks 1 to n in families of at least n children,[6] and $1 - a_n$ represents, at least as a first approximation, the proportion of those women who become sterile between x_{0n} and $x_{0n} + i_n$.

The same proportion sterile is found if, for n and x_0, one substitutes another number of children (m) and another age at marriage (x_1) such that $x_{1m} = x_{0n}$. For low values of x and n, where this equality holds, i_m does not vary significantly from i_n. At the same average age, *as defined above*,[7] the risk of becoming sterile in a given interval following a conception is thus independent of the number of previous conceptions. Let t_x be the risk of becoming sterile during the year following the mean age x. This is a quotient of sterility acquired in marriage and specifically after childbirth. P. Vincent compared t_x and $t_0(x)$ and found that the first is distinctly higher than the second in lower age groups. This result is hardly surprising since the accidental risk of becoming sterile after childbirth is added to the risk associated with aging (common to all women and still minimal at lower ages). I confirmed this finding in Norway but not in Japan. We may note that though premarital conceptions tend to reduce $s_0(x)$, they cause an increase in $t_0(x)$ when they rise in frequency with lower marital age, as must usually be the case.

Despite the differences between sterility acquired extramaritally and that acquired during marriage, the two may be combined partly because of the imprecision of the estimates and partly because the "average woman" is exposed to both risks successively. The probability that a married woman, already a

---

6. Before the end of the fertile period is approached, the average interval between successive births in the same family is not very variable.

7. The italicized is quite important. For an interval of, say, 2.5 years, women married at 20 conceiving their fourth child are the same age as those married at 25 conceiving their second. The difference of two children comes from the difference in age at marriage; there is no selection. It would not be the same if one were to compare, among women married at 20, those who had their fourth conception at 28 with those who had their second conception at the same age.

mother and fecund at age x, will still be fecund at age $x + y$ equals

(2) $$(1 - t_x)(1 - t_{x+1}) \ . \ . \ . \ (1 - t_{x+y-1}) \ .$$

On multiplying this probability by the proportion $1 - s_0(x)$ of women, among those married at age $x - c_0$, who are still fecund at age x, one obtains the proportion of women fecund after age x out of those who married at that age. One thus has, in principle, a fecundity table as a series of proportions by age at marriage. In practice, one can combine those tables referring to the most common marital ages and use an average table calculated for a reasonably low age at marriage, such as 20 years.

Before presenting the results thus obtained, let us subject the method to a critical analysis. It incorporates a sizeable number of simplifying assumptions that may be violated when sterility associated with aging becomes predominant. The last birth is generally separated from the second last by a longer interval than those between earlier births. The risk of sterility in a given interval is thus overestimated by the method described. The increase in the mean delay to conception or in the mean interval between conceptions also leads to an overestimate as soon as the proportion of sterile women grows at an accelerated rate. The risk of error is increased still more if, as might be supposed, fecundability falls appreciably towards the end of the fertile period; the variation in intervals between conceptions would increase and hence the above-mentioned overestimation would likewise be increased.

In addition, it must be admitted that the distinction between fecund and sterile women is not easily justified unless those women considered fecund have a rather high fecundability or, at least, unless there are few among them with very low fecundability. If sterility is preceded by decreasing fecundability as it approaches nullity, the transition from fecundity to sterility becomes indiscernible. This is so serious a problem that the distinction between sterility and fecundity, however natural and useful, may be impossible to maintain beyond a certain age which, for my part, I consider somewhere between 40 and 45. Before that age, and particularly before 35, the distinction remains legitimate. Indeed, the fact that intervals between births are rarely longer than five or even four years indicates that women with extremely low fecundability are quite rare. There is accordingly a real distinction between women already sterile and fecund women.

I must finally mention that, in the investigations I am discussing, $1 - a_0(x_0)$ was equated to the proportion of women sterile at age $x_0 + i_0$ (instead of $x_0 + c_0$), where i_0 is the interval between marriage and the first birth. Ten years later, I no longer see any reason for preferring i_0 to c_0. Furthermore, P. Vincent and I assumed values for i_0 that were too high and perhaps for i_n as well.

For i_0 I took two years, whereas 15 months would have been more suitable for women married at 20–24 or 25–29 years, and a slightly higher value, say 18 months, for those married at 15–19 years. Since the calculations started with the proportion of women married at 15–19 who remained childless, the fecundity table that I devised for England (women married about the middle of the nineteenth century) corresponds to ages lower than those given, the shift being about one year.

For i_n, I took three years but only after calculating results with values of $2\frac{1}{2}$ and $3\frac{1}{2}$ years. At present, I believe that in the lower age brackets an interval of $2\frac{1}{2}$ to three years would have been more appropriate. But at these ages this change would have had only a slight effect on the estimates. We shall therefore assume that a shift of one year as described above is an adequate correction. The same correction can be made to the table for rural Japan established by the same method. For selected ages of the woman, the per cent of subsequently sterile couples is as follows:

	Age in Years				
	20	25	30	35	40
England-Wales, mid-nineteenth century	4	7.5	13	21	36
Rural Japan about 1925	5	12.5	23	38.5	61

The differences between these two series increase with age. One might think that a beginning of birth control in Japan at the relatively recent period when these observations were made might have affected the results. On examination, I discarded this possibility (cf. the article cited). But since there is no fecundity table for any other Asian population, one cannot know whether Japan is a special case.

In studies on historical populations, where the investigator has more control over the data, I have preferred another method. Only fecund couples have children. If the fertility rate of the fecund women were known for a given age, the proportion of fecund women at this age would be obtained if the fertility rate of all women is divided by the fertility rate of the fecund women. For the fertility of fecund women, one may substitute, up to about 40 years of age, the fertility of women subsequently fertile, i.e., of those who have live births at later ages.[8]

The arithmetic means of five series of percentages of sterile women by age obtained in this way are as follows:[9]

	Age in Years				
	20	25	30	35	40
Per cent sterile	3 [a]	5	8	15	32 [a]

[a] Four series rather than five.

Let us examine the shortcomings of this method. The fertility of those women who will subsequently have live births is, by selection, higher than that of all fecund women; hence, there is a risk of overestimating the proportion of sterile women at these ages. The mortality of the historical populations studied was high. It was relatively higher for women of low fertility, despite the additional risks to which childbirth subjected the others. The proportion of sterile women would thus be reduced. This point merits careful examination.

8. On the express condition of a suitable definition of subsequent fertility. If one operates in terms of groups of ages, one can take as subsequently fertile those women who were fertile beyond the higher limit of the group, e.g., for the group aged 30–34 at 35 and more. If one were to work with single years of age, it would be necessary to take as subsequently fertile women who were fertile beyond a period of several years after the end of the year considered.

9. French-Canadians (at the beginning of the eighteenth century), Bourgeoisie of Geneva (generations from 1550–1650), Crulai (end of seventeenth and beginning of eighteenth century), three parishes in the Ile-de-France (1740–1802), Europeans in Tunis (nineteenth century).

No more than the preceding method does this approach permit estimates of sterility at ages beyond 40 years. The proportions estimated for even this age are not very reliable. In conclusion, the statistical estimation of the frequency of sterility gives, or can give, acceptable results up to about 40 years of age. Between this age and the age, about 50, when all women are sterile, there is a gap that is difficult to fill through simple direct interpolation. The procedure would be less arbitrary if data were available showing the proportion of women who have reached the menopause at each age.

One cannot discuss the subject of sterility without saying a few words about terminal infertility. The women who are subsequently infertile include those who are already sterile and those who will become sterile before having had the time to give birth to another child. In the absence of mortality, the numerical determination of subsequently infertile women poses no difficulties; in view of mortality, certain precautions must be taken. The following are the percentages for Crulai, the only locality for which they have been determined.

Age in Years

	20	25	30	35	40	45
Terminal infertility	0	2.5–5	11–12	20.5	54–55	97
Sterility	2	3	7	15	36	

The first series was calculated by two methods which give very similar results except at age 25. Theoretically, the proportions in the first line should be greater than those in the second, as they are from age 30 on. Before that age, due to the small numbers involved, this was not the case at 20 or for one of the estimates at 25 years.

The frequency of terminal infertility increases slowly up to 35 years of age, and much more rapidly after that age. The probability of having another child is about 0.5 at 40; it is practically nil at 45. These results are closely correlated with the age at the last confinement. For women married before 30, it has been found close to 40 in several populations.

FUNDAMENTAL FACTORS IN FERTILITY

It is common knowledge that sexual intercourse is not necessarily and immediately followed by conception, even for a fecund couple; that a pregnant woman cannot conceive anew until the end of her pregnancy and even for some time thereafter; that some pregnancies are interrupted by a spontaneous abortion and that some of those that go to term result in stillbirths; that the age at onset of permanent sterility varies considerably and that it may be a normal consequence of aging or an accidental consequence of a delivery. It is, nevertheless, only in recent years that these obvious facts were successively introduced into demography and employed to construct a coherent theory of natural fertility and of the process of family building.

In 1924, the Italian statistician and demographer C. Gini introduced the concept of fecundability. This is defined as the probability of conception per menstrual cycle or, more simply, per month, outside of periods of pregnancy or of the infecundable periods, of varying length, which follow delivery. Gini indicated methods for evaluating fecundability.[10] For about 30 years, however, this new concept, although fundamental, received little attention from demographers. Considered in isolation, its importance was doubtless not obvious.

I used this notion first in 1953, in a mathematical model of family growth from the time of marriage. This model included only two factors, fecundability and the duration of the infecundability that follows each conception.[11]

Subsequently, I constructed a model in which fertility depended explicitly on three basic functions:[12] (1) fecundability outside of the periods defined below; (2) the probability that a woman is not in a period of immunity or of nonsusceptibility to conception that follows each conception, i.e., that she is not pregnant or in the period before resumption of ovulation or of sexual relations after a delivery or a miscarriage; (3) the probability that a conception will result in a live birth, i.e., the probability of avoiding intrauterine death.

10. C. Gini, ''Premières recherches sur la fécondabilité de la femme,'' *Proceedings of the International Mathematics Congress* (Toronto, 1924), pp. 889–892.

11. L. Henry, ''Fondements théoriques des mesures de la fécondité naturelle,'' *Revue de l'Institut International de Statistique*, XXI (1953), pp. 135–151.

12. L. Henry, ''Fécondité et famille. Modèles mathématiques,'' *Population*, XII (July–Sept., 1957), pp. 413–444; *Population*, XVI (Jan.–March, 1961), pp. 27–48; and *Population*, XVI (April–June, 1961), pp. 261–282.

One may wonder, at first, why the risk of sterility does not appear among the fundamental factors. Physiological sterility is in fact contained in the first function, while pathological sterility may be accounted for in terms of the second.

It might be expected in advance, and has been verified by empirical observations, that the three fundamental functions are not equal for all couples. Each couple is characterized by its own values of these fundamental functions which may, nevertheless, be equal to those of other couples.

In order to construct a complete theory of natural fertility, probability distributions of the parameters should be added to the fundamental functions. Nevertheless, it is essential to many theoretical problems that one first study homogeneous populations, where couples all have the same values for the fundamental functions.

First Hypothesis Concerning the Fundamental Functions

Each of the above three probabilities could be a function of the ages of the spouses, of the duration of their marriage, of achieved parity, or of the time elapsed since the last conception or the last confinement.

Nevertheless, the first models (1953) were constructed in terms of fecundability considered constant from marriage until permanent sterility supervened and in terms of a constant duration of immunity to conception.

In the first investigations subsequently conducted on small yet quite distinct populations (members of the ruling class of Geneva, villagers in France, India and Taiwan), the differences in fertility among women of the same age and of different marital durations were not statistically significant.

I concluded from these investigations that, at least as a first approximation, one could consider as independent variables, only the woman's age for probabilities (1) and (3), and this age plus the interval since the last conception for probability (2).

All women are sterile before puberty and after the menopause. Some of them remain sterile all their lives; for them fecundability remains constant and nil at every age, and the other functions are undetermined. For other women, fecundability must reach a maximum value between puberty and the menopause. In view of the slight variation in fertility observed between the ages of 20 and 30 years, it seems reasonable to assume that the function is flat in the region of the maximum. Therefore it can be approximated by a horizontal line of variable length as was done in my models of 1957 and 1961. I assumed that, from this high level, fecundability decreased almost linearly toward a value of zero.

I also had to make provision for "adolescent sterility," the existence of which was already well known. It could be explained by a variable period of complete sterility after puberty or by a progressive increase in fecundability up to maturity. I chose the second hypothesis as more interesting to study.

Accounting to this first scheme, fecundability, nil until some age a, would then increase until some age b, pass through a constant maximum from age b to age y and then would decrease until an age z when it would become nil again. After age z, the woman would be sterile.

In this model, each woman is characterized in terms of the ages a, b, y, and z as well as by her maximal fecundability. Because of the variations in z from one woman to another, the proportion of sterile women increases with age. For this reason it was unnecessary explicitly to introduce into the model a risk of physiological sterility.

Terminal sterility may also occur prematurely following an illness of either the husband or the wife. To take this into account, it suffices to truncate the curve at the age z', situated between a and z, when such pathological sterility occurs.

This scheme serves as a useful guide since it demonstrates what information is needed from empirical data; the ages at the beginning and end of the three phases ab, by, and vz, and the value of the maximal fecundability, or at a minimum, the mean values of these quantities and, if possible, an index of their dispersion.

I have formulated practically no explicit hypotheses concerning the influence of the woman's age on the second probability. In numerical calculations, I have proceeded as if age had no effect on this probability.

I have, on the other hand, assumed that all women emerge from the postpartum period of immunity after a finite time. To take into consideration accidental sterility following pregnancy, it would have been necessary to introduce permanent immunity for a small fraction of women. As this complicates theoretical investigation, such sterility can, in practice, be included with the already mentioned sterility following illness. This simplification is justified by the fact that, not long after marriage, the distribution of conception over time becomes quite regular.

Neither have I formulated any hypothesis regarding probability (3). It is not necessary in the theoretical study of conceptions and I have not considered it in numerical applications.

Observations

In the United States, a number of results have been obtained relating to observations on conception delays after the interruption of contraceptive use. Since observations of this nature have not been made in France, natural fertility can be studied there only through observations on populations where resort to birth control is nonexistent or little practiced.

P. Vincent focused his investigations on large families (of at least nine children), contestants in a large-family competition established after the First World War. He was thus able to study a large sample of about 15,000 families.[13]

I adopted a different course, orienting my investigations toward the past. First, I studied some genealogies of very high quality of the ruling class of Geneva.[14] However, there are simply not enough genealogies available for demographic purposes. It is therefore more valuable to reconstruct family histories from civil registers (parish registers before 1793) and other documents, if available (church lists, registry lists, tax rolls, notaries' archives). It was through this desire to collect observations on natural fertility that I was led to the study of historical demography, which I now pursue for its own sake.

As of now, the marital history of only a few hundred couples has been reconstructed, from a limited number of villages

---

13. P. Vincent, *Recherches sur la fécondité biologique* (Paris: Presses Universitaires de France, 1961).

14. L. Henry, *Anciennes familles genevoises* (Paris: Presses Universitaires de France, 1956). *Note:* Another demographic study using genealogies is J. Henripin, *La population canadiene au début du XVIIIe siècle* (Paris: Presses Universitaires de France, 1954).

(Crulai in Normandy,[15] Saint-Sernin and Thézels in Quercy,[16] Sottevillelès-Rouen,[17] Saint-Agnan,[18] Ingouville,[19] and three villages in Ile-de-France [20]). To this list must be added, outside of France, the European population of Tunis.[21]

In the framework of a sampling study begun about five years ago in order to reconstruct the population of eighteenth-century France, data were collected on the history of about 30,000 marriages in some 40 villages, which constituted a one-in-a-thousand random sample of French villages. There will be, to be sure, an important deficiency since, because of migrations, a non-negligible fraction of families is lost to observation before enough data are available to make their histories of much use. Experience has shown, however, that in this field of investigation, results may be obtained without numerous observations.

Theoretical Research

P. Vincent directed his investigations principally toward the possible effect of the following factors on the distribution of conceptions and births following marriage: (1) the timing of marriage in the menstrual cycle, (2) variations in fecundability among women, (3) variations in the duration of menstrual cycle among women and within the same woman, and (4) variations in the duration of pregnancy.

An important conclusion of these studies is that the mean fecundability of newlyweds may conveniently be estimated from the distribution of intervals from marriage to first births conceived postnuptially, although sometimes at the cost of rather involved computations.

For my part, I have been concerned primarily with relating

15. E. Gautier and L. Henry, *La population de Crulai, paroisse normande* (Paris: Presses Universitaires de France, 1958).

16. P. Valmary, *Familles paysannes au XVIIIe siècle en Bas-Quercy*, in press.

17. P. Girard, ''Aperçus de la démographie de Sotteville-lès-Rouen vers la fin du XVIIIe siècle,'' *Population*, XIV (July–Sept., 1959), pp. 485–508.

18. J. Houdaille, ''Un village du Morvan: Saint-Agnan,'' *Population*, XVI (April–June, 1961), pp. 301–312.

19. M. Terrisse, ''Un faubourg du Havre: Ingouville,'' *Population*, XVI (April–June, 1961), pp. 285–300.

20. J. Ganiage, *Trois villages de l'Ile-de-France* (Paris: Presses Universitaires de France, 1963).

21. J. Ganiage, *Le population européenne de Tunis au milieu du XIXe siècle* (Paris: Presses Universitaires de France, 1960).

the basic functions to the most common demographic indices: legitimate fertility rates by age or by marital duration and intervals between confinements.

I have also shown that the instantaneous fertility rate (or the rate per menstrual cycle in a discrete model) does not depend on the initial conditions after a sufficiently long time following marriage. This result is equivalent to that obtained by Lotka for stable populations.

The existence of the period of immunity introduces, on the other hand, an asymmetry in the curve of age-specific fertility, even if the curve of fecundability is symmetrical (i.e., phase *ab* and phase *yz* are equal).

When the fundamental functions do not vary with the age of the woman, the instantaneous fertility rate tends toward a constant limit equal to $pv/(1 + gp)$ where p is fecundability, g the mean duration of infecundability and v the probability that a conception will lead to a live birth.

The inverse of this fertility rate is equal to the mean interval between live births. P. Vincent has termed it the characteristic interval of the homogeneous group, or couple, under consideration.

For heterogeneous groups, the instantaneous fertility rate is equal to the inverse of the mean interval between births occurring in a well-defined "period of time."[22] I had shown previously that the fertility rate of subsequently fertile women of a given age group, 25–29 years for example, was equal to the inverse of the mean of all intervals beginning or ending in this age group (those that begin and end in the group being counted twice) and that this relation held approximately in practice, even when fertility varied with age.

These theoretical investigations have provided a more secure basis for analysis and measurement; they have lent a good deal of importance to the intervals between births, a subject long neglected.

I have shown that with relatively simple models, it is possible essentially to reconstruct observations on successive intervals between births in families of the same completed size. In order

22. P. Vincent, *Recherches sur la fécondité* (Paris: Presses Universitaires de France, 1956).

to explain the observed increase in later intervals (the last particularly) in terms of decreasing fecundability, it would be necessary that the decrease take place over a period of 10 to 15 years. The agreement between the simple models studied and reality is still not perfect; in reality, the increase in question appears more abruptly than in the models. If other data confirm this observation, efforts with other models will have to be made.

RESULTS

In the large sample studied by P. Vincent, he estimated the mean effective fecundability (i.e., ignoring fetal death) of newlywed women aged 16 to 25 years as follows. From about 15 per cent at age 16, it increased rapidly to 24 per cent at 18 to 19 years of age. It then increased more slowly, until at 25 years it was found to be 27 per cent. Although each woman in this sample had at least nine children, the effect of this selection on the estimated fecundability seems to be small. In fact, however, the increase in fecundability from ages 18–19 to 25 is probably less marked than in this sample.

These estimates concern fecundability in the strict sense, i.e., the probability of conception per menstrual cycle. Since the average length of menstrual cycles decreases from adolescence to maturity, the probabilities of conception per unit of time (per month, for example), increase a little more than does the effective fecundability as estimated above. The increase in gross fecundability (i.e., including conceptions terminating in miscarriages) is, on the contrary, less marked because of the decrease in intrauterine mortality as the woman passes from adolescence to maturity. Although detailed data are not available on the change in intrauterine mortality with maternal age, it is unlikely that such changes from 16 to 25 years of age are the only cause of a rise in effective fecundability.[23]

The number of observations made to date on historical populations does not allow such detailed study. For Crulai and the three villages of Ile-de-France, considered *in toto*, I estimated the mean effective fecundability as 23 per cent at marriage for

23. S. Shapiro *et al.*, ''A Life Table of Pregnancy Terminations and Correlates of Fetal Loss,'' *The Milbank Memorial Fund Quarterly*, XL (Jan., 1962), pp. 7–45.

those women married at 20–29 whose married life had lasted at least five years (207 women).

The number of very early marriages is small in these populations. Nevertheless, I have found a significant difference between the ratio of births at 8–11 months after marriage to all first births occurring after at least eight months to women married at 15–17, and the same ratio for those married at 20–29 years. There is not doubt, then of the existence and generality of the phenomenon called "adolescent sterility." In fact, this phenomenon is not true sterility, but rather reduced fecundability, since it persists after the first confinement. P. Vincent found, in fact, that the interval between the first and second confinements was longer than subsequent intervals among very young women. Accordingly, phase *ab* of the curve of fecundability is not an almost vertically ascending line, but the rise in fecundability as maturity is approached is spread over several years.

Available observations do not permit an estimate of fecundability after the first birth. Consequently it is not possible to establish whether fecundability indeed depends only on age, as we have assumed.

The slight variability in the fertility of subsequently fertile women between the age groups 20–24 and 25–29 years leads me to believe that the fundamental factors vary little at these ages. The previously cited study of intrauterine mortality showed little variation for women aged 20–24 and 25–29 years. Since, as P. Vincent has shown, effective fecundability varies little (at least between 20 and 25 years of age), the same may be said for gross fecundability.

The changes in gross fecundability after age 30 remain relatively unknown. Originally I tended to ascribe the marked increase in the length of the intervals between the last few births in the completed family (the second last and especially the last interval) to a slow decrease in gross fecundability. Phase *yz* would on the average, then, last about 10 to 15 years, let us say from 30 to 35 to about 45 years of age. But the little we know at present about the marked rise in fetal mortality with age, after age 30, has led me to modify my viewpoint. This rise explains a good part of the decrease, beginning at age 30, in the fertility rates of subsequently fertile women. A recent study has shown, moreover, that the duration of the period of infecundability probably increases with the age of the woman. Consequently, I cannot actually be certain whether gross fecundability falls as the woman ages from 30 to 40 or even 45. I doubt that statistical demography *per se* can answer this question. Observations of biologists or physicians on the frequency of anovulatory cycles and on changes in this frequency with the woman's age seem essential if the effect of the woman's age on gross fecundability is to be determined.

The foregoing has been concerned with averages. Now, fecundability varies from one woman to the other; this is shown by the fact that monthly fertility quotients (the number of first births in the nth month of marriage per thousand subsequently fertile women who have not yet had their first child before the beginning of that month) decrease after the tenth month of marriage. P. Vincent has obtained very good approximations to these quotients by assuming monthly quotients of conceptions as 0.251 for the first month, 0.220 for the second month, 0.198 for the third, etc. On the other hand, I showed in 1953 [24] that the ratio of conceptions in the second month to those of the first enables an estimate to be made of the coefficient of variation in the distribution of fecundability. From the values just given for Vincent's data, this coefficient may be estimated as 0.6.

If one could be certain that fecundability is not modified by the first birth, the duration of immunity after conception would be easy to determine. It would be sufficient to evaluate the conception delay corresponding to the age of the woman and to subtract it from the average interval between deliveries. In view of the uncertainty, other methods have been resorted to. K. Dandekar estimated the fecundability and the duration of immunity for 46 women in Crulai, from the variance between the intervals within each family. [25] Since each variance was estimated from four intervals, the values thus obtained have only limited reliability. One cannot, to my mind, use these estimates

---

24. L. Henry, ''Fondements théoriques des mesures de la fécondité naturelle,'' *Revue de l'Institut International de Statistique*, XXI (1953), pp. 135–151.

25. K. Dandekar, ''Intervals Between Confinements,'' *Eugenics Quarterly*, VI (Sept., 1959), pp. 180–186.

to make acceptable inferences regarding the dispersion of fecundability and of the period of immunity. Besides, the method used in fact gives no more than a lower limit for the average immunity period. It would be equal to the mean duration of immunity only if this period were constant for each woman. This is obviously not the case, even when, as here, the families are limited to those where each child survived for at least a full year. In these families, the average period of immunity after one of the first four conceptions exceeds 21 months.

I took up this problem again, using a slightly different method which is also based on the internal variance between intervals, but in a different form.[26] The method provides an estimate for a lower limit for the duration of immunity by maternal age. At about 30 years of age, this lower limit is of the order of 20 months for Crulai and the three villages of Ile-de-France. The lower limit increases with maternal age. Since the lower limit at 35–39 is greater than the upper limit at 25–29, the duration of immunity must increase between these age periods. As of now, however, it cannot be concluded that this duration increases continuously with maternal age. Particularly is this the case since the number of preceding pregnancies probably has some effect on it. According to the available data, intervals between confinements for the same woman tend to increase fairly regularly, on the average, from the second to the second last interval. But when the interval between the first and second confinements (first interval) begins at maturity or later, say after age 20, the increase from this interval to the next is greater, on the average, than between subsequent intervals. This change, related to a specific birth order, cannot be ascribed to age; it is an effect of the first pregnancy. According to medical observation, amenorrhea during lactation is much less frequent in the case of the first child than for subsequent children; the above observation would then be a result of this difference in frequency.

Once more, I present only uncertain conclusions, due to deficiencies in available biological data. When newborns live at least a year, the internal variance of the duration of immunity is

26. L. Henry, ''Mesure de temps mort en fécondité naturelle,'' *Population*, XIX (June–July, 1964), pp. 485–514.

closely associated with the internal variance of postpartum amenorrhea. If the latter were known, the former could be evaluated and hence the real duration of immunity could be estimated.

The period of immunity varies considerably from woman to woman. Fecundability similarly varies; it may therefore be asked whether differences in fertility among women depend more on one of these variations than on the other. The following observation suggests that variations in the period of immunity are more important. The mean interval between confinements is greater when the preceding child survives to the age of one year (a "normal" interval) than if the child dies before this age (interval after death). There is a marked inverse relationship between the mean length of normal intervals and completed family size. This relation is much less marked for intervals after a death, which depend less on the duration of immunity. Thus large families are more often associated with short immune periods than with high levels of fecundability.

PART IV

Biological Aspects of
Natality and Its Control

Dugald Baird

VARIATIONS IN FERTILITY ASSOCIATED WITH CHANGES IN HEALTH STATUS

INTRODUCTION

In many countries where child death rates are high, maximum use has been made of high fertility to produce as many babies as possible since only in this way could populations be maintained. Today, with falling death rates and rising standards of health, planned parenthood and a drastic reduction in family size are more often the rule. In this way a baby's survival is much less a matter of chance or even "natural selection." Some think that this will lead to serious dangers and that one effect of the lower death rates, brought about by the rising standard of living in general and higher standards of obstetric and pediatric care in particular, will be the survival of the unfit who would previously have died. They, in turn, will produce more substandard infants and so lead in time to an increase in the percentage of substandard people. There is as yet little evidence to support this view.

According to the family census of 1946 conducted by the Royal Commission on Population,[1] 11.7 per cent of couples in

1. *Report of the Family Census of 1946,* VI (London: Royal Commission on Population, 1954).

Britain who married in the years 1900–09 were childless after 10 years. The percentages by age at marriage were as follows:

Under 20	20–24	25–29	30–34	35–39	40+
6.2	8.4	14.3	22.7	39.4	68.2

Amongst those who marry at 25 years of age or over, no change in childlessness occurs with increasing length of marriage beyond 10 years. There was very little difference in the rate between the social classes. This was at a time when according to Lewis-Fanning[2] not more than four per cent of couples used birth control at marriage.

As birth control spread down through the social classes the effect was shown in increasing childlessness, first of all in the nonmanual workers and later in the manual workers.

Figures for Irish women marrying in the period 1876–81 show few childless women. For example, in those marrying at the ages of 20–24 and 25–29 the rates of childlessness were 4.4 and 5.9 per cent respectively. Glass and Grebenik[3] thought that these figures might be artificially low since women marrying in Ireland in that period might have been "selected" to some extent for physiological fertility.

Amongst the Hutterites in Dakota, Eaton and Mayer[4] found that the median age of marriage of women was 22.0 years and the median number of children 10.6. The actual size of the Hutterite family was 1–3 children fewer than the theoretical maximum which these women might have produced because most of them were over 20 years of age before they married. There was no variation in fertility with socioeconomic status but in this society class distinctions scarcely existed. The peak of fertility was the 22nd year of life when seven out of every 10 women who were married between 1941–50 had a live child.

2. E. Lewis-Faning, *Report on the Enquiry into Family Limitation and Its Influence on Human Fertility During the Last Fifty Years*, I (London: Royal Commission on Population, 1949).

3. D. V. Glass and E. Grebenik, *The Trend and Pattern of Fertility in Great Britain*, VI (London: Royal Commission on Population, 1954), p. 254.

4. J. W. Eaton and A. J. Mayer, "The Social Biology of the Very High Fertility Amongst the Hutterites: The Demography of a Unique Population," *Human Biology*, XXV–XXVI, pp. 206–264.

Fertility in the age group 25–29 was also very high: 498 babies were born per year to every 1,000 women in this specific age group. Unfortunately there is no accurate information about stillbirth rates. The infant mortality in the years 1946–50 was 48 per 1,000 compared to 38.3 per 1,000 in the United States in 1945. It is not possible to say what proportion of these deaths occurred in the neonatal period.

In Hutterite communities in South Dakota, death rates were higher in females than males in every age group over the age of 15, except over the age of 60 when the position was reversed. It was thought that this might be explained by a high death rate in childbirth. Home deliveries were the rule and many of the midwives were self-taught.

These figures show that the reproductive capacity in a healthy population is high, and far above what is required for replacement. Formerly early marriage was associated with large families but today, although the average age at marriage is decreasing, the average family size has risen only slightly. This makes it clear that more women now have children because they want them and not because they cannot prevent pregnancy. It will be shown later that improved health and growth of young mothers which is a concomitant of these changes should help to ensure that reproductive wastage is kept to a minimum.

A follow-up in 1955 of 804 women who had a first baby in Aberdeen in 1949 showed that in Social Classes I and II, 13 per cent had had a second delivery within 18 months and a further 23 per cent within three years; at the end of five years 36 per cent had had no further children. In Classes IV and V the corresponding figures were 23, 35, and 23. In other words, spacing was widespread in all social classes but the interval was greater in Classes I and II and the number of children smaller. The interval was shorter in all classes if the baby was stillborn or died later. Family limitation is least practiced and least effective where material conditions are worst—mainly in Classes IV and V. Apathy, hostility, and lack of knowledge on the subject of birth control are still prevalent. There is little or no discussion between husband and wife. Social Classes IV and V provide one quarter of all first births and one half of all seventh or subsequent births. They have received a poor education and have lower than average intelligence test scores. They also tend to be of poor physique and living conditions are substandard. About four per cent of the women followed up were found to have had a postpartum sterilization performed because of multiparity and debility and inability to prevent conception. They came from the lowest socioeconomic groups amongst whom death rates are high. In the National Birthday Trust Perinatal Mortality Survey of 1958 [5] the perinatal death rate in the Para 4+ category was 50.5 compared to 33.6 in Para 0 and 23.5 in Para 1. It is clear, therefore, that in the conditions prevailing in many large industrial cities many of the wives of semiskilled or unskilled manual workers are ill-grown, unhealthy, and unable to limit the size of their families.

It seems that much more severe environmental conditions are required before they affect adversely the capacity to conceive, as, for example, in the famine conditions which prevailed over a six-month period in Holland in 1944 when amenorrhea was widespread and fecundity was seriously affected. Even more severe effects were reported by Antonov [6] during the siege of Leningrad where hardships of all kinds were greater and of longer duration.

FACTORS AFFECTING FERTILITY

Important biological factors are the mother's age and number of previous pregnancies. Maternal health and physique, which are influenced by genetic factors, and the type of environment in which she has been reared, greatly affect the mother's response to pregnancy. Finally, the standards of obstetric and pediatric care greatly influence the mortality and morbidity associated with childbirth for both mother and child.

These various factors are however so interrelated that it is difficult to isolate the effect of any one of them. For example, the influence of age is obscured by the fact that in Britain at least those who start childbearing at the age of 18 are very different people in many respects from those who postpone childbearing

5. *Perinatal Mortality: The First Report of the British Perinatal Mortality Survey* (Edinburgh and London: Livingstone, 1963).
6. A. M. Antonov, *Journal of Pediatrics*, XXX (1947), p. 250.

till the age of 28. Again they may, for a variety of reasons, receive very different standards of obstetric care which again will further complicate the study of "biological" effects of age. This has been carried to such lengths today that if we wish to demonstrate statistically the effect of age on length of labor or perinatal mortality we are forced to use data collected 25 years ago when obstetric practice was much more conservative and less selective.

Another difficulty is that hospital patients may not represent a true cross section of the childbearing women in a community, either because, as in some areas of Britain, a high percentage are confined at home or because the hospital in question may be situated in a particular area of a city which may not contain a representative cross section of the society. For this reason I shall, in this paper, make free use of Aberdeen material since 85 per cent of all women in the city and all primigravidae are confined in the only specialist hospital in the city.

Health and Physique of the Mother

It is reasonable to assume that healthy and well-grown mothers will be more efficient reproducers than those who are undergrown and unhealthy. Unfortunately we have no objective and easy method of measuring health and physique. However, the social class to which a woman belongs does more than signify what kind of home she lives in and how much money she has. It tells us about her way of life, and indirectly about her health, physique, and intelligence. Those brought up by well-to-do parents in a good environment will have better food, more fresh air and exercise, a better education, and better medical care than those brought up by poor parents in a poor environment.

Thus we can assume that upper social class women are more likely to reach the maximum stature permitted by their genetic makeup, while those who grow in less satisfactory conditions will fail to attain the maximum possible. The poorer the living conditions in a community the higher the proportion of small women resulting from stunting of growth. In the city of Aberdeen the percentage of primigravidae less than 61 inches in height varies from less than 10 per cent in the wives of professional and business men to 29 per cent in the wives of semiskilled or unskilled workers, and the percentages measuring 64 inches or more are 47 and 21 respectively.

Bernard [7] reported from the results of X-ray pelvimetry in 100 young women under 5 ft. and 100 of 5 ft. 4 in. or more in height that not only were the pelves in the short women generally smaller than those of the tall women but that 34 per cent of them had flattened pelvic brims compared to only seven per cent of the tall women. He also found that those women assessed clinically as being in very good health had less flattening of the pelvic brim than those found to be in poor general health. Bernard found exactly similar differences in the pelves of tall and short men. Indeed he was of the opinion that the triangular, so-called "android," pelvic brim is almost certainly a form of flattening, a sign of stunting and not of masculinity. In a few cases the promontory of the sacrum projected forwards to produce a kidney-shaped pelvic brim indistinguishable from that seen in women with other signs of having had rickets in childhood.

Statistical analysis shows that the incidence of difficult labor due to disproportion decreases with increasing height of the mother. As one would expect, the Caesarean section rate for obstructed labor and the perinatal death rate from birth trauma also decrease with increasing height of the mother. In addition, however, the perinatal death rate from all *other causes* decreases with increasing maternal stature. This also seems logical since if superior environmental conditions in childhood favor maximum growth of the skeleton they should also favor maximum growth and development of all body tissues and thus promote maximum efficiency in childbearing. It is interesting to note that while in the upper social classes the perinatal mortality and prematurity rates fall steadily with increase in stature in primigravidae right to the uppermost limits of height, in the lowest social classes the rates rise in women over 5 ft. 4 in. This suggests that in poor lower class homes where diets are inadequate it may be disadvantageous to have a very high growth potential since in these circumstances requirements are less

7. R. N. Bernard, ''The Shape and Size of the Female Pelvis,'' Proceedings of the Edinburgh Obstetrical Society, *Edinburgh Medical Journal,* LIX (1952), p. 1.

likely to be fully met than in those children whose requirements are less. They may succeed in growing tall but may not develop fully, and therefore may grow up to be rather unhealthy adults.

Table 1 gives the results of an attempt by obstetricians at the

TABLE 1

Incidence of Obstetric Abnormalities in Aberdeen Primigravidae by Maternal Health and Physique as Assessed at the First Antenatal Examination. Twin Pregnancies Have Been Excluded

	Health and Physique			
	Very good	Good	Fair	Poor: very poor
Prematurity a(%)	5.1	6.4	10.4	12.1
Caesarean section (%)	2.7	3.5	4.2	5.4
Perinatal deaths per 1,000 births	26.9	29.2	44.8	62.8
Percentage tall (5 ft. 4 in. or more)	42	29	18	13
Percentage short (under 5 ft. 1 in.)	10	20	30	48
No. of subjects	707	2,088	1,294	223

a Birth weight of baby 2,500 g. or less.

Aberdeen Maternity Hospital to grade the health and physique of primigravidae into one of four categories at the first visit to an antenatal clinic. Statistical analysis of the outcome of the pregnancies shows that women thought to be in poor health had high rates of prematurity, perinatal mortality, and Caesarean section. They were short in stature, nearly 50 per cent being less than 61 inches. On the other hand, those judged to be in very good health were much taller; only 10 per cent measured less than 61 inches; they had low perinatal, prematurity, and Caesarean section rates.

As a general rule, those born and brought up in an upper social class environment marry into the same class. Illsley [8] has shown that there is considerable social mobility in Britain today and that more women move up in the social scale on marriage

8. R. Illsley, "Social Class Selection and Class Differences in Relation to Stillbirths and Infant Deaths," *British Medical Journal*, XI, p. 1520.

than move down. He showed that in Aberdeen those who move up on marriage are taller and have lower perinatal death rates and prematurity rates than those who do not move up on marriage. Given a uniformly good standard of obstetrical care the perinatal mortality level into which any particular married woman is likely to fall can be predicted with surprising accuracy even before pregnancy if her height, age, and her father's and her husband's occupations are known. The National Birthday Trust Perinatal Mortality Survey of 1958 gave Illsley the opportunity to confirm his findings in a National sample.

Table 2 shows that the highest percentages of tall women (65 inches or more) was found in those whose fathers and husbands both belonged to the professional classes (46 per cent), whereas the lowest percentage of tall women (24 per cent) occurred where both the father and the husband had semiskilled or unskilled occupations. The percentage of mothers who had education over the minimum followed the same pattern.

TABLE 2

Height of Wives, Educational Standard and Mortality Ratio (All Parities) by Socio-economic Group of Father and Husband; National Birthday Trust Mortality Survey 1958

| | Father's Socioeconomic Group | | | | | | | | | | | |
| | Professional | | | Nonmanual | | | Skilled | | | Unskilled | | |
Husband's socioeconomic group	(a) [a]	(b) [b]	(c) [c]	(a)	(b)	(c)	(a)	(b)	(c)	(a)	(b)	(c)
Professional	46	84	(71)	40	71	(72)	37	47	(76)	32	39	(93)
Nonmanual	43	73	(76)	36	44	(85)	30	30	(83)	26	18	(89)
Skilled	34	48	(81)	32	32	(89)	28	17	(94)	23	11	(104)
Unskilled	27	42	(117)	28	20	(82)	26	12	(102)	24	10	(124)
All	41	69	(79)	34	43	(85)	29	21	(91)	25	12	(111)

[a] Per cent 65 in. or more in height.
[b] Per cent educated beyond the minimum.
[c] Mortality ratio.

The mortality ratio compared to a mean of 100 was distributed in the same way, the lowest (71) being in those who were daughters of professional men and who were married to professional men. The highest (124) was in those who were daughters of semiskilled or unskilled laborers and who were married to semiskilled or unskilled laborers. The number of women who rise in the social scale on marriage was twice as great as those who moved down. They were also taller and had a lower mortality ratio.

These trends are the effect of the rising standard of living which offers opportunities to those with the ability to rise in the social scale. Since more move up than down, the lowest social class becomes smaller; but because of the resultant greater concentration of poorer types, perinatal mortality rates do not fall and, in fact, may rise. Thus the gap in mortality between the social classes is maintained or may widen.

This helps to explain the fact that the fall in mortality and morbidity with rising standards of living among unskilled manual workers is less than might be expected. Another factor is that the women in this group are least likely to make full use of the services provided either for themselves or their children. They tend to be very conservative in their habits and to lack initiative. The fact that they tend to remain in the same neighborhoods and to take the most unattractive and worst paid jobs means that they tend to marry inside the same social class so that the effects of undesirable hereditary characteristics may be added on to those resulting from the unfavorable environment.

Age and Parity

The outcome of pregnancy depends on the age and the parity of the mother. In each parity maternal age has an important influence. The interpretation of age and parity trends is complex since age at any given parity is affected by social circumstances.

Thus in Britain, until recently, it has been exceptional for the well educated woman with a good social background to bear her first child before the age of 20—many were nearer 30. Primigravidae under 20 therefore come from the lowest social group and may include many unmarried women and many more who conceived before marriage. They are, as a group, of inferior health and physique and living in poor conditions and in many cases have made no preparations for acquiring a home. Under the Aberdeen Town Council's housing policy most young married couples have little chance of getting a house of their own. Many start married life in a room sublet from parents or, less often, from a stranger.

In the Aberdeen Maternity Hospital in the age group 15–19, eight per cent are 65 inches or taller and 44 per cent are under 62 inches whereas in the age group 30–34, 20 per cent are 65 inches or taller and only 28 per cent are less than 62 inches. This is to a large extent a social class effect, although not entirely, since in all social classes the percentage of tall women is highest in those who have their first child between the ages of 25 and 34. In England and Wales young primigravidae are much taller than in Scotland so that the difference in height distribution by age is much less. This is a measure of the fact that the standard of living, especially amongst the semiskilled and unskilled workers, is much higher in England than in Scotland. Industrial Scotland, with the closing of the coal fields and the decline in ship building, can be classified as a depressed area.

Age, however, has a more direct biological meaning. It would be surprising if primiparae who had postponed childbearing for many years after they have attained sexual and physical maturity preserve their reproductive efficiency intact, and it is well recognized that the "elderly primigravida" (say, aged 35 or over) is particularly liable to experience difficulty even when she is in good health. It is not so well known, however, that efficiency begins to decline very much earlier. For example, if the management of labor is conservative, the incidence of spontaneous delivery in less than 24 hours is highest in the 15–19 age group and the chance of an intact perineum, i.e., one which is elastic enough to stretch without tearing or without the need for an episiotomy incision, is about 10 per cent less in the 15–19 age group than in the age group 20–24 [9]

Hytten [10] has shown that enlargement of the breasts during pregnancy and the output of fat and of total milk output is considerably lower in primiparae in the age group 20–24 than in the 15–19 age group.

9. D. Baird, F. E. Hytten, and A. M. Thomson, "Age and Human Reproduction," *Journal of Obstetrics and Gynaecology of the British Empire*, LXV (1958), No. 6, p. 865.

10. F. E. Hytten, "The Relationship Between the Age, Physique and Nutritional Status of the Mother to the Yield and Composition of Her Milk," *British Medical Journal*, XI (1954), p. 844.

In the village of Imesi in Western Nigeria, I have, through the kindness of Miss Woodland, the resident health nurse, been able to study all the first births occurring in one year—47 in all. Seventeen of the mothers were less than 17 years old and only one of these was more than 64 inches tall; 8 of the 17 babies were less than 2,500 g. at birth. In 14 having the first child between the ages of 19–22, six were more than 64 inches tall and only two babies were under 2,500 g. Women having a second child at 18 were well up to the height of the older primigravidae. The high prematurity rate in the very young primigravidae was related to the fact that the mothers themselves were not fully grown. It is not known with certainty whether or not there were any social stigmata attached to childbearing at a very early age. Most of the Aberdeen primigravidae in the 15–19 age group were 18 or 19 years of age and had stopped growing. Thus, while it seems clear that the age of 16 is too soon for efficient childbearing, there is strong evidence that the primigravida, especially if she has been reared in good environment, is most efficient at about 18 years of age. The importance of youth in parturition helps to explain the fact that in many underdeveloped countries where childbearing starts at an early age the actual labor is so often easy and uneventful. When the mother is young and well developed it is very seldom necessary to apply forceps to complete a labor because the mother is unable to do so herself.

After the age of about 22, however, a steadily increasing percentage of mothers seem to require assistance to complete the delivery for no other reason than they are unable to expel the baby themselves. With increasing age the risk of unexplained intrauterine death (possibly due to placental insufficiency) increases, more particularly if the pregnancy is prolonged much beyond 40 weeks; in addition hypertension and pre-eclampsia are more frequent and add to the risks. Today a very high proportion of primigravidae over 35 years of age are delivered by Caesarean section. In many instances this is done primarily in the interests of the baby. This policy has been successful in reducing the very high perinatal mortality which has been characteristic of the elderly primigravida.

In the young primigravida, despite her poor health and physique, the risk of intrauterine death at or near term is much less and the risks of anoxia [shortage of oxygen in infant's brain] during labor are also less. This is because at this age uterine action is good and the cervix dilates quickly so that labor is not prolonged except occasionally where there is contracted pelvis and a big baby and disproportion. In such cases the decision to perform Caesarean section can be taken fairly quickly. This is in contrast to the problem of difficult labor in the elderly primigravida, where the cause of delay is more likely to be cervical dystocia or disordered uterine action, and where much more time may be required before a decision can be taken as to whether vaginal delivery is possible or not.

In the young primigravida death rates from prematurity (cause unexplained) and malformations of the central nervous system are high. Such causes cannot, of course, be easily prevented by any treatment during pregnancy.

Table 3 shows that the perinatal mortality is lowest in Social

TABLE 3

Perinatal Mortality by Height and Social Class of Husband; All Aberdeen Primi-gravidae, 1948–57

Height	Social class			All classes
	I & II	III	IV & V	
64 in. and over (Tall)	14	25	35	25
63 in.–61 in. (Medium)	22	33	37	33
Less than 61 in. (Short)	35	36	55	42

Classes I and II, and that in each social class the death rate rises with decreasing stature. The lowest rate, 14 per 1,000, is found in tall women in Social Classes I and II and the highest, 55 per 1,000, in short women in Classes IV and V.

Table 4 shows that the lowest perinatal mortality—12 per 1,000—occurs in tall primigravidae aged 25–29. In the age groups 20–24 and 15–19 the Caesarean section rate is much less than that in the 25–29 age group, but the perinatal mortality is much higher. For the reasons stated above there is no idication for increasing the Caesarean section rate. The younger age groups contain many women from the lower social classes whereas the 25–29 age group is predominantly upper social class. Even at the comparatively early age of 25–29 it has been found necessary to increase the Caesarean section rate to 2.4 per

TABLE 4

Primigravidae, 1953–60, All Aberdeen; Caesarean Section Per Cent; Perinatal Deaths Per Thousand

Height	Age group					
	20	20–24	25–29	30–34	35 +	Total
Tall						
Caesarean section	0.4	1.1	2.4	9.6	24.6	2.9
Perinatal deaths	44	21	12	28	43	22
Medium						
Caesarean section	1.1	2.4	5.4	12.5	34.3	4.6
Perinatal deaths	34	25	25	34	40	27
Small						
Caesarean section	5.1	7.0	13.5	13.3	48.6	9.3
Perinatal deaths	47	28	49	38	54	37
All heights						
Caesarean section	2.1	3.1	5.8	11.6	33.7	5.1
Perinatal deaths	39	25	25	34	43	28
Numbers (total)	1,064	4,240	2,229	656	208	8,397

cent even in tall women, the indication being usually uterine disfunction or fetal distress. Any further increase in age is associated with a higher incidence of these conditions. A decrease in stature results in a rise in the Caesarean section rate for disproportion. It is clear therefore that the perinatal mortality rate and Caesarean section rates would decline if the average height were to increase and the age to decrease.

The age at marriage has been declining and the average stature increasing in the United States ever since World War II and this is now happening in Britain. The steady decline in perinatal mortality in England and Wales between 1959 and 1962, after it had been stationary between 1948 and 1958, may be due, in part at least, to these influences making themselves felt in the younger members of the childbearing population.

Perinatal mortality has been low for years in Norway, Sweden, Denmark, and Holland, where people are tall. For example, Boyne and Leitch [11] showed that the average height of young service men in Denmark increased by 5.4 cm. between 1915 and 1956 and is now 174.4 cm. (5 ft. 8½ in.), which is equivalent to that of young men in Great Britain coming from

11. A. W. Boyne and I. Leitch, *Nutritional Abstracts Review*, XXIV (1954), p. 255.

Social Classes I and II. There are no satisfactory observations of secular change in adult stature in Britain, but it is well recognized that school children in Britain today are much taller and healthier than before World War II and that this will result in an increase in the average stature of young adults.

Spacing of Children

It has been shown by Heady *et al.*,[12] that in the case of stillbirth increased age is an adverse factor at any parity. Even in a fourth pregnancy under the age of 25 the rate is very low. In the case of postneonatal deaths, on the other hand, increased age appears to be favorable till over the age of 35. In the first four weeks of life extremes of age and youth in the mother are unfavorable.

Since the women having a fourth pregnancy before the age of 25 usually come from the lowest socioeconomic group and tend to live in substandard houses and in conditions of great overcrowding, it is not surprising that the postneonatal death rate is high. It does seem surprising that such women, who are often underdeveloped and in poor health, should have such low stillbirth rates. Spacing of children, by increasing the mother's age, would have the effect of raising the stillbirth rate in her later pregnancies. On the other hand, spacing might have the effect of lowering the postneonatal death rate indirectly if it brought about improvements in living conditions and in the standard of health generally. It has been shown earlier, however, that the reproductive pattern is greatly influenced by the social background. In the upper social groups, where there may be a considerable interval between pregnancies, the increase in the age of the mother may be the most important factor in determining the outcome.

It is unfortunate that more information is not available about stillbirth and infant mortality rates in the Hutterites since this must be one of the few societies where increasing size of family does not result automatically in a steady decline in living standards.

12. J. A Heady, C. Daly, and J. N. Morris, ''Social and Biological Factors in Infant Mortality—Variations of Mortality with Mothers' Age and Parity,'' *Lancet*, I (1955), pp. 395–397.

Diet in Pregnancy

Do tall women enjoy better diets during pregnancy than short women? Thomson and Billewicz,[13] as a result of careful dietary surveys in 1950–53, have found that they do. The tall women, being heavier than the short women, would be expected to take more calories. After standardization, by regression of the calorie intakes to the mean body weight for all heights, tall women still took about 240 calories per day more than the short women. Many of the differences in the intake of nutrients were attributable to the differences of calorie intake but tall women took more calories and more Vitamin C than could be explained on this basis. However, even in wives of semiskilled and unskilled workers, who had the lowest incomes and the least education, there was little correlation between the dietary and the clinical findings. Were the diets even in the poorest social group so "adequate" that none of the women could be regarded as malnourished? The conclusion reached was that, within the range of nutritive values found in the diets of Aberdeen women during the postwar years, there was little evidence that the course and outcome of pregnancy were appreciably influenced by the diet taken during pregnancy.

Yet, although obvious deficiency disease was totally absent amongst the women, many of them were undoubtedly of inferior health and physique and looked "poorly nourished." It seems reasonable to suppose that the nutritional history of the women during growth and adolescence may be more important than dietary experience during pregnancy itself. On this hypothesis, women who have been well fed during growth would usually do well in obstetric terms, even if the diets they took during labor were relatively poor.

In 1946 a subcommittee of the Scientific Advisory Committee to the Department of Health for Scotland[14] published a report in which they concluded that in prewar Scotland "working class

13. A. M. Thomson and W. Z. Billewicz, "Nutritional Status, Maternal Physique and Reproductive Efficiency," *Proceedings of the Nutrition Society*, XXII (1963), p. 55.

14. Department of Health for Scotland, *Infant Mortality in Scotland*, Report of a Subcommittee of the Scientific Advisory Committee, Edinburgh (London: Her Majesty's Stationery Office, 1946).

mothers are often underfed and their diets are of poor quality . . . . Such diets are important causes of poor physique and maternal ill-health, premature birth and low vitality of the child.'' Orr, Garry and Thomson [15] found that rats reared for 2½ years on a working class human diet had relatively small litters with slightly reduced survival rates.

Wartime experience helped our understanding of the importance of diet during pregnancy. Between 1928 and 1938 the perinatal mortality was stationary in England and Wales. From 1940 to 1945 a very rapid fall occurred. The improvement was greatest in the areas where the rate was highest. For example, in South Wales where there had been very severe industrial depression in the coal fields for many years, the stillbirth rate fell from 55 in 1931 to 25 in 1948. This was attributed to full employment during the War and the Government's enlightened food policy in terms of which pregnant women were treated as a priority group. This led, amongst other things, to a great increase in the consumption of milk and vitamins during pregnancy. A high level of employment has been maintained since. Possibly dietary surveys carried out in the 1950's by Thomson were done too late to give clear-cut results and yet we know that many diets are defective.

There were, amongst 489 subjects, 14 cases of perinatal death (stillbirths and deaths in the first week). The diets of the mothers who lost their babies did not differ appreciably from those of normal subjects. The numbers do not suffice for a satisfactory analysis of cause of death. This negative result does not mean that there is no association between death rates and diet in pregnancy but rather that the association is too small to appear in the present data. National statistics show that in 1945, 97 per cent of babies were born alive compared to 96 per cent in 1940. During this five-year period, a national food policy was applied with all the special powers available in wartime. If a similar change were expected in a controlled feeding experiment it would be necessary to use more than 5,000 experimental subjects and a similar number of control subjects to be reasonably sure of obtaining a statistically significant result.

15. J. B. Orr, W. Thomson, and R. C. Garry, *Journal of Hygiene*, XXXV (Cambridge: 1936), p. 476.

TABLE 5

Incidence of Certain Abnormalities by Weight-for-Height in 4,215 Aberdeen Primigravidae [a]

	Underweight	Average weight	Overweight
Pre-eclampsia (%)	4.8	6.3	8.3
Prematurity [b] (%)	9.6	6.9	4.1
Caesarean section (%)	3.7	3.0	5.8
Perinatal death (%)	2.8	2.7	3.1
No. of subjects	1,049	2,112	1,054

[a] Birth weight of baby 2,500 g. or less.
[b] Under and overweight women constitute the lightest and the heaviest 25 per cent respectively at each height.

In Holland in 1944 at the time of the famine, one cohort of women were submitted to starvation diets during six months of their pregnancy. There was little or no rise in the stillbirth rate during that time and the average weight of the baby was reduced by less than half a pound. In fact between 1940 and 1945 the stillbirth rate fell from 25 to 20 and a substantial part of the fall in the death rate was attributed to a decrease in the incidence of pre-eclamptic toxaemia. One could postulate that before 1940 Dutch women ate too much during pregnancy and had excessive rates of pre-eclampsia as a result. The decreased incidence during the War might be due to a decrease in food consumption during pregnancy.

TABLE 6

Clinical Outcome in Relation to Amount of Weight Gained in the 16-Week Period, 20th to 36th Week

Weight gained lb.	kg.	Pre-eclampsia (per cent)	Prematurity [a] (per cent)	Percentage of prematures [a] with pre-eclampsia	Perinatal mortality per 1,000	No. of cases
<8	<3.6	2.6	12.1	9	36.0	273
8	3.6	3.3	8.3	9		671
12	5.4	3.1	5.5	16	11.9	1,090
16	7.3	5.7	4.4	25	27.8	1,009
20	9.1	9.2	4.9	35		651
24	10.9	13.5	5.7	47	32.9	296
28 +	12.7 +	26.0	8.5	66		177

[a] Birth weight 5½ lb. (2,500 g.) or under.

Table 5 shows that underweight primigravidae have lower rates of pre-eclampsia than those who are overweight. They have however more than twice the incidence of babies weighing 2,500 g. or less.

Table 6 shows that primigravidae who put on more than one lb. per week between the 20th and 36th weeks of pregnancy have an increased incidence of pre-eclampsia. A low weight increase is associated with a high incidence of prematurity. The lowest perinatal mortality is found in those who gain slightly less than one lb. per week during this period.

Racial Factors

It is known that in many underdeveloped countries babies are much lighter than in Western Europe and North America, but accurate statistics are difficult to obtain.

Ventatachalam,[16] in a very thorough study of prematurity in Coonon, Hyderabad, and Madras, found the mean birth weight to be much greater in the upper than in the lower socioeconomic groups. The prematurity rates were 13.8 and 29.3 per cent respectively. It seems very probable that many of these women were of short stature and we know that many of them were light, under 100 lb. in weight. Ventatachalam found that his patients gained about six kg. in weight during pregnancy, which is about half the European figure, and many of them gained little or no weight in the last trimester. If taken into the hospital for the last month of pregnancy and given a plentiful, well-balanced diet, the babies were on the average about 200 g. heavier than those not admitted.

In areas of the world where the prematurity rate is very high, a very high proportion of those classified as premature weigh between 4½ and 5½ lb. and are near full time, so that when born they do not behave like the typical premature baby and progress is, as a rule, good. Weight for weight the death rate is lower than in European or North American babies where overall prematurity rates are low. This is probably because the birth of a baby of five lb. or less to a tall, well-developed mother is more likely to be associated with a serious abnormality of pregnancy

16. P. S. Ventatachalam and C. Gopalan, *Indian Journal of Medical Research,* XLVIII (1960), p. 507.

which may threaten the baby's survival. The lower first week death rate in the highly developed countries depends on the low incidence of prematurity rather than the low death rate in premature babies. In fact, first week death rates are lowest in babies weighing between 7½ and 8½ lb. (3,500–4,000 g.) and such babies constitute a high percentage of the total in the highly developed countries.

While the birth of small babies to small women, as described in Madras, may be regarded as a fairly satisfactory adaptation to chronic food shortage, it cannot be accepted as a desirable state of affairs from the long term point of view.

In many areas in Africa, on the other hand, food is not in such short supply and women are taller and the prematurity rate much less. For example, in a rural village of Western Nigeria, 32 per cent of mothers were 64 inches or more in height and 20 per cent were under 61 inches. They were therefore taller than Aberdeen women. The prematurity rate was 15 per cent. The perinatal mortality was higher in short than in tall women. The women put on much less weight during pregnancy than Aberdeen women and there was little, if any, pre-eclampsia, although during labor eclampsia occurred with little rise of blood pressure.

Table 7 shows that in primigravidae in Hong Kong rates of prematurity, perinatal mortality, and Caesarean section are influenced by the height of the mother in the same way as in

TABLE 7

Incidences of Prematurity, Caesarean Section, and Perinatal Mortality in Aberdeen and in Chinese (Hong Kong) Primiparae

Height (in.)	Prematurity [a] (per cent) Aberdeen	Hong Kong	Caesarean section (per cent) Aberdeen	Hong Kong	Perinatal deaths (per 1,000) Aberdeen	Hong Kong
Under 57	16.3	19.3	25.8	20.5	40.7	19.2
57–58		11.6	12.5	5.0		
59–60	10.3	6.6	5.3	3.1	28.6	17.3
61–62	6.9	6.7	3.3	2.3	25.7	14.4
63–64	6.2	5.7	2.7	1.8		
65 and over	3.7		2.4		24.4	

[a] Birth weight of baby 2,500 g. or less.

Aberdeen. A striking feature is that the perinatal mortality in the Hong Kong series is very much less than in Aberdeen. The Hong Kong women were all delivered in the University teaching hospital and received a high standard of obstetric care. The great majority of the Chinese women came from poor families in the dock area. They were on the average two inches shorter than Aberdeen women. The death rate from every cause of death was lower in the Hong Kong series. The lower rate from pre-eclampsia might be associated with the fact that the women are lighter and put on less weight during pregnancy than the average women in Britain. The death rates from malformations were 1.9 and 5.2 per 1,000 in Hong Kong and Aberdeen respectively. In a high proportion of lethal malformations in Britain the lesion is in the central nervous system and the death rates from anencephaly [absence of the brain] are particularly high in the industrial cities of the north and in the unskilled social groups. Slum conditions in Hong Kong do not seem to predispose to central nervous system malformations in the same way as in Britain.

TABLE 8

Community Obstetrical Study, Hartford County, Connecticut; Progress Report 1960; Infant Malformations

	White (total 16,080 women)		Nonwhite (total 1,953 women)	
	No.	Rate per 1,000	No.	Rate per 1,000
Cardiac malformations	108	6.7	7	3.5
Genito-urinary	151	9.4	13	6.6
Genito-skeletal	199	12.3	12	6.1
Alimentary	81	5.0	7	3.6
Central nervous system	81	5.0	4	2.0
Spina bifida	19 ⎤			
Hydrocephalus	17 ⎥			
Anencephal	10 ⎥ 62		1	
Meningocele	8 ⎥			
Meningomyelocele	7 ⎥			
Encephalocele	1 ⎦			
Others	19		3	
Umbilical hernia	15	0.9	13	6.6
Multiple including CNS	55	3.4	2	1.0
All others	108	6.7	5	2.5
All	798	49.4	63	31.9

Table 8 compares the incidence of malformations of all types in white and nonwhite patients in a Community Obstetrical Study, Hartford County, Connecticut.[17] The overall incidence of malformations was 49.4 and 31.9 per 1,000 for white and non-white respectively. Table 8 shows the only malformation with a higher incidence in the nonwhite is umbilical hernia where the rate is six times that in the white patients. On the other hand serious central nervous system malformations are five times as common in white patients as in nonwhite—this despite the fact that the nonwhite came very largely from the lowest socioeconomic groups. The relative absence of serious central nervous system malformations, such as anencephaly, has been noted in populations as far apart as West Africa, Singapore, and Malaya and in nonwhite in the United States and suggests that in the nonwhite populations there is a low predisposition to these malformations even in conditions which predispose to a high rate in white races.

Standard of Obstetric Care

In Britain, 41 per cent of births take place at home and 13 per cent in small maternity hospitals under the care of the family doctor. Only 40 per cent take place in a hospital under specialist supervision. In most countries of Western Europe and in North America, where perinatal death rates are low, the incidence of hospital delivery is very high. The one exception is Holland where the hospital delivery rate is about 30 per cent. De Haas-Posthuma [18] shows that in the regions with a hospital delivery rate of over 30 per cent the perinatal mortality was 25 per 1,000, and in the areas where the hospital delivery rate was under 20 per cent the perinatal mortality was just over 30 per 1,000. These figures suggest that with good organization in a country like Holland, where the standard of health and physique is high and lines of communication are easy, it is possible to have low perinatal death rates with a high incidence of domiciliary midwifery. Nevertheless it seems as if the rate could be

17. *Community Obstetrical Study, Hartford County, Connecticut, Progress Report* (New York: State University of New York, 1960).

18. J. H. De Haas-Posthuma, *Perinatale sterfte in Nederland* (Van Gorcum-Assen: Organization for Health Research T.N.O., 1963).

lowered still further by an increase in hospital deliveries over the 1954–57 rates.

In the city of Aberdeen, 85 per cent of all births take place in one teaching hospital under the care of specialists, and the perinatal mortality is considerably lower than in the 1958 National Birthday Trust Survey cases. The difference is greatest in the type of case where birth trauma, pre-eclampsia and placental insufficiency are important causes of death and least in the cases where prematurity and malformations are relatively more important. Thus the Aberdeen rates are much better in first pregnancies and in the Para 4+ group and slightly worse in Para 1 than in the National Survey. In primigravidae the

TABLE 9

Perinatal Mortality in Para 0 (Single Births) by Age and Height of Mother. (S) National Birthday Trust Perinatal Mortality Survey 1958 (A) Aberdeen City 1953–62

Height	Age group										Mortality ratio [c] per cent
	15–19		20–24		25–29		30 +		All		
	S [a]	A [b]	S	A	S	A	S	A	S	A	
Tall											
(65 in. or more)	32.8	34.0	24.6	10.9	26.7	14.1	27.8	32.6	26.8	16.7	62
Medium	36.4	30.3	33.8	26.2	41.1	18.7	54.7	34.2	38.2	25.6	67
Small	36.6	40.8	45.5	26.8	52.4	46.3	80.6	41.2	48.3	34.8	72
(Less than 62 in.)											
All heights	37.7	35.3	35.9	24.1	45.0	26.3	56.8	36.4	33.4	27.5	82
Per cent less than 62 in.	26	45	23	39	19	31	21	30	21	36	

[a] S National Birthday Trust Perinatal Mortality Survey, 1958.
[b] A Aberdeen City, 1953–62.
[c] Aberdeen Perinatal Mortality as percentage of Survey Mortality in each height group.

difference in perinatal death rates is most marked over the age of 25 years where a high standard of care is combined with induction of labor to avoid prolonged pregnancy in the elderly primigravida and liberal use of Caesarean section in cases of fetal distress. In the high parity group, again, the women over 35 years of age must be most carefully watched and immediate action may be called for in cases of malposition of the fetus or prolapse of the cord. In a second pregnancy, however, the outcome of the labor depends much more on the reproductive efficiency of the woman herself and such complications as difficult labor, malpresentation, and pre-eclampsia are least common. The Aberdeen women are much shorter (twice as many are under 62 inches in height as in the Survey cases) and by implication have been reared in a less favorable environment. Not surprisingly, the perinatal mortality was slightly higher in the Para 1 group in Aberdeen than in the National Survey.

Table 9 shows that the difference between the Aberdeen rate and that of the Survey is greatest in tall and least in short women. The explanation is that tall women are superior in health and physique to short women and thus a smaller proportion of the deaths in the tall women are related to prematurity and malformations and more to conditions such as asphyxia, birth trauma, and placental insufficiency, which can more easily be avoided by a high standard of care. Thus, although the rates in the Survey cases are least in tall women in the age groups 20–24 and 25–29, it is in these groups that the difference between the Aberdeen and the Survey cases is greatest. The fact that these women come largely from the professional classes helps to explain why improvements in standards of obstetric care do not necessarily lead to a narrowing of the gap in mortality between the social classes.

CONCLUSIONS

It may be concluded that the essentials for easy and efficient childbearing are youth and first class physical development and nutrition. If in such women the first child is born by the age of 20, the total is restricted to four, and the last is born before the age of 30, the perinatal mortality would be very low, probably less than 15 per 1,000 from all causes, given a good standard of obstetric care.

This rate can be achieved today in the socially advanced countries by certain sections of society, but even in such countries the overall national perinatal death rate is not less than 25 per 1,000. National rates will not fall much below this figure until the levels of health and nutrition of the women in the lowest social classes have been raised and until they have been educated to make better use of the health services. More research is required in depth into the physiological changes which occur in pregnancy in women of varying levels of health and reproductive efficiency. Since this may involve longitudinal studies of women in successive pregnancies, long-term plans must be laid, including the establishment of careers for those who wish to make clinical research their lifework.

Robert G. Potter,
Mary L. New,
John B. Wyon, and
John E. Gordon

APPLICATIONS OF FIELD STUDIES TO RESEARCH ON THE PHYSIOLOGY OF HUMAN REPRODUCTION: LACTATION AND ITS EFFECTS UPON BIRTH INTERVALS IN ELEVEN PUNJAB VILLAGES, INDIA

INTRODUCTION

From a variety of sources—genealogies, parish records, and special field studies—it has been found that in societies practicing little or no birth control,[1] average birth intervals range from barely more than two years to nearly three years. Factors associated with lactation are believed to play a fundamental role in this large variation from group to group.[2] Within populations, older mothers tend to have longer birth intervals than younger mothers. Averaging the experience of several historical European populations presumably practicing little birth control, Henry found an increase of roughly seven months between ages 20–24 and ages 35–39.[3] However, for want of direct data, the relative importance of various factors contributing to this increase has remained vague.

1. R. G. Potter, "Birth Intervals: Structure and Change," *Population Studies*, XVII (Nov., 1963), pp. 160–162.
2. L. Henry, "Aspects biologiques de la fécondité," *Proceedings of the Royal Society*, CLIX B (Dec., 1953), pp. 85–87; L. Henry, "La fécondité naturelle: Observation–théorie–résultats," *Population*, XVI (Oct.–Dec., 1961), pp. 633–634.
3. L. Henry, "Some Data on Natural Fertility," *Eugenics Quarterly*, VIII (June, 1961), p. 87.

Mathematical models developed by Henry,[4] Vincent,[5] and more recently by Perrin and Sheps [6] have greatly advanced the theoretical analysis of birth intervals in terms of pregnancy wastage, gestation, postpartum amenorrhea, and menstruating interval. (By "menstruating interval" is meant the number of months a woman menstruates after the end of postpartum amenorrhea and before the next conception.) The great lack at present is not theory, but data. Needed is the kind of information that permits one to resolve birth intervals into interpregnancy intervals and these subintervals into their basic components—gestation, postpartum amenorrhea, and menstruating interval—and then to correlate these components with such factors as outcome of previous delivery, survival of last infant, and length of lactation.

Information of this sort is obtainable only by special field studies featuring prospective as well as retrospective data. The purpose of this paper is to present new results from one such study, the India-Harvard-Ludhiana Population Study, hereafter abbreviated as the Khanna Study.[7] Field work took place in 11 villages of the Punjab, India, during the years 1953–59.

PREVIOUS STUDY

The relevance of lactation to birth spacing has long been suspected. Several studies, the first in 1942,[8] have shown that when the infant survives, the average birth interval is as much as a year longer than when the child is born dead or dies

4. L. Henry, "Fécondité et famille," *Population*, XII (July–Sept., 1957), pp. 413–444; L. Henry, "Fécondité et famille: Modèles mathématiques (II)," *Population*, XVI (Jan.–March, 1961), pp. 27–48; (April–June, 1961), pp. 261–282.

5. P. Vincent, *Recherches sur la fécondité biologique*, Institut National d'Études Démographiques, 1961, Travaux et Documents, Cahier No. 37, pp. 166–232.

6. E. B. Perrin and M. C. Sheps, "Human Reproduction: A Stochastic Process," *Biometrics*, XX (March, 1964), pp. 28–45; M. C. Sheps and E. B. Perrin, "The Distribution of Birth Intervals Under a Class of Stochastic Models," *Population Studies*, XVII (March, 1964), pp. 321–331.

7. J. E. Gordon and J. B. Wyon, "Field Studies in Population Dynamics and Population Control," *American Journal of Medical Sciences*, CCXL (Sept., 1960), pp. 361–368. See also J. B. Wyon and J. E. Gordon, "A Long-term Prospective Type Field Study of Population Dynamics in the Punjab, India," *Research in Family Planning*, ed. C. V. Kiser (Princeton: Princeton University Press, 1962), pp. 17–32.

8. H. Hyrenius, "Fertility and Reproduction in a Swedish Population Group with Family Limitation," *Population Studies*, XII (Nov., 1958), pp. 124–128.

neonatally.[9] From such indirect evidence, however, one cannot tell whether lactation operates primarily through postpartum abstinence from coitus or by prolonging amenorrhea as well as possibly increasing the number of anovulatory menstrual cycles. For several reasons the prolonging of amenorrhea is coming to be regarded as the dominant mechanism, though unquestionably abstinence does reinforce the physiological effects of lactation in many instances. In the first place, long average birth intervals believed to be without birth control are found in societies thought not to abstain from coitus for more than a few months after delivery. Secondly, clinical studies in the West have demonstrated that lactation does prolong postpartum amenorrhea and that conception rates are low during this type of amenorrhea. These studies have suffered the defect that few of the mothers were nursing for as long as a year. Nor have these studies determined conclusively whether lactation increases the number of anovulatory cycles directly following postpartum amenorrhea. Thirdly, in two Indian areas, where prolonged nursing is customary, postpartum amenorrhea averages in the vicinity of a year.[10] Finally, in Bombay, Baxi[11] has demonstrated that interpregnancy intervals are appreciably longer when the infant is breast fed than when it is not nursed or born dead. More important, Baxi had information enough to show that these differences depended primarily on differential postpartum amenorrhea, and not on the relatively brief durations of postpartum abstinence reported by his respondents. The chief limitation of Baxi's study is the selected character of his 500 hospital patients, 25 per cent of whose pregnancies ended in wastage.

Three factors may be cited to explain why birth intervals increase as mothers age, even when they are not practicing

9. Many statements in this section are guided by the thorough review of C. Tietze, ''The Effect of Breast Feeding on the Rate of Conception,'' *International Population Conference: New York, 1961*, II (London, 1963), pp. 129–136.

10. K. Dandekar, *Demographic Survey of Six Rural Communities* (Poona: Gokhale Institute of Politics and Economics, 1959), p. 62; World Health Organization *Final Report on Pilot Studies in Family Planning*, I (New Delhi: W.H.O. Regional Office for South East Asia, Sept., 1954), p. 33.

11. P. C. Baxi, ''A Natural History of Childbearing in the Hospital Class of Women in Bombay,'' *Journal of Obstetrics and Gynecology of India*, VIII (Sept., 1957), pp. 25–51.

deliberate birth control. First is the increasing frequency of spontaneous pregnancy wastage, documented in several Western studies.[12] Second is the lengthening of menstruating intervals owing to such age-dependent factors as declining coital frequency and more numerous anovulatory cycles. The apparent lengthening of menstruating intervals is further increased by that part of the rising incidence of fetal wastage that goes unreported. On the basis of indirect evidence, Henry has hypothesized a third factor: longer postpartum amenorrhea among older lactating mothers.[13]

SAMPLE

The Khanna Study provides a broad scope of prospective as well as retrospective data for approximately 1,500 couples of childbearing potential. These prospective data were collected on the basis of monthly visits to each wife aged 15–44 years over a three to five-year period. Not all such histories are used in the analysis below. This analysis relates to "interpregnancy intervals" defined as intervals from delivery to next conception. Thus, unless a wife has at least one pregnancy termination during the prospective period and experience following it, her fertility history is not usable.

Accordingly three main categories of resident wives aged 15–44 have been excluded as ineligible for purposes of this study. (The numbers cited pertain to wives resident in the villages during December, 1959.)

First are menopausal women operationally defined as women aged over 35 and amenorrheic for longer than a year for reasons unrelated to lactation. Thirty women were classified as menopausal during an initial interview. Thirty-eight additional wives were adjudged menopausal on the basis of information collected during monthly household visits.

Second are the 217 wives, most of them young brides, who had not yet had a first pregnancy or who had not had time to

12. *Foetal, Infant and Early Childhood Mortality*, Population Studies, I, No. 13 (New York: United Nations, 1954), pp. 23–26. See also S. Shapiro, E. W. Jones, and P. M. Densen, "A Life Table of Pregnancy Terminations and Correlates of Fetal Loss," *Milbank Memorial Fund Quarterly*, XL (Jan., 1962), pp. 15–17.

13. L. Henry, "La fécondité naturelle: Observation–théorie–résultats," *Population*, XVI (Oct.–Dec., 1961), p. 633.

accumulate experience after a first pregnancy before the end of the study. Special factors operate to affect the interval between marriage and first pregnancy, including the bride's frequent visits back to the home of her parents, so that this initial interval is best kept separate from intervals following termination of a pregnancy.

Third are 170 wives with at least one previous pregnancy who menstruated more or less regularly throughout the three to five-year period of prospective observation. These women are excluded because there is no reliable information dating either the last delivery or the span of postpartum amenorrhea following it.

An idea of coverage is afforded by Table 1 which classified wives residing in the villages during December of 1959 by age

TABLE 1

Wives Aged 15–44 Years, and Resident in Eleven Punjab Villages, December, 1959, by Eligibility for Study of Interpregnancy Intervals and Response Status

Status of wife	Age of wife					All
	15–19	*20–24*	*25–34*	*35–39*	*40–44*	*15–44*
Eligible						
Completed interpregnancy history	48	294	645	200	109	1,296
Defective history	1	8	15	1	5	30
No history collected	1	4	4	2	14	25
Total eligible	50	306	664	203	128	1,351
Ineligible	90	91	82	71	130	464
Total wives	140	397	746	274	258	1,815

and eligibility and also subclassified eligible wives by whether useful interpregnancy data were collected from them or not. Coverage of eligible wives is high for all relevant ages, at least for the chosen month of December, 1959, coinciding with the end of field work. A further 226 wives aged 15–44 were resident at some time during the study but had died or were widowed, separated, or residing elsewhere by December, 1959. Examination of their records indicates a maximum of 38 nonexistent or defective interpregnancy histories. Hence it appears safe to assume that except for the first few months of field work, coverage of eligible wives during earlier stages of the study was comparable to that depicted in Table 1.

The fertility of the 11 villages is high, there being an average of 7.5 live births among once-married wives aged 45 or more. Nor has age-specific fertility declined much among the younger wives studied below.[14] Contraception and induced abortion were limited but certainly not absent. Mothers characteristically nurse their infants 18 months or longer. The coital frequencies reported in one village are somewhat lower than those published for United States samples, but significantly the great majority of couples in the Khanna Study villages reported that they had resumed sexual relations within six months after delivery.

DATA

Reporting of contemporary events yielded data which are more detailed and presumably more reliable than the data obtained from pregnancy histories. Accordingly three types of interpregnancy interval are distinguished. First, if the delivery and conception marking the start and finish of an interval fell within the prospective period of contemporary recording of events, the interval is called Entirely Prospective. Second are the Truncated Prospective Intervals that started in the prospective period but were truncated by end of the Study, by outmigration or by death of one of the spouses. Third are the Partly or Entirely Retrospective Intervals whose reliability is open to question. Even those portions of Partly Retrospective Intervals that extended into the prospective period must be questioned since any measurement of amenorrhea or lactation length depends in part on the woman's memory of when she had her last delivery.

Attention will be confined to the Entirely Prospective and Truncated Prospective Intervals. Six pieces of information are available for each Entirely Prospective Interval: (1) total length; (2) length of postpartum amenorrhea; (3) length of menstruating interval; (4) length of lactation; (5) outcome of

14. R. G. Potter, M. L. New, J. B. Wyon, and J. E. Gordon, "A Fertility Differential in Eleven Punjab Villages," *Milbank Memorial Fund Quarterly*, XLIII (April, 1965), pp. 188–190.

previous delivery; and (6) survival of the last child born. Corresponding details are available for those portions of Truncated Prospective Intervals that come under prospective observation.

Four limitations of the data need mention.

1. Lengths of exposure are coded in whole calendar months. Months containing a conception, a delivery, or the first menses postpartum are distinguished as such. Otherwise the month is classified as representing gestation, menstruation, or postpartum amenorrhea, and simultaneously as a month of lactation or not. This coarseness of measurement results in biases of two weeks or more, which are troublesome chiefly when the duration under consideration is short, as instanced by postpartum amenorrhea following a miscarriage.

2. The ideal of visiting every eligible household each month was only partially realized. The most serious breach occurred during the last 18 months of the study when, in seven of the villages, couples viewed as poor prospects for contraception were visited only once every three months. However, the record of dates of household visits reveals only a low incidence of gaps exceeding two months between visits. The question arises whether a wife's passage from postpartum amenorrhea to menstruation was always promptly recognized and whether there is not a positive bias attaching to amenorrhea lengths and a corresponding negative bias applying to menstruating intervals. However, if these biases exist, they must be small since the proportion of conceptions belonging to Entirely Prospective Intervals that are coded as occurring during postpartum amenorrhea (four per cent) agrees well with an estimate of five per cent derived by Tietze on the basis of several Western studies.[15]

3. The apparent lengths of menstruating intervals were increased by a limited practice of contraception and by unreported fetal wastage. It is estimated that, on the average, contraception did not extend menstruating intervals by more than a month or two, though in a minority of interpregnancy intervals its effect must be much larger. It is also concluded that the reporting of stillbirths and late abortions was fairly complete, but early abortions were somewhat less completely re-

15. C. Tietze, *op. cit.*, p. 132.

ported than in certain recent United Sates studies. An overall wastage rate (including stillbirths) of 14 per 100 pregnancies was recorded for the 11 villages.[16]

4. The length of lactation was measured rather arbitrarily. If lactation extended into the next pregnancy, this overlap was ignored and the duration of nursing was taken as that of the interpregnancy interval. Actually lactation often extended several months into a full term pregnancy and in cases of miscarriage frequently extended the full duration of the pregnancy and beyond. The dependence of an infant upon breast milk was a matter of degree, being total for a median length of just over six months.[17] In the way that lactation was recorded in this study, no provision was made for this matter of degree.

RESULTS BASED ON ENTIRELY PROSPECTIVE INTERVALS

By themselves the Entirely Prospective Intervals were a selected set of intervals, being biased toward brevity. The shorter an interpregnancy interval, the more chance it had of fitting entirely within the prospective period. However, there is no reason to suppose that Entirely Prospective Intervals of a particular length are biased with respect to the lengths of their components—lactation, postpartum amenorrhea, and menstruating interval. Hence it is legitimate to study the manner in which these components change as a function of interpregnancy length.

When the previous pregnancy ended in a miscarriage or stillbirth, there was no lactation and postpartum amenorrhea was short. In such cases interpregnancy length depended almost entirely on length of the menstruating interval. Essentially the same was true when the infant died in the first month of life so that lactation, if it was established at all, lasted less than one month. Roughly half of all Entirely Prospective Intervals following a live birth that were nine months or shorter were of this type, and most of those were six months or shorter.

16. R. G. Potter, J. B. Wyon, M. L. New, and J. E. Gordon, ''Fetal Wastage in Eleven Punjab Villages,'' *Human Biology*, XXXVII (Sept., 1965), pp. 262–273.

17. In a series of 775 infants, less than half were receiving only breast milk by the sixth month after delivery. (J. E. Gordon, I. D. Chitkara, and J. B. Wyon, ''Weanling Diarrhea,'' *American Journal of the Medical Sciences*, CCXLV [March, 1963], pp. 146–147.)

When the infant survived longer than a month, the picture changed drastically. Fig. 1, based on 604 Entirely Prospective Intervals following a live birth, presents mean durations of postpartum amenorrhea, menstruating interval, and lactation by length of interpregnancy interval. The rates of increase of postpartum amenorrhea and menstruating interval with increasing interpregnancy length are roughly equal. However, for inter-

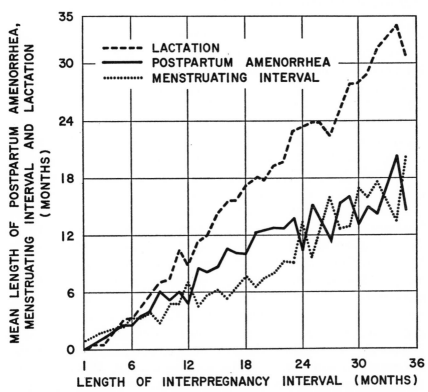

Fig. 1. Mean lengths of postpartum amenorrhea, menstruating interval, and lactation, by length of interpregnancy interval, for 604 entirely prospective intervals following live birth.

pregnancy intervals longer than 30 months, confident generalization is impossible owing to the paucity of cases. From Partly Retrospective data it is evident that most very long interpregnancy intervals depend on long menstruating intervals. Therefore it is likely that for each monthly increase in interpregnancy length up to 30 months or so, duration of postpartum amenorrhea increases by nearly one half month until it approaches 15 or 16 months, when this increase would become much reduced.

In the experience of this study virtually any child not established on breast milk died.[18] Conversely, if the infant survived longer than a month, it meant that nursing had been established and usually continued longer than a year. Indeed, unless the interpregnancy interval was longer than 30 months, lactation typically extended into the next pregnancy.

LIFE TABLE RESULTS

One way to overcome the biases of Entirely Prospective Intervals is to combine them with Truncated Prospective Intervals. At the same time it increases the number of observations. The problem is how to do it. For example, a particular interpregnancy interval started eight months before the end of the study. If the woman was still lactating and in amenorrhea at the end of the study, the final lengths of her amenorrhea, menstruating interval, lactation, and interpregnancy interval are all unknown.

To solve this problem we have used a life table technique. Suppose that a distribution of postpartum amenorrhea is to be derived, using Entirely Prospective and Truncated Prospective Intervals. The proportion of wives who menstruated the first month after delivery is first calculated. Next, among those amenorrheic during the first month, the proportion who resumed menstruation during the second month is computed. More generally, among those amenorrheic during the $(n-1)$th month, the proportion who resumed menstruation during the nth month is calculated. A diminishing number of women contributed experience to these successive, conditional, monthly probabilities of resuming menstruation. The complements of these monthly probabilities define the conditional probabilities of continuing in amenorrhea another month. Finally, by taking accumulative products of these probabilities, one obtains the likelihoods of still being in amenorrhea during the second, the third, and more generally, the nth month after delivery.

An example of a life table relating to postpartum amenorrhea

18. *Ibid.*, p. 361.

is given in the Appendix. Each life table includes estimates of standard errors. The procedure followed to test the significance of a difference between two life tables is also described in the Appendix.

Table 2 compares the lengths of interpregnancy intervals,

TABLE 2

Proportion of Wives in Postpartum Amenorrhea, Lactating, and Not Yet Pregnant at the End of Specified Numbers of Months Following Birth of an Infant That Survived One Month or More, Based on Prospective Observation in Eleven Punjab Villages, 1955–1959

Months since previous delivery	In postpartum amenorrhea ($l_1 = 1,418$)	Still lactating ($l_1 = 1,415$)	Not yet pregnant ($l_1 = 1,418$)
0	1.00	1.000	1.000
1	.94	.999	1.000
3	.86	.996	.996
6	.74	.98	.98
12	.43	.89	.89
18	.17	.60	.62
24	.07	.41	.47
30	(.03) [a]	.26	.35
36		.16	.29

[a] Based on the experience of fewer than 25 women.

lactation and amenorrhea when the previous pregnancy ended in the birth of an infant surviving one month or longer. The number of women who contributed experience decreases rapidly as duration from delivery increases. Proportions are placed in parentheses when based on the experience of less than 25 women. It is to be kept in mind that a low level of contraceptive practice together with some unreported pregnancy wastage was extending menstruating intervals and therefore interpregnancy intervals and also indirectly lactation. In other intervals, a child death was shortening lactation and therefore postpartum amenorrhea. The median length of postpartum amenorrhea is 11 months and the central 50 per cent of the amenorrhea lengths span a range of 6 to 16 months. The median duration of lactation is 21 months, with the first and third quartiles falling in the 15th and 30th months. The median interpregnancy interval is 22 months, while first and third quartiles coincide with months 15 and 42 respectively.

Table 3 presents durations of amenorrhea following a miscarriage, stillbirth, birth of an infant that died in the first month of life, and, in the last two columns, following births of an infant that survived 2 to 12 months and 13 months or longer. The proportions of women still amenorrheic at specified durations

TABLE 3

Proportion of Wives Still in Postpartum Amenorrhea at the End of Specified Numbers of Months Following Previous Delivery, by Outcome of That Delivery, Based on Prospective Observation in Eleven Punjab Villages, 1955–1959

| Months since previous delivery | Outcome of Previous Delivery | | | | |
| | | | | *Infant survives* | |
	Miscarriage ($l_1 = 184$)	*Stillbirth* ($l_1 = 54$)	*Neonatal death* ($l_1 = 102$)	*2–12 months* ($l_1 = 89$)	*13 months or longer* ($l_1 = 1,301$)
0	1.00	1.00	1.00	1.00	1.00
1	.12	.50	.49	.87	.94
3	(.01) [a]	(.20)	.21	.75	.87
6		(.12)	(.09)	.54	.75
12			(.06)	(.12)	.46
18					.17
24					.08
30					(.03)

[a] Proportions are placed in parentheses when based on the experience of fewer than 25 women.

after delivery should not be taken as exact. Coding was in terms of whole calendar months and errors up to nearly two months are possible. It is believed that the bias is not serious except when intervals are short. Lengths originally coded as zero or one months probably average several weeks longer. Table 3 is useful mainly for the broad contrasts that it presents.

Postpartum amenorrhea following a miscarriage was obviously brief, which is in agreement with Western clinical experience. The distributions of amenorrhea length after a stillbirth or a neonatal death are virtually the same and barely longer than after a miscarriage, though this small difference is statistically significant. Six per cent of the infants surviving the first month failed to survive 12 months. The 89 mothers suffering such a loss exhibited a distribution of postpartum amenorrhea lengths intermediate between those of mothers experiencing a neonatal death and those whose infant survived at least 12 months.

We now turn to menstruating intervals. The results from Tables 2 and 3 have pertained to durations measured from the previous delivery. What are being called menstruating intervals are measured from the resumption of menstruation at the end of postpartum amenorrhea. Length of menstruating interval as related to the outcome of the previous delivery is given in Table 4. None of the differences are very large. Menstruating intervals

TABLE 4

Proportion of Wives, Still Menstruating and Not Yet Pregnant at End of Specified Number of Months Since First Menses Postpartum, by Outcome of Previous Delivery, Based on Prospective Observation in Eleven Punjab Villages, 1955–1959

Completed months since first menses postpartum	Outcome of Previous Delivery				
	Miscarriage ($l_1 = 183$)	Stillbirth ($l_1 = 49$)	Neonatal death ($l_1 = 92$)	Miscarriage, stillbirth, or neonatal death ($l_1 = 324$)	Infant survives one month or more ($l_1 = 966$)
0	1.00	1.00	1.00	1.00	1.00
1	.93	.94	.88	.92	.88
3	.80	.77	.61	.74	.78
6	.60	.61	.53	.58	.68
12	.43	(.38)	(.25)	.37	.47
18	.35	(.30)	(.21)	.31	.33
24	(.24) [a]			.22	.27
30	(.23)			(.20)	.23
36				(.20)	(.20)

[a] Proportions are placed in parentheses when based on the experience of fewer than 25 women.

were barely longer following a miscarriage or stillbirth than following a neonatal death. Partly because of the small number of cases, these differences do not reach a high level of statistical significance. On the average, menstruating intervals were longest when the infant survived one month or more. The difference between these menstruating intervals and all other menstruating intervals (i.e., following fetal wastage or a neonatal death) is highly significant statistically.

This difference does not appear to have depended upon postpartum abstinence. It was hypothesized that when the mother was nursing, the couple would refrain from marital relations longer and therefore postpartum abstinence would extend more often into the menstruating interval. In a subsample of 631 wives, nearly two thirds reported abstaining from intercourse for four months or less following a delivery, while 20 per cent reported continence lasting five or six months and 15 per cent reported continence lasting seven months or more. Greater detail including the relative length of postpartum amenorrhea and abstinence, and therefore the length of any overlap between postpartum abstinence and menstruating interval, was available for 212 interpregnancy intervals. As seen from Table 5, postpartum abstinence was more likely to extend

TABLE 5

Relative Length of Postpartum Abstinence and Amenorrhea, by Outcome of Previous Delivery, Based on Prospective Observation in One Punjab Village, 1955–1959

	Relationship of Postpartum Abstinence and Amenorrhea			
Outcome of pregnancy	Abstinence shorter	Abstinence equal	Abstinence longer	Total
Surviving live birth [a]	135	19	29	183
Neonatal death	2	0	4	6
Stillbirth	1	0	1	2
Abortion	0	11	10	21

[a] Infant survived one month or longer.

into the menstruating interval if following an abortion or else following an infant stillborn or dying in the first month of life than if the infant survived one month or longer. To be sure, when the infant survived, abstinence tended to be longer, averaging 4.7 months as opposed to 2.2 months when the infant did not survive. Nevertheless because lactation prolonged postpartum amenorrhea longer than it did postpartum abstinence, this abstinence less often extended into the menstruating interval. Among the 183 mothers (Table 5) whose infant survived one month or longer, the mean overlap between abstinence and menstruating interval was roughly a half month. This figure compares with an average overlap exceeding one month among the remaining 29 mothers who experienced either fetal wastage or an early infant death. Delay in the start of sexual intercourse after childbirth apparently had little effect on the length of menstruating intervals of these women.

The longer menstruating intervals associated with lactation may have depended in part upon contraception. The relationship between use and nonuse of contraception during menstruating intervals and three outcomes of previous delivery is given in Table 6. The six entries of this table yield a chi square value that

TABLE 6

Use and Nonuse of Contraception During Menstruating Intervals,[a] by Outcome of Delivery and Survival of Infant, Based on Prospective Observation in Eleven Punjab Villages, 1955–1959

Use of contraception during menstruating interval	Infant Survived One Month or More		Infant Died in First Month		Stillbirth or Abortion	
	Number	Per cent	Number	Per cent	Number	Per cent
Yes	261	45.7	14	33.3	56	39.7
No	308	54.3	28	66.7	85	60.3
Total	569	100.0	42	100.0	141	100.0

[a] The 751 interpregnancy intervals used in this table are either Entirely Prospective Intervals or Truncated Prospective Intervals that include one month or more of menstruation.

would be exceeded by chance about 15 per cent of the time. While the relationship is not strong, or statistically highly significant, it is of a form favoring the observed differences in menstruating interval. As among the three outcomes of delivery, use of contraception was greatest and menstruating intervals were longest when the infant survived. In contrast, use of contraception was least and menstruating intervals shortest when the infant was born dead or died in the first month of life.

A third possibility is that lactation not only postponed menstruation but increased the number of initial anovulatory cycles once it had returned. Unfortunately it is impossible to separate the effect of this factor from that of contraception since no direct data on anovulatory cycles are available from the Khanna Study. Thus whether additional anovulatory cycles play an important role in the association of lactation with longer menstruating intervals remains unclear.

The next two tables, which are predicated on the previous delivery producing a live born child who survives one month or longer, compare events during the first and second half of the reproductive period. Among women aged 30 and over the median length of postpartum amenorrhea was 12 months as opposed to 10 months among women aged 20–29 (Table 7). The

TABLE 7

Proportion of Wives in Postpartum Amenorrhea, Still Lactating, and Not Yet Pregnant at the End of Specified Numbers of Months Following Birth of an Infant That Survived One Month or More, by Age, Based on Prospective Observation in Eleven Punjab Villages, 1955–1959

Months since previous delivery	In Postpartum Amenorrhea		Still Lactating		Not Yet Pregnant	
	Aged 20–29 ($l_1 = 795$)	Aged 30 or over ($l_1 = 501$)	Aged 20–29 ($l_1 = 790$)	Aged 30 or over ($l_1 = 495$)	Aged 20–29 ($l_1 = 811$)	Aged 30 or over ($l_1 = 509$)
0	1.00	1.00	1.000	1.000	1.000	1.000
1	.93	.96	.998	1.000	1.000	1.000
3	.84	.92	.996	.996	.996	.996
6	.69	.84	.98	.99	.98	.99
12	.38	.53	.87	.92	.87	.92
18	.14	.23	.54	.69	.56	.71
24	(.05) [a]	.11	.36	.53	.41	.60
30	(.01)	.05	.18	.38	.26	.52
36			(.10)	(.25)	.20	.44

[a] Proportions are placed in parentheses when based on the experience of fewer than 25 women.

number of months required for 25 and 75 per cent to resume menstruation was 8 and 17 for the older women, 5 and 14 months for the younger. The older wives also showed longer menstruating intervals (Table 8). In both age groups 25 per cent had conceived little more than three months after resuming menstruation, but it required 14 months for half of the women 30 years and over to conceive as compared to 10 months for wives in their twenties. Three quarters of the younger women had conceived by the 19th month, but less than 60 per cent of the older women.

With longer postpartum amenorrhea and longer menstruating

TABLE 8

Proportion of Wives Still Menstruating and Not Yet Pregnant After Specified Number of Months Since First Menses Postpartum, Following Birth of an Infant That Survived One Month or More, by Age, Based on Prospective Observation in Eleven Punjab Villages, 1955–1959

Months since first menses postpartum	Aged 20–29 ($l_1 = 571$)	Aged 30 or more ($l_1 = 333$)	All ages ($l_1 = 966$)
0	1.00	1.00	1.00
1	.88	.87	.88
3	.78	.76	.78
6	.67	.67	.68
12	.41	.53	.47
18	.26	.44	.33
24	(.17) [a]	.40	.27
30	(.13)	(.38)	.23
36		(.34)	(.20)

[a] Proportions are placed in parentheses when based on the experience of fewer than 25 women.

intervals, the older women necessarily had longer intervals from previous birth to next conception (Table 7). The median interval from a birth to next conception for wives 30 years and older was 30 months as compared to 20 months for wives aged 20–29. Corresponding first quartiles were 17 and 14 months. Within 31 months after childbirth, three quarters of the younger women had conceived again while barely more than half of the older women had conceived so quickly.

With the next conception setting an upper limit for lactation length, it is not surprising that the older women also showed longer durations of nursing (Table 7). Median lengths were 16 and 14 months for older and younger women respectively. The central 50 per cent of lactation lengths spanned 25 to 36 months among wives aged 30 years and over and 19 to 27 months among those aged 20–29. It is to be kept in mind that the increase in menstruating interval with older age, and indirectly that for lactation length, was exaggerated by the slightly greater use of contraception by the older women and by their higher incidence of abortion, induced as well as spontaneous, which was probably incompletely reported.

The direct relationship between age of mother and length of

postpartum amenorrhea, which is highly significant statistically, bears out the hypothesis of Henry to which he was led by indirect evidence. If this finding is corroborated, it will necessitate a more complicated view of the progressive lengthening of birth intervals as a function of age than has sometimes been taken.[19] This lengthening is not just a matter of more frequent pregnancy losses and a declining fecundability. In part it reflects the fact that older lactating mothers are slower to start menstruating again after childbirth.

DISCUSSION

It is evident that in the Punjab villages of the Khanna Study lactation substantially prolonged postpartum amenorrhea. When an infant survived one month or more, lactation usually lasted well over a year, and the median length of postpartum amenorrhea was 11 months. Whereas if the child was stillborn or died in the first month of life the mother did not lactate and the median length of postpartum amenorrhea stayed in the vicinity of two months.

The long period of postpartum amenorrhea fostered by lactation helps to explain why average birth intervals exceeding 30 months were commonplace in this and other similar populations even in the absence of deliberate birth control. From an unfinished analysis of Khanna Study materials involving Partly Retrospective as well as Entirely Prospective and Truncated Prospective data, it is estimated that the mean length of postpartum amenorrhea following a live birth is 11 months while that for menstruating intervals is 10 months. It is further estimated that without contraception the mean menstruating interval would be one or two months shorter. The average prolongation of birth intervals by pregnancy wastage is gauged at two months. Now 11 months of postpartum amenorrhea, nine months of gestation, eight months of menstruating interval (in the absence of contraception), plus two months added by pregnancy wastage sum to 30 months.

The long period of postpartum amenorrhea associated with lactation also helps to explain why contraception and abortion sometimes have limited impact. Contraception affects only the

19. R. G. Potter, *op. cit.,* pp. 159–160.

length of "ovulatory exposure" (i.e., menstruating interval less anovulatory cycles), which comprises only a small fraction of the birth interval described above. According to fragmentary data from the West,[20] the mean number of anovulatory cycles following the birth of an infant that is not nursed or nursed only briefly is in the neighborhood of two and it remains an open question whether the frequency of anovulatory cycles is further increased when lactation is lengthy. If allowance is made for anovulatory cycles and for the limited contraception practiced by the Khanna Study couples, then their mean ovulatory exposure may be estimated as six or seven months, say six for definiteness of illustration. Roughly half of the average prolongation of birth intervals by pregnancy wastage is composed of ovulatory exposure. Given all the above assumptions, the ratio of ovulatory exposure to average birth interval without contraception becomes 7/30. This result means that even if contraception was 50 per cent effective and was doubling ovulatory exposure, it would be augmenting the total birth interval by a factor of only 7/30, or less than 25 per cent. Likewise, the impact of induced abortion is reduced because, in the absence of contraception, the average marriage duration required for one live birth with its attendant extra months of gestation, postpartum amenorrhea and anovulatory cycles is equivalent to the average duration required for nearly three second or third month abortions. That is, it takes on average almost three induced abortions to have the equivalent of one birth averted.

As usual in demographic matters, age plays an important qualifying role. In the present sample as mothers passed from their early twenties to their late thirties and early forties fetal wastage doubled [21] and menstruating intervals lengthened substantially. At the same time, length of postpartum amenorrhea associated with lactation increased appreciably. The findings reported suggest that this result is not attributable to contraception or to under-reporting of fetal wastage. If this result is corroborated in future studies, it confronts the endocrinologist with a new phenomenon to explain.

20. C. Tietze, *op. cit.*, p. 131.
21. R. G. Potter *et al.*, "Fetal Wastage in Eleven Punjab Villages," p. 265 (see footnote 16).

ACKNOWLEDGEMENTS

The original data were collected under grants from the Rockefeller Foundation and the Government of India. The Health Ministers and officials of the Government of India and of the Punjab encouraged and assisted in numerous ways during six years of field work. The present analysis has been supported in part by grants from the National Institutes of Health (Grant GM 10760–01), the Population Council, the National Science Foundation (Grant G-22677), and the Higgins Fund. Use of a life table approach was originally suggested by Dr. Jane Worcester. The writers gratefully acknowledge the manifold assistance of Mrs. Margaret Parker, the programming work of Mr. Arthur Le Gasse, and the kind permission of Dean James A. Crabtree and Dr. Antonio Ciocco to use the computing facilities of the Graduate School of Public Health, University of Pittsburgh.

APPENDIX

The details of the first 24 months of exposure of a life table pertaining to postpartum amenorrhea are reproduced in Table A–1. l_x signifies the number of couples exposed during month x to the risk of stopping postparum amenorrhea, or, what is the same, of resuming menstruation. c_x designates the number of couples who resume menstruation during month $x.w_x$ represents the couples for whom observation terminates at the end of month x. Thus, w_x includes both the c_x couples who resume menstruation during month x and the couples who drop from observation at the end of month x because of end of the study, outmigration, or death of one of the spouses. Given the restriction to Entirely Prospective and Truncated Prospective Intervals, all couples start their exposure during month one. Successive values of l_x are determined by the equation $l_{x+1} = l_x - w_x$.

The probability of ending postpartum amenorrhea during month x is estimated by c_x/l_x, while the complementary probability of continuing in amenorrhea during month x is given by $p_x = 1 - q_x$. The cumulative product

$$P(x) = \prod_{i=1}^{x} p_x$$

represents the probability of remaining in postpartum amenorrhea during the first x months. First differences of these probabilities, namely $R(x) = P(x-1) - P(x)$, gives the proportions resuming menstruation during any specified month x. The final column of the table furnishes approximate standard errors for the $P(x)$ column. The formula used, namely,

$$S_x = P(x) \left(\sum_{i=1}^{x} \frac{q_i}{l_i p_i} \right)^{\frac{1}{2}}$$

where p_i, q_i, l_i and $P(x)$ have the same meanings as above, is discussed elsewhere.[22] This estimator becomes less and less efficient as sample size decreases. Given moderate or small samples, the formula tends to be biased downward, owing to the neglect of a host of positive covariance terms.

The entire life table has been programmed for a Royal MacBee LCP-30 by Mr. Arthur LeGasse of the University of Pittsburgh.

To test the significance of a difference between two life tables, based on independent samples, the following approximate critical ratio has been used:

$$[P'(x) - P''(x)]/[(S'_x)^2 + (S''_x)^2]^{\frac{1}{2}},$$

where the single and double primes distinguish the two life tables. One problem is to select in advance the month of exposure on which to base the test. It is certainly not legitimate to hunt for that x which gives the largest $P'(x) - P''(x)$ difference. The procedure followed has been to choose that month which gives the $P(x)$ value closest to .500 for whichever life table is based on the smaller sample. For instance, if the life table in Table A–1 has the smaller l_1-value, the significance test would be based on month 11.

A better solution to the problem above would be to test the significance of differences between $P'(x) - P''(x)$ at several time points rather than at an arbitrarily selected single point.

22. R. G. Potter, ''Additional Measures of Use-Effectiveness of Contraception,'' *Milbank Memorial Fund Quarterly*, XLI (Oct., 1963), pp. 412–414.

TABLE A-1

Life Table of Postpartum Amenorrhea Following a Live Birth That Survives One Month or More, Based on Entirely Prospective and Truncated Prospective Intervals

Month of exposure x	Observation terminates at end of month x w_x	Number of couples exposed l_x	Number of couples resuming menstruation c_x	Probability of resuming menstruation (c_x/l_x) q_x	Probability of remaining amenorrheic $1 - q_x$ P_x	Probability of remaining amenorrheic x months $P(x)$	Probability of resuming menstruation during month x $R(x)$	Standard error of $P(x)$ $S(x)$
1	129	1,390	88	.0633093	.9366906	.9366906	.0633093	.006468
2	84	1,261	41	.0325138	.9674861	.9062351	.0304554	.007765
3	90	1,177	55	.0467289	.9532710	.8638877	.0423474	.009241
4	83	1,087	47	.0432382	.9567617	.8265347	.0373530	.010305
5	74	1,004	50	.0498007	.9501992	.7853726	.0411621	.011298
6	77	930	59	.0634408	.9365591	.7355479	.0498247	.012295
7	82	853	53	.0621336	.9378663	.6898456	.0457022	.013028
8	67	771	44	.0570687	.9429312	.6504770	.0393686	.013564
9	73	704	54	.0767045	.9232954	.6005824	.0498945	.014112
10	76	631	53	.0839936	.9160063	.5501373	.0504451	.014525
11	78	555	56	.1009008	.8990991	.4946280	.0555093	.014833
12	73	477	60	.1257861	.8742138	.4324106	.0622173	.014983
13	67	404	58	.1435643	.8564356	.3703318	.0620787	.014885
14	67	337	51	.1513353	.8486646	.3142875	.0560442	.014552
15	55	270	44	.1629629	.8370370	.2630703	.0512172	.014080
16	37	215	27	.1255813	.8744186	.2300336	.0330367	.013671
17	31	178	28	.1573033	.8426966	.1938485	.0361850	.013119
18	26	147	21	.1428571	.8571428	.1661559	.0276926	.012559
19	22	121	17	.1404958	.8595041	.1428116	.0233442	.012002
20	15	99	8	.0808080	.9191919	.1312713	.0115403	.011705
21	15	84	12	.1428571	.8571428	.1125182	.0187530	.011215
22	19	69	7	.1014492	.8985507	.1011033	.0114149	.010875
23	9	50	7	.1400000	.8600000	.0869489	.0141544	.010587
24	11	41	6	.1463414	.8536585	.0742246	.0127242	.010232

Needed for this purpose is a procedure yielding joint confidence intervals for the functions $P'(x) - P''(x)$. An asymptotic solution to this problem is offered by A. Berger and R. Gold.[23] Unfortunately, the present authors were not aware of this work during preparation and revision of the present paper.

23. A. Berger and R. Z. Gold, ''On Comparing Survival Times,'' *Proceedings of the Fourth Berkeley Symposium on Mathematical Statistics and Probability*, ed. J. Neyman (Berkeley: University of California Press, 1961), IV, pp. 67–76.

Christopher Tietze

INDUCED ABORTION AND STERILIZATION AS METHODS OF FERTILITY CONTROL

While induced abortion, with or without legal sanction, and surgical sterilization are important methods of fertility control in many countries, no comprehensive information is available on the extent of their use. Illegal abortion, in particular, is probably the least explored area within the scope of public health.

This statement is as true for the United States as it is for any other country in the world. A committee appointed by the Conference on Abortion at Arden House, New York, in April, 1955,[1] concluded its report with the observation that "a plausible estimate of the frequency of induced abortion in the United States could be as low as 200,000 and as high as 1,200,000 per year." The group saw "no objective basis for the selection of a particular figure between these two estimates as an approximation of the actual frequency." No new data have become availa-

---

1. M. S. Calderone (ed.), *Abortion in the United States* (New York: Paul B. Hoeber, 1958), p. 180.

ble since 1955 on which a more reliable estimate could be based.

Information on the frequency of illegal abortion in other countries is equally unsatisfactory and it would serve no useful purpose to burden this report with a series of more or less—all too often less—informed guesses. The following discussion of abortion is, therefore, limited to legal interruptions of pregnancy according to the laws of the countries concerned.

LEGAL ABORTIONS

United States

In the United States, the laws of most states stipulate a threat to the life of the pregnant woman as the sole legal ground on which pregnancy may be interrupted. This permission is extended, in a few states by statute and elsewhere by practice, to cases where a serious threat to health is to be averted. In some hospitals certain eugenic indications such as German measles in the first trimester of pregnancy are recognized, although the law does not provide for this type of indication. In general, however, the interpretation of the law by physicians and hospital administrators tends to be conservative.

In New York City, where all fetal deaths must be registered, the annual numbers of therapeutic abortions have declined from about 700 in the middle 1940's [2] to 284 in 1961; [3] the ratio per 1,000 live births has fallen from 4.7 to 1.7. This overall trend conceals a sharp and continuing decline in traditional medical indications and an increase in the incidence of abortion on psychiatric grounds. The proportion of therapeutic abortions in New York City performed for psychiatric indications has increased from about one tenth to about one half.

No reliable estimate can be made of the number of therapeutic abortions in the United States as a whole. If it is arbitrarily assumed that the ratio per 1,000 live births is the same as that reported for New York City in recent years, i.e., two per 1,000,

2. C. Tietze, ''Therapeutic Abortions in New York City, 1943–1947,'' *American Journal of Obstetrics and Gynecology*, LX (July, 1950), pp. 146–152.
3. J. P. Greenhill, ''World Trends of Therapeutic Abortion and Sterilization,'' *Clinical Obstetrics and Gynecology*, VII (March, 1964), pp. 37–42.

the current total for the country as a whole would be about 8,500 per year. However, a rough estimate of this sort can do no more than indicate an order of magnitude.

Legislation and practices with regard to abortion in Canada, the United Kingdom, France, and many other countries are similar to those prevailing in the United States.

Sweden and Denmark

In a few countries, such as Sweden and Denmark, abortion policies are substantially more liberal.[4] The first comprehensive legislation on abortion in these countries was enacted in the late 1930's. It provided for a broad extension of the traditional medical indications for the interruption of pregnancy and added new indications that had not been recognized previously. In both countries the abortion laws were subsequently amended and liberalized: in Sweden, most recently in 1946, and in Denmark in 1956. The range of acceptable indications is roughly the same in the Swedish and the Danish laws. In each instance the law recognizes medical indications, extended medical indications, eugenic indications, and humanitarian indications. The medical and extended medical indications require a serious threat to the life or health of the pregnant woman.

The extended medical indication, also known as the "social-medical" indication, allows consideration of the pregnant woman's social environment in the assessment of the threat to her life or health. In Sweden since 1946, the law provides that an abortion may be induced "when it can be assumed, considering the conditions of life of the woman and other circumstances, that her physical or mental strength will be seriously reduced by the birth and care of the child." It is not necessary that any threat to life or health actually exist at the time when the interruption of pregnancy is recommended. The Danish law prescribes that "consideration is to be given not only to physical or mental illness, but also to actual or threatening states of physical or mental stress, based on an evaluation of all circumstances, including the conditions under which the woman has to live." Medical and extended medical indications account for the

4. C. Tietze, ''Legal Abortion in Scandinavia,'' *Quarterly Review of Surgery, Obstetrics and Gynecology*, XVI (Oct.–Dec., 1959), pp. 227–230.

great majority of legal abortions in Sweden and Denmark. In recent years between 70 and 85 per cent of legal abortions in these two countries have been performed primarily on psychiatric grounds, including conditions described as "exhaustion."

In regard to the eugenic indication, the Swedish law of 1946 mentions only the hereditary transmission of mental disease, mental deficiency, and other severe illness or defect. The Royal Medical Board has, however, authorized the interruption of pregnancy on extended medical indication in many cases of German measles and at least one celebrated case of thalidomide poisoning. The more recently amended Danish law includes damage or disease acquired during intrauterine life. The humanitarian indication, called "juridical" indication in Denmark, applies in the case of pregnancies resulting from certain offenses against the penal code, such as rape and incest, and to pregnanies in children less than 15 years of age.

As shown in Table 1, the number of legal abortions in Sweden increased from about 400 in 1939 to more than 6,300 in 1951. During the same period the ratio of abortions per 1,000 live births rose from 5 to 57.[5] A parallel development occurred in Denmark, pushing the number of legal abortions from about 500 in 1939 to 5,400 in 1955 and the ratio per 1,000 live births from 7 to 70.[6]

In recent years the upward trend of legal abortions has been reversed. In Sweden the number declined to about 3,000 per year, and in Denmark to less than 4,000 per year. The current ratios per 1,000 live births are on the order of 30 in Sweden [7] and 50 in Denmark.[8] In part, this reversal of the trend appears to reflect a more restrictive practice of authorization. It is not clear to what extent other factors are also involved, such as a change of attitude toward abortions on the part of pregnant women or a more general and more skillful use of contraceptives.

5. Sweden: Medicinalstyrelsen, *Allmän hälso– och sjukvård, 1959* (Stockholm, 1961), p. 70.

6. Denmark: Sundhedsstyrelsen, *Medicinalberetning for Kongeriget Danmark, 1955* (Copenhagen, 1957), p. 127.

7. Sweden: Medicinalstyrelsen, *Allmän hälso– och sjukvård, 1960* (Stockholm, 1962), p. 103; *Ibid.*, 1961 (Stockholm, 1963), p. 97; *Ibid.*, 1962 (Stockholm, 1964), p. 105.

8. Denmark: Sundhedsstyrelsen, *Medicinalberetning for Kongeriget Danmark, 1959*, I (Copenhagen, 1961), p. 110; *Ibid.*, 1960, I (Copenhagen, 1962), p. 97.

TABLE 1

Legal Abortions in Sweden and Denmark: 1939–1963

Year	Number		Ratio per 1,000 Live Births	
	Sweden	Denmark	Sweden	Denmark
1939	439	484	5	7
1940	506	522	5	7
1941	496	519	5	7
1942	568	824	5	10
1943	703	977	6	12
1944	1,088	1,286	8	14
1945	1,623	1,577	12	17
1946	2,378	1,930	18	20
1947	3,534	2,240	28	24
1948	4,585	2,543	36	30
1949	5,503	3,425	45	43
1950	5,889	3,909	51	49
1951	6,328	4,743	57	62
1952	5,322	5,031	48	65
1953	4,915	4,795	45	61
1954	5,089	5,140	48	67
1955	4,562	5,381	43	70
1956	3,851	4,522	36	59
1957	3,386	4,023	32	53
1958	2,823	3,895	27	52
1959	3,071	3,587	29	48
1960	2,792	3,918	27	51
1961	2,909	4,124	28	54
1962	3,205	3,996	30	51
1963	3,528	3,971	31	48

Sources: Sweden 1939–59: Sweden: Medicinalstyrelsen, *Allmän hälso-och sjukvård*, 1959 (Stockholm, 1961), p. 70; Sweden 1960: *Ibid.*, 1960, p. 103; Sweden 1961: *Ibid.*, 1961, p. 97; Sweden 1962: *Ibid.*, 1962, p. 105; Sweden 1963: data supplied by Medicinalstyrelsen. Denmark 1939–54: Denmark: Sundhedsstyrelsen, *Medicinalberetning for Kongeriget Danmark*, 1955 (Copenhagen, 1957), p. 127; Denmark 1955–58: *Ibid.*, 1959, I, p. 110; Denmark 1959–60: *Ibid.*, 1960, I, p. 97; Denmark 1961–63: data supplied by Sundhedsstyrelsen.

While laws and practices in matters of abortion are much more liberal in countries such as Sweden or Denmark than they are in the United States, these countries have not "legalized" abortion in the sense in which this term is often used. Japan and a number of countries in Eastern Europe have adopted far more radical policies, and it is to these countries that we shall now turn our attention.

Japan

In Japan, the Eugenic Protection Law of 1948 authorized interruption of pregnancy for economic as well as for medical reasons.[9] The crucial passage is contained in Article 14 of the law and permits the interruption of pregnancy in a woman "whose health may be affected seriously from the physical or economic viewpoint by the continuation of pregnancy or by confinement." The subsequent interpretation of this paragraph by the medical profession, by the authorities, and by the public, has been tantamount to making abortion available on request.

As shown in Table 2, the reported numbers of legal abortions in Japan rose from 246,000 in 1949 to 1,170,000 in 1955, corresponding to an annual rate of 13.1 abortions per 1,000 population. Since 1955, the number of abortions has declined by 16 per

TABLE 2

Live Births and Legal Abortions in Japan, 1949–1963
(Rates per 1,000 Population)

Year	Live Births		Legal Abortions	
	Number	*Rate*	*Number*	*Rate*
1949	2,696,600	33.2	246,100	3.0
1950	2,337,500	28.2	489,100	5.9
1951	2,137,700	25.4	638,400	7.6
1952	2,005,200	23.5	798,200	9.3
1953	1,868,000	21.5	1,068,100	12.3
1954	1,769,600	20.1	1,143,100	13.0
1955	1,730,700	19.4	1,170,100	13.1
1956	1,665,300	18.5	1,159,300	12.9
1957	1,566,700	17.2	1,122,300	12.3
1958	1,649,800	18.0	1,128,200	12.3
1959	1,622,800	17.5	1,098,900	11.9
1960	1,603,000	17.2	1,063,200	11.4
1961	1,586,400	16.9	1,035,000	11.0
1962	1,613,100	17.0	985,400	10.4
1963	1,657,400	17.3	955,100	10.0

Source: 1949–57: M. Muramatsu, "Effect of Induced Abortion on the Reduction of Births in Japan," *Milbank Memorial Fund Quarterly*, XXXVIII (April, 1960), pp. 153–166; 1958–63: data supplied by Dr. Muramatsu.

9. *Eugenic Protection Law in Japan* (rev. ed.) (Tokyo: Institute of Population Problems, Aug., 1960).

cent and the rate by 21 per cent. The numbers reported are believed to fall short of the actual totals by several hundred thousand, owing—it has been alleged—to the reluctance of physicians to pay income tax on their full earnings.[10]

Eastern Europe

In Eastern Europe, abortion policy has undergone several major changes since November 8, 1920, when interruption of pregnancy at the request of the pregnant woman was legalized in the U.S.S.R. by a joint decree of the Commissariats of Health and Justice. On June 27, 1936, another decree restricted legal abortion to a list of specified medical and eugenic indications. On November 23, 1955, the policy was once more reversed and the restrictive decree of 1936 repealed by the Presidium of the Supreme Soviet.[11]

Following the example of the U.S.S.R., most of the countries of Eastern Europe have adopted similar legislation.[12] The stated aims of this legislation, in the words of the preamble to the Soviet decree, are "the limitation of the harm caused to the health of women by abortions carried out outside of hospitals" and to "give women the possibility of deciding by themselves the question of motherhood."

Throughout Eastern Europe, official concern with over-population or rapid population growth is proscribed by Marxist philosophy. Moreover, several of the countries concerned have a very low birth rate, and none has a high birth rate by global standards. At least two countries (Czechoslovakia and Hungary) pursue an active population policy by means of family allowances for third and later children.

Within the overall pattern of legal abortion, considerable variation between the individual countries is apparent. Abortion at the request of the pregnant woman is currently permitted in the U.S.S.R., Bulgaria, and Hungary. In Poland, the law of

---

10. M. Muramatsu, ''Effect of Induced Abortion on the Reduction of Births in Japan,'' *Milbank Memorial Fund Quarterly*, XXXVIII (April, 1960), pp. 153–166; I. B. Taeuber, *The Population of Japan* (Princeton: Princeton University Press, 1958), p. 276.

11. M. G. Field, ''The Re-legalization of Abortion in Soviet Russia,'' *New England Journal of Medicine*, CCLV (Aug. 30, 1956), pp. 421–427.

12. C. Tietze and H. Lehfeldt, ''Legal Abortion in Eastern Europe,'' *Journal of the American Medical Association*, CLXXV (April 1, 1961), pp. 1149–1154.

1956 stipulated a "difficult social situation" as an acceptable reason for the interruption of pregnancy and made the physician responsible for the determination of its existence. Since early 1960, however, an oral declaration by the pregnant woman suffices to establish her "difficult social situation."

In Czechoslovakia, the law permits abortion for reasons "worthy of special consideration," among which the Ministry of Health lists: (a) advanced age; (b) three or more living children; (c) death or disability of the husband; (d) disruption of the family; (e) predominant economic responsibility of the woman for the support of the family or the child; and (f) a difficult situation arising from the pregnancy of an unmarried woman. In Yugoslavia, interruption of pregnancy may be authorized if the birth of the child "would result in a serious personal, familial, or economic situation for the pregnant woman which cannot be averted in any other way."

Commissions for the authorization of abortion, consisting of physicians and representatives of the social services, have been established in Czechoslovakia and Yugoslavia. Medical boards also exist in Hungary, but their function has become purely formal since they must now assent if the applicant insists on having her pregnancy interrupted. In Poland, abortion is authorized by a certificate from a single physician.

Throughout Eastern Europe abortion is prohibited in pregnancies of more than three months' duration, except for medical reasons, and is forbidden if the applicant had undergone an induced abortion during the preceding six months. The operations must be performed by physicians in appropriately equipped and staffed hospitals, which in Eastern Europe are public institutions. The typical period of hospitalization is two or three days, followed by sick leave if the woman is a wage earner.

Abortions for medical reasons are performed free of charge. Those done on request or on "social indications" must be paid for by the applicant, except in Czechoslovakia, where fees for abortion on social indications were abolished in 1960. The charges cover only part of the costs of the operation and hospitalization.

The new legislation has resulted in spectacular increases in the incidence of legal abortions throughout Eastern Europe.

The most comprehensive statistics are available for Hungary and Czechoslovakia (Table 3). None are available for the U.S.S.R. In Hungary strong efforts were made in 1952 and 1953 to enforce existing laws against criminal abortion. These efforts

TABLE 3

Live Births, Stillbirths, and Abortions: Hungary, 1949–1963, and Czechoslovakia, 1953–1963 (Rates per 1,000 Population)

	Live Births		Stillbirths		Legal Abortions		Other Abortions [a]	
Country and year	*Number*	*Rate*	*Number*	*Rate*	*Number*	*Rate*	*Number*	*Rate*
Hungary								
1949	190,400	20.6	4,500	0.5	1,600	0.2	31,600	3.4
1950	195,600	20.9	4,200	0.4	1,700	0.2	34,300	3.7
1951	190,600	20.2	3,700	0.4	1,700	0.2	36,100	3.8
1952	185,800	19.5	3,500	0.4	1,700	0.2	42,000	4.4
1953	206,900	21.5	3,500	0.4	2,800	0.3	39,900	4.2
1954	223,300	23.0	3,700	0.4	16,300	1.7	42,000	4.3
1955	210,400	21.4	3,400	0.4	35,400	3.6	43,100	4.4
1956	192,800	19.5	3,000	0.3	82,500	8.3	41,100	4.2
1957	167,200	17.0	2,500	0.3	123,400	12.5	39,500	4.0
1958	158,400	16.0	2,200	0.2	145,600	14.7	37,400	3.8
1959	151,200	15.2	2,200	0.2	152,400	15.3	35,300	3.5
1960	146,500	14.6	2,000	0.2	162,200	16.2	33,800	3.4
1961	140,400	14.0	1,700	0.2	170,000	17.0	33,700	3.4
1962	130,100	12.9	1,600	0.2	163,700	16.3	33,900	3.4
1963	132,300	13.1	1,700	0.2	173,800	17.2	34,100	3.4
Czechoslovakia								
1953	271,700	21.2	3,200	0.2	1,500	0.1	29,100	2.3
1954	266,700	20.6	3,100	0.2	2,800	0.2	30,600	2.4
1955	265,200	20.3	3,200	0.2	2,100	0.2	33,000	2.5
1956	262,000	19.8	2,900	0.2	3,100	0.2	31,000	2.3
1957	252,700	18.9	3,000	0.2	7,300	0.5	30,200	2.3
1958	235,000	17.4	2,600	0.2	61,400	4.6	27,700	2.1
1959	217,000	16.0	2,400	0.2	79,100	5.8	26,400	1.9
1960	217,300	15.9	2,300	0.2	88,300	6.5	26,300	1.9
1961	218,400	15.8	2,200	0.2	94,300	6.8	26,000	1.9
1962	217,500	15.7	2,000	0.1	89,900	6.5	26,000	1.9
1963	235,900	16.9	2,100	0.1	70,700	5.0	29,200	2.1

[a] Hospital admissions.

Sources: Hungary 1949–58: I. Hirschler, "Die Abortsituation in der Volksrepublik Ungarn," *Internationale Abortsituation, Abortbekämpfung, Antikonzeption*, ed. K.-H. Mehlan (Leipzig: Georg Thieme, 1961), pp. 114–122; Hungary 1959–63: Statisztikai Idöszaki Közlemények, *Magyarország Népesedése, Demográfiai Evkänyv 1963*; Czechoslovakia 1953–57: M. Vojta, "Die Abortsituation in der Tschechoslowakischen sozialistischen Republik," *Internationale Abortsituation, Abortbekämpfung, Antikonzeption*, ed. K.-H. Mehlan (Leipzig: Georg Thieme, 1961), pp. 107–113; Czechoslovakia 1958–62: V. Srb and M. Kučera, "Potratovost v Československu v letech 1958–62," *Demografie*, V (1963), pp. 289–307; 1963: Ministerstvo Zdravotnictví, *Zdravotnictvi ČSSR 1963*. All data on live and stillbirths from *United Nations Demographic Yearbook* and *Population and Vital Statistics Report*.

were followed by an increase in births in 1953 and 1954. At about the same time, medical boards for the authorization of therapeutic abortions were established. The growing numbers of legal abortions indicate the progressive liberalization of the policies of these boards from 1953.[13] After the decree of June 3, 1956, had introduced the interruption of pregnancy on request, the number of legal abortions increased rapidly until in 1963 it reached 173,800, exceeding the number of live births by almost one third.[14]

In Czechoslovakia, legalization of abortion for nonmedical reasons was preceded by almost two years of public discussion. Moderate increases in therapeutic abortions in 1956 and 1957 reflect the changing attitude of the medical profession. Promulgation of a new and liberalized abortion law in December, 1957 was followed by a steep rise in legal abortions in 1958, continuing at a decelerating pace until 1961.[15] The trend was reversed with a drop to 70,700 in 1963.[16]

In each of the countries of Eastern Europe where abortion was legalized, a decline of the birth rate has ensued. By 1962, compared with the early 1950's, the decline ranged from 15 per cent in the U.S.S.R. to almost 40 per cent in Hungary. No such decline occurred in the two countries which had not legalized abortion (Albania and East Germany) nor, generally speaking, in Western Europe. The difference in natality trends is sufficiently marked to justify the conclusion that the legalization of abortion has had a depressant effect on the birth rate.[17]

Complications

Up-to-date information on the risk to life associated with the legal interruption of pregnancy comes mainly from Eastern

13. I. Hirschler, ''Die Abortsituation in der Volksrepublik Ungarn,'' *Internationale Abortsituation, Abortbekämpfung, Antikonzeption*, ed. K. -H. Mehlan (Leipzig: Georg Thieme, 1961), pp. 114–122.

14. Statisztikai Időszaki Közlemények, *Magyarország Népesedése, Demográfiai Evkönyv 1963.*

15. M. Vojta, ''Die Abortsituation in der Tschechoslowakischen sozialistichen Republik,'' *Internationale Abortsituation, Abortbekämpfung, Antikonzeption*, ed. K. -H. Mehlan (Leipzig: Georg Thieme, 1961), pp. 107–113.

16. V. Srb and M. Kučera, ''Potratovost v Československu v letech 1958–62,'' *Demografie*, V (1963), pp. 289–307; 1963: Ministerstvo Zdravotnictví, *Zdravotnictvi ČSSR 1963.*

17. C. Tietze, ''The Demographic Significance of Legal Abortion in Eastern Europe,'' *Demography*, I (1964), pp. 119–125.

Europe. The Japanese, who have reported more than 13 million legal abortions since 1949, have been curiously unwilling or unable to study the implications of their policy in terms of mortality or morbidity.

Mortality associated with legal abortion has been exceedingly low in Eastern Europe. For Hungary, Hirschler's thorough investigation reported 15 deaths following 269,000 abortions during the two-year period 1957–58, corresponding to a mortality rate of six per 100,000. More recent figures, reported by Szabady for the two-year period 1960–61, point to the even lower mortality rate of three per 100,000 legal abortions, based on nine deaths among 332,000 cases. In Czechoslovakia, a mortality rate of four per 100,000 was achieved in 1959–60; there were six deaths among 167,000 legal abortions. In 1961, no deaths were reported.[18] In Yugoslavia, according to Mojić,[19] eight deaths occurred in 1960–61 among 177,000 legal abortions, corresponding to a rate of less than five per 100,000 cases. It is almost certain that the low level of mortality in Eastern Europe reflects primarily the restriction of legal abortion to the first three months of pregnancy except in cases with a medical indication.

While many physicians cling to the belief that interruption of pregnancy even under the most favorable conditions often produces sterility, this outcome is, in fact, comparatively rare. The majority of recent follow-up investigations of women who had undergone legal abortion, carried out mainly in Scandinavia and summarized by Lindahl,[20] have reported an incidence of involuntary sterility as low as one to six per cent, roughly corresponding to the incidence of secondary sterility after confinement.

Some physicians have been concerned with possible psychological sequelae of legal abortion. It is true that some women are disturbed about the operation and may even regret it. In Ekblad's carefully studied group of 479 cases from Stockholm, one fourth reported mild or serious self-reproaches. However, a

18. M. Vojta, personal communication.
19. A. Mojić, *Abortion as a Method of Family Planning*, paper presented at the IPPF Regional Conference (Warsaw, 1962).
20. J. Lindahl, *Somatic Complications Following Legal Abortion* (Stockholm: Svenska bokförlaget, 1959), p. 150.

"closer study of the case histories of these women . . . shows that even if their subjective sufferings due to the abortion were severe, from the psychiatric point of view, their depression must in general be designated as mild. It is only rarely that the women's working capacity has been impaired or that they have needed to consult a doctor on account of their mental troubles. . . ." [21] Moreover, it is necessary to consider not only the possible emotional sequelae of legal abortion, but also the consequences of unwanted parenthood for mother and child, family and community.

None of the Asian countries committed to a governmental program of fertility control as a matter of population policy, such as India or Pakistan, has given serious consideration to the legalization of abortion. While this restraint doubtless reflects religious beliefs and traditional medical attitudes, it may also be justified on the basis of lack of medical personnel and facilities.

It is well to remember that the development of an oral abortifacient, suitable for use in the human, has not had a high priority in the laboratories of the pharmaceutical industry or in academic research.

Many compounds have been investigated in animals, mainly in the context of teratogenesis. Most of these are too toxic for use in humans but at least one folic acid antagonist has been successful, with "only a slight and transitory depressing effect on the hemoglobin and white blood counts of the mothers," [22] in 10 out of 12 therapeutic abortions. The social implications of an effective and truly safe abortion pill are beyond the scope of this paper.

STERILIZATION

History

Let us now turn to surgical sterilization as a method of fertility control. Surgical sterilization was originally used to

21. M. Ekblad, "Induced Abortion on Psychiatric Grounds: A Follow-up Study of 479 Women," *Acta psychiatrica et neurologica Scandinavica*, Suppl. 99 (1955), p. 234.

22. J. B. Thiersch, "Therapeutic Abortions with a Folic Acid Antagonist, 4-aminopteroylglutamic acid (4-amino P.G.A.), Administered by the Oral Route," *American Journal of Obstetrics and Gynecology*, LXIII (June, 1952), pp. 1298–1304.

protect women whose life or health was threatened by pregnancy. Dr. James Blundell of London is credited with having first proposed the procedure in 1823 to avoid the necessity of repeated Caesarean section or destruction of the child in cases of severe pelvic contraction. Effective techniques were developed in the latter part of the nineteenth century when aseptic surgery and anesthesia became available. At about the same time, sterilizing operations began to be widely used on males, mainly in connection with operations on the prostate. The sterilizing effects in these cases, however, were only incidental and not the purpose of the operation.

Growing confidence in the efficacy and safety of surgical sterilization led to its use for eugenic purposes, i.e., to prevent persons suffering from hereditary disabilities from having offspring. The most important indications have been mental deficiency, psychoses, and idiopathic epilepsy. In the United States, 32 states adopted legislation between 1907 and 1937 regulating the practice of eugenic sterilization. Some of these laws have been declared unconstitutional, but the majority are still in force. However, only a few states have used their authority extensively and the total number of persons sterilized under the eugenic laws was 63,000 through 1961.[23] During the period 1957–61, the number of eugenic sterilizations averaged about 600 per year.

In recent years, discussion has centered on the legality and propriety of voluntary sterilization as a method of family limitation and on the use of sterilization in countries where high birth rates and rapid population growth threaten to produce serious economic and social difficulties.[24]

Risk

It should be noted that neither tubal sterilization nor vasectomy is 100 per cent successful in preventing future pregnancies. According to 10 major studies, published since 1948 and covering about 10,000 women on whom salpingectomy had been

23. Human Betterment Association, *Sterilizations Performed Through December 31, 1962 Under U.S. State Sterilization Statutes* (New York, March, 1963).

24. C. P. Blacker, ''Voluntary Sterilization: Transitions Throughout the World,'' *Eugenics Review*, LIV (Oct., 1962), pp. 143–162.

performed, the incidence of known pregnancies during a follow-up period of several years was on the order of one per cent.[25] Fragmentary information suggests that failures of vasectomy may be more common than failures of sterilizing operations on females.

While salpingectomy is a major operation, requiring the opening of the abdominal cavity and hospitalization, it hardly lengthens the period of bed rest when performed immediately following delivery. In the male, vasectomy can be performed through a small incision in the scrotum or groin under local anesthesia, and does not require hospitalization.

Attempts to restore fecundity by a second operation have been made in both men and women. The results of these efforts have been only moderately encouraging. In general, therefore, fertility control by surgical methods should be considered irreversible. This fact should restrict sterilization to persons permanently ineligible for parenthood and to mature couples who have all the children they want or are likely to want in the future.

According to a number of studies, the great majority of sterilized patients are satisfied with the result, feel relieved from the nagging fear of pregnancy, and have no complaints. Regrets and more serious psychological side effects have, however, been occasionally noted in sterilized persons of both sexes, who were poorly chosen or not suitably prepared for the operation. Such undesirable side effects are most likely to occur if the marriage was seriously unhappy or when the operation was accepted reluctantly, under pressure from a spouse or from other persons.

Prevalence

Comprehensive information on the prevalence of voluntary sterilization in the United States during the late 1950's was obtained in the second round of the Growth of American Families Study. I am greatly indebted to the late Professor Whelpton[26] and his associates for their permission to include

25. C. Tietze, ''The Current Status of Fertility Control,'' *Law and Contemporary Problems*, XXV (Summer, 1960), pp. 426–444.
26. P. K. Whelpton, personal communication.

some of their findings in this paper. An operation, on either the wife or husband, which made pregnancy impossible was reported by 255 among 2,684 white and nonwhite respondents. In 112 cases, the sterilizing effect was incidental to the correction of a pathological condition, such as the removal of a tumor. In almost all of these cases the wife had been the patient. In the remaining 143 cases (5.3 per cent of all couples) the operation had been performed to prevent conception. Among the latter group, 90 wives and 53 husbands had undergone surgery. Among couples with a wife 18–29 years of age, 2.7 per cent reported a contraceptive operation; the corresponding figure for couples with a wife in her thirties was 7.6 per cent. It would appear on the basis of these figures that the incidence of voluntary sterilization for contraceptive purposes in the United States during the late 1950's was on the order of 110,000 per year, including about 65,000 operations on women and 45,000 vasectomies.

The popularity of voluntary female sterilization in Puerto Rico is well known far beyond the confines of that island. According to an often-told story, it started in the early 1940's when a number of women were sterilized in a missionary hospital. The hospital ". . . was attacked in a pastoral letter. The reading of the letter in the rural churches was followed by a wave of inquiries at public health clinics and to private doctors as to the availability of the operation which had been denounced by the bishop." [27]

By 1950, the number of sterilizations in Puerto Rico was authoritatively estimated at between 3,000 and 4,000 per year. Several surveys taken in 1953–54 led to the conclusion that one sixth of all women of childbearing age were sterilized.[28] Recourse to surgical birth control was reported more often among the better educated than among women with little or no school-

27. C. Senior, "An Approach to Research in Overcoming Cultural Barriers to Family Limitation," *Proceedings of the Annual Meeting of the Population Association of America*, ed. G. F. Mair (Princeton: Princeton University Press, 1949), pp. 148–151.

28. K. W. Back, R. Hill, and J. M. Stycos, "Population Control in Puerto Rico: The Formal and Informal Framework," *Law and Contemporary Problems*, XXV (Summer, 1960), pp. 558–576.

ing. The popularity of female sterilization in Puerto Rico is not shared by the comparable operation on the male.

In Japan, surgical sterilization is regulated by the Eugenic Protection Law of 1948 which permits sterilization of women who have given birth to "several" children, or of their husbands, for reasons of the woman's health. This provision has been broadly interpreted by the medical profession and there can be little doubt that the great majority of sterilizations in Japan are performed for economic, social, and personal reasons, as an alternative to contraception.[29]

According to official statistics, about 450,000 sterilizations, including 14,000 vasectomies, were reported in Japan from the time of the adoption of the Eugenic Protection Law through 1962. Official statistics are, however, incomplete and many sterilizations are performed under "black market" conditions. According to the most recent survey of family limitation practices, conducted in 1961 by the Population Problems Research Council,[30] 4.7 per cent of the wives and 0.9 per cent of the husbands in the interviewed sample were sterilized, corresponding to a total of about 800,000 couples for Japan as a whole.

In India, surgical sterilization is an important part of the official family planning program. Thanks in part to financial support from the central government, facilities for free surgery are available on a fairly wide scale. Government employees and industrial workers are given a week's special leave. To others, some State governments offer a modest bonus of Rs 10 to Rs 30 ($2.00 to $6.00), described as a compensation for loss of wages, and free transportation.[31]

Since 1956 an estimated 400,000 persons have been sterilized in India, including about 250,000 men and 150,000 women. India seems to be unique in having more men than women accept surgical birth control. Another special feature is the use of

29. Y. Koya, "Sterilization in Japan," *Eugenics Quarterly*, VIII (Sept., 1961), pp. 135–141.

30. Population Problems Research Council, *Sixth Opinion Survey on Family Planning and Birth Control: A Preliminary Report* (Tokyo: Mainichi Newspapers, 1962).

31. B. L. Raina, *Family Planning Programme Report for 1962–63* (processed, New Delhi, April, 1963), pp. 11–12.

"sterilization camps" in rural areas during the winter months when farm work is slack. These camps are usually operated for several days during which more than 1,000 men may undergo vasectomy.

The demographic effectiveness of the Indian sterilization program should be evaluated against the somber computations of Dandekar.[32] If all married males would accept vasectomy after the birth of their third living child, the birth rate would decline only 30 per cent below its present level. To achieve this goal, a backlog of 32 million men would have to be sterilized, in addition to an annual increment of more than two million newly eligible fathers.

In summary, then, surgical sterilization, as well as abortion, is widely used throughout the world, and their utilization as methods of fertility control is a matter for serious consideration. In the meantime, until mankind has learned to master the "passion between the sexes" or until effective, safe, and convenient contraceptives are universally accepted and available, sterilization and abortion will continue, with or without official encouragement or prohibition.

32. K. Dandekar, "Sterilization Programme: Its Size and Effects on Birth Rate," *Artha Vijnana*, I (Sept., 1959), pp. 220–232.

A. S. Parkes

BIOLOGY OF HUMAN FERTILITY AND ITS CONTROL

It has often been said that until the advent of the Pincus pill [1] less than ten years ago, methods of controlling human fertility were archaic in principle and a disgrace to science in this age of spectacular technical achievement. With an eye to the future, it is useful to ask why this sad state of affairs lasted so long. In retrospect, two main factors seem to have been responsible: (1) whatever may have been private practice, public acknowledgement and discussion of the problem was taboo; (2) we were largely ignorant of the relevant biology, especially in man.

The origin of the taboo was no doubt complex, but some probable influences can be discerned. With high mortality, the lot until recently of most of the human race, high fertility has a major survival value and the necessity for exploiting it can well become built into social customs. Moreover, in more primitive

1. Eds. note: Contraceptive pills, also known as oral contraceptives. The mechanism of action of these pills is discussed in the body of the paper. See Pincus in list of references.

417

societies, an abundance of children demonstrates a man's much prized virility and later on provides cheap labor or social influence. Here, too, we see the origin of the slight stigma attaching to sterility. On the ideological plane, whether religious or political, another factor comes in—that leaders of causes, good or bad, naturally want their followers to outbreed others, and prohibitions against restricting fertility become part of the body of dogma under which the sect or party operates. Naturally, there are many exceptions to these generalizations—infanticide, for instance, has not uncommonly sprung up under the harsh pressures of life, but the general principles remain. Here then, we have a biological explanation of the irrational and often hysterical opposition to attempts at organized birth control which characterized the early years of this century. Biologists and medical scientists were not immune from such influences and, however strong their private practical endorsement of birth control may have been, mostly made no effort to carry out the research necessary for understanding the problems involved and for rendering methods more effective and aesthetic.

Two exceptions must be made to this generalization. In the middle 1930's, Dr. J. R. Baker in Oxford undertook the first systematic investigation of the properties of chemical spermicides and of the conditions necessary for their effective vaginal application.

The second exception, of course, is the work of Knaus and Ogino. Up to about 1920, although the cyclic changes in the human endometrium were well known, their relation with the ovarian cycle was still a matter of debate and it was often supposed that a woman could ovulate and therefore could get pregnant at any time of the cycle. Even the homology of the menstrual cycle in women was uncertain, and attempts to homologize menstruation with the pro-estrous bleeding of the dog, instead of with the end of progestational phase, still lingered on. This uncertainty was brought to an end by work which showed that the one and only ovulation taking place in a menstrual cycle did so at about its mid-point. At about the same time it became realized that the most mammalian sperm and ova had a very limited life in the female tract—possibly three days and one day respectively in the case of man. It followed that coitus could be fertile only during some four days of the menstrual cycle, and that coitus outside this short fertile period would necessarily be sterile and therefore safe from the point of view of contraception. This idea of the safe period was postulated nearly simultaneously, but independently, by Knaus in Vienna and Ogino in Japan.

RHYTHM METHOD

This so-called rhythm method was eagerly seized on by many people who had scruples of one sort or another about the use of mechanical or chemical devices. It was especially favored by those to whom it seemed to conform to "natural laws," as defined by ecclesiastics without knowledge of biology, and glowing reports of its effectiveness appeared. For instance, two authors claimed to have records of 49,356 intercourses during the safe periods in 11,249 cycles without a single pregnancy. Such statistics must be regarded with some caution.

The basic principle of the rhythm method is of course entirely sound, but it has been well said that knowledge of it is more useful in securing pregnancy than in avoiding it. Certainly, the difficulties of its practical application for contraception, except in an attenuated form, are obvious. There is no way of determining in women that ovulation is about to occur, or even of detecting it at the time it occurs except in the few women who feel a momentary pain on one side or the other. Estimation of the probable time must therefore depend on rough arithmetic, but even in a conventional 28-day cycle, the time of ovulation will be affected by ordinary biological variability. More especially, even in a woman with an average cycle length of 28 days, variability from month to month is considerable. In any large group of women variation is of course much greater. Women with modal cycle lengths of 29, 27, or even 25 days are not uncommon and in a large sample, cycles of 27 or 29 days may be nearly as frequent as those of 28 days, and those of 25, 26, and 30 days considerably more than half as frequent.

This variability would be less important if ovulation followed at a definite time after the end of menstruation, but as menstruation marks the end of the luteal phase initiated by ovulation, ovulation is tied not to the preceding menstruation, but to the one that will occur if conception does not take place. There is evidence too, originally derived from the study of monkeys, that the luteal phase of the menstrual cycle tends to be more regular in length than the follicular phase, so that the time of ovulation should best be calculated back from the expected time of the next menstruation, which can be predicted only within limits. The idea that the luteal phase is more regular than the follicular one is not accepted unanimously, but it is strikingly confirmed by hormone excretion patterns during short and long cycles.

Evidently, the variables to be allowed for in calculating the safe period are formidable, and many formulas have been put forward. Knaus maintained that ovulation always occurred 15 days before the date of the next expected menstruation, i.e., in a 28-day cycle 13 days after the preceding menstruation, and that allowance must be made for variation in total cycle length over the previous year. Thus, where the variation had been from 26–30 days, ovulation was to be expected 11–15 days after the preceding menstruation. Excluding the time of menstruation, this leaves 18–19 days for the infertile, i.e., the safe period. Evidently, however, some allowance must be made for variability in the length of the luteal phase, and the safe period is reduced accordingly. These matters are comprehensively dealt with by Hartman in his recent and most useful book on *Science and the Safe Period*.

The use of the rhythm method is to some extent facilitated by basal temperature records, which, because of the thermogenic effects of progesterone, may indicate within a day or two that ovulation has occurred. This technique, however, like the estimation of urinary pregnanediol, the excretion product of progesterone, is more useful retrospectively to decide whether or not ovulation occurred in a cycle than as a basis for current action. The real need is for a simple method, suitable for domestic use, of predicting ovulation in women three days in advance. At present there is no promising lead in this direction. When such a lead appears, its successful exploitation would be worth a tremendous research effort. In the meantime, what other possibilities exist?

At the meeting organized by the American Academy of Arts

and Science in Boston last year,[2] John Rock put forward the attractive idea of expediting ovulation, that is, getting it over and done with at a known time in the cycle. The difficulties, however, are formidable. First, a follicle can be made to ovulate only after a certain stage of development—when does that occur in any particular cycle? Second, human gonadotrophins which would do the job are not active by mouth, and monthly injection, possibly multiple monthly injections, would not be practicable. It is unfortunate that estrogens, some of which are active by mouth, precipitate ovulation in some species, but delay or suppress it in man. And this brings me to my next topic.

THE SUPPRESSION OF OVULATION

If ovulation cannot at present be accelerated and disposed of in that way, it can by contrast be suppressed altogether. And here it may be that a closer study of three conditions in which women do not ovulate would provide useful information, i.e., during anovular cycles, pregnancy, and early lactation. Anovular cycles, in which ovulation does not take place, are of normal length and terminate in an overtly normal menstruation, which is the result of bleeding from a resting rather than a progestational endometrium. Such cycles are of interest in showing that cycle length in man is not dependent on the presence of a corpus luteum and that menstrual bleeding, although the normal termination of it in an infertile cycle, is not dependent on progestational development of the endometrium. The lack of ovulation is presumably the result of a deficiency of hypophysial gonadotrophin, or of decreased sensitivity of the target organ, because it can be remedied by administration of human hypophysial gonadotrophin. Evidently, much further study of this interesting condition is required.

After conception in women, ovulation is in abeyance until some time during lactation. During pregnancy, especially late pregnancy, the organism becomes tolerant to very large amounts of estrogen produced by the placenta, amounts which would cause alarming symptoms in a nonpregnant woman. At the same time, the hypophysis becomes almost devoid of gonado-

2. See R. O. Greep, ''Human Fertility and Population Problems,'' in list of references.

trophin, very probably under the pressure of high circulating estrogen. After parturition, gonadotrophin reappears in the hypophysis, but increases only slowly, amenorrhea usually being terminated by one or more anovular cycles before ovulation and fertility return. With a rapid sequence of pregnancies, therefore, hypophysial gonadotrophic activity and ovulation are suppressed almost continuously for years. This fact may have some relevance in considering possible consequences of the long term artificial suppression of hypophysial gonadotrophic activity. This brings me to my next theme—the Pincus pill. What is the background of this remarkable medication?

When the pituitary gonadotrophins were discovered more than 35 years ago, it was quickly realized that there must be some feedback to the hypophysis so as to prevent overstimulation of the gonads. This necessary mechanism proved to depend on the fact that the presence of excessive amounts of the gonad hormones in the circulating blood damped down pituitary activity, thus creating a reciprocating mechanism. This pituitary depressing activity is exerted by exogenous gonad hormones, and is not sex-specific. Thus androgens are effective in females and estrogens and progesterone in males. Among many other results obtained in this field, it was shown that administration of estrogens, starting early in the cycle, suppressed ovulation in women, and this reaction was exploited in the treatment of dysmenorrhea, which does not occur in the absence of ovulation. Unfortunately, prolonged treatment with estrogen was generally regarded as hazardous and to require some therapeutic justification, and the use of estrogen in this way for contraceptive purposes was not pursued. In these circumstances it is rather odd to see estrogens now being used for contraception in the form of sequential therapy, that is, estrogen to inhibit ovulation followed by estrogen and progestagen to regulate menstruation.

Androgens, though at one time used in women to control menorrhagia, could not be administered indefinitely because of masculinizing effects. Finally progesterone, more benign than either estrogens or androgens, was inactive by mouth—a fatal disadvantage. Here, if we except the preparation of a weak orally-active progestagen, ethisterone, about 1937, the situation rested until the early 1950's when biological analogues of progesterone with high activity by mouth were prepared. Pincus and Rock, to their great credit, saw and seized the opportunity presented, and after extensive animal experiments, oral contraception, based on the suppression of ovulation by the use of orally active progestagens with a small mixture of estrogen, came into existence. Acceptability, in spite of the necessity for consuming a pill each day during days 5 to 25 of the cycle, has proved to be remarkably good and when properly used, the technique has proved to be extraordinarily effective. Effectiveness is in fact so high that the effects of the exogenous progestagen on the endometrium and cervical mucus are probably supplementary antifertility factors, and prevent conception even in the event of a breakthrough ovulation.

The endometrial effect may be important because implantation of a fertilized egg depends on appropriate priming of the endometrium before and for some days after ovulation, a state of affairs not likely to be found after exposure to exogenous progestagens for two weeks or more. The cervical mucus reaction is also of considerable interest and was at one time thought to have possibilities for contraception in its own right. During the follicular phase of the normal cycle, the mucus which plugs the cervix becomes thin and runny and by the time of ovulation is easily penetrated by spermatozoa. After ovulation, during the luteal phase, it becomes thick and tacky, and resistant to the passage of spermatozoa. This change is brought about by progesterone and can be stimulated, when it would not otherwise occur, by the administration of progestagens. It is hard to avoid the conclusion that this reaction is a factor in the defence against conception provided by oral progestagens.

The idea of administering highly active steroids for the greater part of each cycle for an indefinite period has not unnaturally raised among endocrinologists some queries which require careful consideration. We may dismiss the question of immediate side effects—headache, nausea, etc.—which are not serious and tend to disappear in a few months. Medical complications occurring in association with the taking of oral progestagens, e.g., thrombo-embolic conditions, etc., require more attention, but, so far as I know, it has still to be shown that such emergencies occur more frequently among the hundreds of thousands of women using the pill than among other women of similar age and history.

Two other contingencies, largely hypothetical, are also much discussed. The first is that the long-term suppression of its ovulation-producing activity will utimately damage the pituitary gland. This possibility is difficult to refute because it is difficult to prove a negative and impossible to do so in advance. The fact that the ovulation-producing activity of the human pituitary gland is suppressed for a year or so during pregnancy and lactation has already been mentioned, and a rapid succession of pregnancies is certainly compatible with the normal functioning of the reproductive machinery. In any case, the argument about ultimate damage boils down to the Gilbertian situation that no women should be kept on the pill for, say, 20 years until a substantial number of women have, in fact, been kept on the pill for 20 years to demonstrate its harmlessness.[3]

The second hypothetical possibility urged against the use of the pill is that the ovulation-inhibiting action of the oral progestagen is at least partly a direct one on the ovary, and that there may therefore be adverse genetic effects on the oocytes. This ingenious succession of assumptions is based on observations that (1) the mid-cycle rise in urinary gonadotrophin of hypophysial origin-associated with ovulation—may still be found to some extent in women receiving oral progestagens and (2) exogenous gonadotrophin does not always overcome their ovulation-inhibiting effects. At present, evidence of this kind is quite inadequate to prove that the effect of the oral progestagens is a direct one on the ovary, and I doubt if there is any evidence that, even if it were, there would be genetic damage to the oocytes. In experimental animals, depression of pituitary activity, as by hypophysectomy, conserves the oocyte population, not only by preventing ovulation, but by decreasing follicular atresia. In the case of women, it is known that fertility returns, possibly at a higher level than before, immediately after the end of progestagen medication, and, so far as I know,

3. Eds. note: During the Symposium discussion, it was mentioned that long-term animal experiments (on mice) are now in progress to examine this question. Perhaps experiments on a number of species would be of value.

no genetic effects definitely attributable to the use of the pill have been reported. The question of the possible conservation of oocytes is of some interest, because it has been suggested that if it happens in women using oral progestagens the span of reproductive life might be increased and the menopause postponed. The possibility of damage to the ovary other than to the oocytes should not, of course, be overlooked.

POSSIBLE AGENTS FOR USE BY MALES

It should be urged, however, that very long-term continuous exposure to the pill need not be visualized because its use from an early age would probably be interrupted by planned pregnancies. Moreover, possibly the most useful place for the pill is after completion of a family, and especially in the control of the menopause and of the hazards to both mother and child of a belated pregnancy. The most important point here, however, is that it will almost certainly be unnecessary to contemplate the use of the Pincus pill for indefinitely long periods because of the probability that a fertility-control pill for males is on the way. When this arrives it will be possible for man and woman to take alternate, say alternate yearly, shifts in consuming pills, and so to avoid the possible adverse effects on either of long-term medication. Effects in the male would offer an instructive comparison with those in the female. In the latter, the pill inhibits ovulation in the first cycle of its use and thus becomes effective immediately. In the male, even if antispermatogenic substances stopped spermatogenesis immediately, existing spermatozoa would survive in the epididymis for some weeks, so that fertility would persist until they were used up or ceased to be viable. Antifertility medication of the man, therefore, would have to start at least a month before that of the woman stopped. At the reverse changeover, no overlap would be necessary.

Such alternation of antifertility medication might be very satisfactory. It would certainly be highly sophisticated. What are the chances of its becoming a reality? There are two different approaches to the problem of the biological control of fertility in the male. As in women, fertility in men is dependent on the production of gonadotrophins by the anterior pituitary body, and the cutting off of this supply stops spermatogenesis.

Also, as in the female, a feedback mechanism exists from the gonad to the hypophysis and the administration of exogenous steroid hormones suppresses hypophysial activity and, therefore, spermatogenesis in the male as well as ovulation in the female. Unfortunately, depression of hypophysial activity in the male also results in failure of the androgen-producing interstitial cells of the testis. The speed and extent of the loss of sex drive resulting from loss of testicular androgens is extremely variable in man, but the probability of an appreciable effect makes unacceptable the control of fertility in the human male by the use of oral progestagens. The use of androgens, while depressing pituitary activity, would presumably replace the lost androgenic activity of the testes, and so suppress spermatogenesis without affecting *libido*; unfortunately a really effective orally active androgen is not yet known. Alternatively, a compound selectively inhibiting pituitary FSH but not ICSH should suppress spermatogenesis without affecting the androgenic activity of the interstitial cells, but, again, such a compound is unknown at the present time.

The second approach is to attack spermatogenesis directly and this requires the use of antimeiotic substances. Several types of such substances are known, but not all are sufficiently free from side effects to be suitable for extensive field trials in man. This applies particularly to certain bis-(dichloracetyl)-diamine compounds investigated by Warren Nelson, and presumably to the cadmium salts which were found by Parizek to have devastating effects on the seminiferous tubules of rats, apparently because of the competitive inhibition of zinc. There are good indications, however, both from animal experiments and from initial tests on man, that one or more compounds, apparently meeting the necessary specifications and requiring relatively infrequent administration, are likely to become available. Relay medication of the two sexes is likely, therefore, to become a practical proposition in the visible future.

Inhibition of release or production of gametes are thus the antifertility techniques of practical biological interest at the present time. There are, of course, several other biological approaches which have so far made less progress. For instance, immunological aspects of reproduction, especially the antigenic properties of reproductive cells and tissues, are being actively investigated at the present time and it may well be that methods based on immunological phenomena will become available in due course. These would probably have the disadvantage of involving one or more injections, but they would also probably have the advantage of being effective over a long period and of being acceptable and easily organized among populations already inured to mass immunization programs.

INTERFERENCE WITH IMPLANTATION

A further possibility now attracting much attention is that of preventing, by biological methods, the implantation of the fertilized egg. This would presumably require medication during the third week of the cycle whenever there was a possibility of an egg's having been fertilized. Such a method would have the disadvantage of depending on calculations about the probable time of ovulation, but the arithmetic involved would be much less critical than that required by the use of the rhythm technique. Moreover such a method would have the enormous advantage of being retrospective rather than anticipatory, and therefore of being effective in cases of unexpected intercourse, which is presumably not uncommon, and for which the Pincus pill of course is useless after the first day or two of the intermenstrual cycle. In some experimental animals the overall effect of preventing implantation can easily be achieved, either by using antizygotic compounds to inactivate the fertilized egg before it becomes implanted or by rendering uterine conditions unsuitable for implantation. In experimental animals, the administration of estrogen soon after mating effectively blocks pregnancy, probably by a combination of those effects. The reaction is particularly well produced by ethinyl estradiol and stilbestrol administered orally. It is remarkable, therefore, that 25 years after highly orally-active estrogens became available in quantity, the obvious experiment of brief administration of estrogen to women in the third week of the cycle for contraceptive purposes has not been made, or at least not reported.

The scope for other studies of factors affecting implantation is well illustrated by the facts that (a) in newly mated female mice implantation is prevented by the smell of males of a different strain, an effect mediated through the olfactory receptors, the hypothalamus, the hypophysis and the corpora lutea in the ovary and (b) the transplanted mouse blastocyst will implant in the kidney or spleen of the female at any time of the cycle, or even better in the testis of the male, whereas it will do so in the uterus only under complex endocrinological conditions. The study of the conditions necessary for implantation and its control should, therefore, be pushed on with all speed in the hope that it will lead to practical results. Unfortunately, the biological requirements in man of a method of contraception based on the prevention of implantation are ill-defined. I should add that I use the word "contraception" advisedly, because I have repeatedly stated my view that conception means implantation of the blastocyst, not fertilization of the egg, so that contraception can properly be practiced up to the time of implantation.

INTRAUTERINE CONTRACEPTIVE DEVICES

Such then are some of the biological aspects of fertility control in man. Until recently, it was confidently expected that biological methods would supersede the mechanical ones. In the last two or three years, however, an entirely different possibility has appeared in the guise of a modern intrauterine contraceptive device (IUCD), a coil or spiral of flexible plastic. This is a descendant of the Gräfenberg ring, but is far more practical because it can be fed through a straight, narrow transcervical cannula [a hollow tube] into the uterus, where it regains its coiled or spiral shape. A short, soft tail can be left protruding through the cervix to facilitate removal or checking. This device appears to be reasonably effective. The ease with which it can be inserted and removed and its indefinite period of operation may well make it the method of choice for population control for which a method must essentially be acceptable, cheap, and nonrepetitive, but need not be 100 per cent reliable provided it has the desired effect of cutting the birth rate. The coil cannot be regarded as a purely mechanical device, but unfortunately the nature of the biological effect by which it prevents pregnancy is unknown. It is likely that implantation of the blastocyst is prevented in some way, but until more definite information on this point is available, together with proof of its local harmlessness in long-term use, the coil method must be regarded as *sub-judice*. It is not unlikely, however, that it will prove to have wide practical application, and will provide the next stage in the evolution of methods of controlling human fertility. The sequence of mechanical, chemical, biological, and biomechanical methods is most thought-provoking. What next?

REFERENCES

R. O. Greep (ed.), *Human Fertility and Population Problems* (Cambridge, Mass.: Schenkman Publishing Co., Inc., 1963).

C. G. Hartman (ed.), *Science and the Safe Period* (London: Balliere, Tindall, and Cox, 1962).

———, *Mechanisms Concerned with Conception* (London: Pergamon, 1963).

M. C. N. Jackson, "Oral Contraception in Practice," *Journal of Reproduction and Fertility*, VI (1963), p. 153.

H. Knaus, *Periodic Fertility and Sterility in Woman* (Vienna: Wilhelm Maudrich, 1934).

G. Pincus, "Fertility Control with Oral Medication," *Proceedings of the Society for the Study of Fertility*, X (1958), p. 3.

A. Tyler and K. A. Laurence (eds.), *Proceedings of a Conference on Immuno-Reproduction* (New York: Population Council, 1962).

DISCUSSION

WARREN O. NELSON: I should like to discuss briefly the question of regularization of cycles, and of ovulation incident to them, so that the rhythm method might be used more effectively. In this country, regularizing estrus in domestic animals for purposes of mass insemination is common practice. This makes it more convenient to inseminate most of a herd at a given time, since the use of some of the steroids brings about 70 per cent of a herd of cows or sows into heat at the same time. There is thus a consequent reduction in labor and in cost for the artificial insemination. No one, as far as I know, has attempted to do this in a human being, that is to so regularize the cycle as to induce predictable ovulation. I am not sure why such is the case, but the cycles are not so different in the domestic animal and the primates that it should not be possible to do it. Perhaps someone might speculate on this: as to whether it would be or would not be feasible.

I wonder whether you were serious, too, in saying in your paper—that women who had been on the oral contraceptives might be more fertile when they discontinued use. I do not think *fertile* women would be more fertile. They certainly do become pregnant very quickly after they discontinue use, but these women were already fertile before they took the pills, and they very likely would have become pregnant if they had not used them.

It is true—and we have known this for a long time, longer than the present pills have been used—that if infertile women are given artificial cycles over a period of some months, some of them do conceive when they are thrown upon their own physiological resources. But I doubt very much if women, really fertile women, have ever been made more fertile.

I say this, although I believe the only laboratory evidence that might support the idea was provided by Dr. A. B. Lachsman and myself, when we studied ovulation in rats that had been treated with 19-nor steroids. These rats were first treated for a period of 90 to 120 days, and after discontinuation of treatment were compared with a group that had not been treated. In the treated animals a significantly larger number of ova were ovulated. However, I am not sure I believe that our own experiments are applicable to fertile women.

I am sure that you did have your tongue in your cheek when you said that women who have been on the pills for some time might have their reproductive life prolonged with postponement of the menopause. In this regard we, of course, cannot be certain as yet since not enough women have come off the pills—but there is some reason for us to believe that they probably will enter the menopause at the same time as they would have, because as you know, there are a significant number of women who have gone through most of their reproductive lives either pregnant or lactating, with few menstrual periods during 30 or so years, and yet have come to the menopause at the expected age.

In this connection there is also a very interesting group of women, not a large number as yet, that have been observed since we have known how to treat congenital adrenal hyperplasia. This condition occurs from birth. Puberty does not occur in these girls, who otherwise may be normal, because their ovaries are suppressed by the abnormal adrenal function. Now that the syndrome is understood, we know that we can treat them with cortisone, and that they are returned quickly to a perfectly normal reproductive life of ovulation, sex maturation, and even pregnancy.

Some of these girls have been treated in the later 30's. They had never ovulated nor menstruated prior to treatment yet they came to menopause during the following decade of life.

Thus, I believe that you need not fear that the menopause will be prolonged until 80 years or so in some women. However, I think all this does raise an interesting point as to when women taking pills into their 40's should discontinue medication. When should this type of contraception be stopped? As long as they use this therapy, they will menstruate, even after they would have gone into a spontaneous menopause. In my opinion this is a question that will need an answer.

Christopher Tietze

HISTORY AND STATISTICAL
EVALUATION OF INTRAUTERINE
CONTRACEPTIVE DEVICES

The modern history [1] of intrauterine contraceptive devices (IUCD's) begins in 1928 when Dr. Ernst Gräfenberg of Berlin reported on handmade stars of silkworm gut, which he had inserted into the uterine cavity for contraceptive purposes.[2] These stars consisted of three strands knotted at the ends and tied in the center with fine silver wire.

Observing that the stars tended to be expelled by contractions of the uterus, Gräfenberg tried a new device made by rolling the silkworm gut into rings and binding them with silver wire to hold them in shape. Later he replaced the silkworm gut ring with a pliable coil of silver wire. It is this device that is known as the Gräfenberg ring.

Although the insertion of the ring was a relatively simple

---

1. C. Tietze, ''Intra-Uterine Contraceptive Rings: History and Statistical Appraisal,'' *Intra-Uterine Contraceptive Devices*, ed. C. Tietze and S. Lewit (Amsterdam: Excerpta Medica International Congress, 1962, Series No. 54, pp. 9–20.

2. E. Gräfenberg, ''Silk als Antikonzipiens,'' *Geburtenregelung: Vorträge und Verhandlungen des Ärztekursus vom 28–30. Dezember 1928*, ed. K. Bendix (Berlin: Selbstverlag, 1929), pp. 50–64.

432

procedure, Gräfenberg stressed that "a certain amount of gynecological experience is absolutely essential." The anterior lip of the cervix was grasped with a tenaculum forceps and the cervical canal dilated to Hegar size 6. The ring could then be inserted easily by means of a specially designed instrument with a forked tip. An instrument ending in a slender hook was used for the removal of the ring.[3]

The reception accorded to Gräfenberg by the medical profession ranged from enthusiasm to complete condemnation. His most important follower was Dr. Norman Haire of London, who discussed the method at the meeting of the Germany Gynecological Society in Frankfurt-am-Main in 1931.[4] Haire used the ring for a number of years, but "because of the possibility that it may be an unsuitable method, in a considerable portion of women," he did not recommend it in his last article, written shortly before his death in 1952.[5]

Another early enthusiast was Dr. J. H. Leunbach of Copenhagen, who, starting in the fall of 1929, inserted 175 rings in eight months. By June, 1930, after observing a number of pregnancies and two cases of severe pelvic inflammation, Leunbach reversed his earlier judgment and rejected the device as harmful and unreliable.[6]

The great majority of gynecologists did not wait until they had gained experience with the Gräfenberg ring but condemned the new method out of hand. The opposition was so universal and so strong, especially in Germany and in the United States, that with one single exception,[7] no physician who himself had used IUCD's published a report in any medical journal of the

3. E. Gräfenberg, "Die Intrauterine Methode der Konzeptionsverhütung," *Third Congress of the World League for Sexual Reform* (1929), pp. 116–125; E. Gräfenberg, "An Intrauterine Contraceptive Method," *Seventh International Birth Control Conference* (1930), pp. 33–47.

4. N. Haire, "Zehnjährige intensive Erfahrungen über Preventivverkehr," *Archiv für Gynäkologie,* CXLIV (1931), pp. 342–345.

5. N. Haire, "Methods of Contraception," *Indian Medical Journal,* XLVI (May, 1952), pp. 119–122.

6. J. H. Leunbach, "The Graefenberg Ring," *Seventh International Birth Control Conference* (1930), pp. 56–58; J. H. Leunbach "Erfahrungen mit Graefenbergs intrauterinem Silberring," *Archiv für Gynäkologie,* CXLIV (1931), pp. 347–352; J. H. Leunbach, "The Graefenberg 'Silver Ring' and Inter- and Intra-Uterine Pessaries," *Journal of State Medicine,* XL (Jan., 1932), pp. 37–45.

7. M. Halton, R. L. Dickinson, and C. Tietze, "Contraception with an Intra-uterine Silk Coil," *Human Fertility,* XIII (March, 1948), pp. 10–13.

western countries between 1934 and 1959. Textbooks of gynecology, if they discussed contraception at all, mentioned the intrauterine ring "only to condemn it." Because of this attitude, Gräfenberg used his device rarely and with great reluctance after 1940 when he came to the United States.

By 1959 the time seemed ripe for a re-evaluation of the IUCD. Because no American physician could be found who both had had personal experience with the method and was willing to report on it, the editors of the *American Journal of Obstetrics and Gynecology* invited Dr. W. Oppenheimer of Israel to contribute an article on the subject.[8] Between 1930 and 1957, Oppenheimer had equipped 329 women with a total of 866 rings, silver at first, and silkworm gut later. His experience covered an aggregate exposure of 793 woman-years with 20 pregnancies, corresponding to a failure rate of 2.5 per 100 years of exposure. Oppenheimer considered the method both harmless and reliable.

At about the same time, the *Yokohama Medical Bulletin* published an article by Dr. Atsumi Ishihama on clinical experience in the use of intrauterine rings in Japan, based on 973 personal observations and a much larger but less intensviely studied series of 18,594 cases in 149 hospitals.[9] Japanese physicians had been interested in the subject since 1934 when Ota [10] described a modification of the Gräfenberg ring consisting of an outer coil in the center of which a small, hollow, lentil-shaped capsule was suspended by three radial springs. The Ota ring, made either of metal or of plastic with a flat disk substituted for the hollow capsule, is still widely used in Japan.

Experience with the intrauterine ring in Ishihama's report was as favorable as Oppenheimer's had been. Among his own patients, only 1.4 per cent conceived. The incidence of pregnancy was slightly higher (2.3 per cent) in the large hospital series. Nor did Ishihama observe any serious side effects.

8. W. Oppenheimer, "Prevention of Pregnancy by the Graefenberg Ring Method," *American Journal of Obstetrics and Gynecology*, LXXVIII (Aug., 1959), pp. 446–454.

9. A. Ishihama, "Clinical Studies on Intrauterine Rings, Especially the Present State of Contraception in Japan and the Experiences in the Use of Intrauterine Rings," *Yokohama Medical Bulletin*, X (April, 1959), pp. 89–105.

10. T. Ota, "A Study on the Birth Control with an Intrauterine Instrument," *Japanese Journal of Obstetrics and Gynecology*, XVII (June, 1934), pp. 210–214.

The two articles from Israel and Japan stimulated interest in IUCD throughout the world and encouraged other physicians to admit that they had been using the "condemned" devices. An outstanding example is the article by Drs. Herbert Hall and Martin Stone of New York City published in March, 1962.[11] Hall had been a close associate of Gräfenberg, with experience extending over a period of 12 years. His rings were made of a coil spring of stainless steel. While the rings were left *in situ* for indefinite periods, patients were examined at intervals of six months. The aggregate exposure of the 128 women included in this study amounted to 648 years with six pregnancies, corresponding to a failure rate of 0.9 per 100 years of exposure. Once more, no serious side effects of any kind were observed.

NEW DEVICES

Even before the publication of the reports by Oppenheimer and by Ishihama, Dr. L. C. Margulies of Mt. Sinai Hospital in New York City had begun to develop a new type of IUCD. He experimented with a variety of shapes and a large number of plastic materials, finally settling on a spiral of polyethylene. The first of these spirals was inserted in September, 1960. It underwent a series of modifications until the current model (Spiral 5) was introduced in December, 1961. This model replaced all earlier types of spirals. A smaller spiral (5/J for "Junior") has been available since April, 1962.[12]

Dr. Jack Lippes of the University of Buffalo School of Medicine started his study of IUCD in October, 1959. He first obtained, from Japan, plastic Ota rings from which he removed the central disk. Later he developed his own device in the shape of a double S and made of polyethylene, which he calls a loop. This device has been in use since February, 1961. A year and a half later, Lippes recognized that his first model (Loop 1) did not offer adequate protection probably because it was too

11. H. H. Hall and M. L. Stone, "Observations on the Use of the Intrauterine Pessary, with Special Reference to the Grafenberg Ring," *American Journal of Obstetrics and Gynecology*, LXXXIII (March, 1962), pp. 683–688.

12. L. C. Margulies, "Permanent Reversible Contraception with an Intra-Uterine Plastic Spiral (Perma-Spiral)," *Intra-Uterine Contraceptive Devices*, ed. C. Tietze and S. Lewit (Amsterdam: Excerpta Medical International Congress, 1962), Series No. 54, pp. 61–68.

small. He replaced it with a large model (Loop 2) and recommends that Loop 1 be used for nulliparous women only.[13]

A third IUCD, recently developed by Dr. Charles Birnberg of Brooklyn, is shaped like an hourglass with one of the two component triangles slightly larger than the other. This device will be referred to as the "plastic bow."

Because the IUCD's of Margulies, Lippes, and Birnberg are made of a chemically inert plastic material, they, like the stainless steel ring of Hall and Stone, may remain in the uterus for indefinite periods; they need not be changed at periodic intervals, as was necessary with Gräfenberg's silver ring. Another characteristic of the plastic is its flexibility. All of the pastic devices can be stretched and inserted into the uterus by means of a narrow plastic tube, a method of insertion first developed by Margulies. When the device is pushed out from the tube, the plastic's "memory" asserts itself and the spiral, loop, or bow resumes its original shape. Dilatation of the cervix is required in nulliparous women only.

The IUCD's of Margulies and Lippes are both equipped with an appendage or "tail" which passes through the cervical canal into the vagina. The tail of the spiral is a thin polyethylene stem with seven small beads; after insertion all beads, except one, protruding from the external os are cut off. The loop carries a monofilament suture. The purpose of these tails is two-fold: (1) for easy removal and (2) for checking the continued presence of the device. The wearer is taught to examine herself after each menstrual period and to report to the physician if she cannot feel the bead or suture. Birnberg's plastic bow and the stainless steel ring have no tails and are removed with a hook similar to that used by Gräfenberg.

PRESENT STUDY

In the spring of 1962 a two-day conference on IUCD was held in New York City under the auspices of the Population Council.[14] Dr. Alan F. Guttmacher, then Chief of the Department of

---

13. J. Lippes, "A Study of Intra-Uterine Contraception: Development of a Plastic Loop," *Intra-Uterine Contraceptive Devices*, ed. C. Tietze and S. Lewit (Amsterdam: Excerpta Medica International Congress, 1962), Series No. 54, pp. 69–75.

14. C. Tietze and S. Lewit (eds.), *Intra-Uterine Contraceptive Devices* (Amsterdam: Excerpta Medica International Congress, Series No. 54, 1962).

Fig. 1. Intrauterine contraceptive devices.

Obstetrics and Gynecology at Mt. Sinai Hospital and now President of the Planned Parenthood Federation of America, served as chairman. About 50 physicians from all parts of the world participated—from the United States and the United Kingdom, Puerto Rico, Mexico, and Chile, Egypt and Israel, Japan and China (Taiwan), India and Pakistan. The consensus of this conference as to the effectiveness, acceptability, and safety of IUCD was so encouraging that a number of new clinical studies were undertaken. Most of the new investigators as well as several of the pioneers have joined a cooperative statistical program, the implementation of which has been assigned to the National Committee on Maternal Health

(NCMH). The remainder of this paper is based on the experience through February 29, 1964, of 33 institutions and investigators in private practice participating in the cooperative program. Most of these are located in the United States.

The total number of cases (patients) reported to the NCMH by February 29, 1964, was 10,324. The number of *active* cases, ie., women presumed to be wearing the IUCD and remaining under observation was 8,114. The remaining 2,210 women had discontinued the use of the device either temporarily or permanently, or had been lost to follow-up and had thus become *closed* cases. The aggregate period of use for all cases—active and closed—was 89,305 woman-months.

Because many patients have experienced more than one insertion of the same type or of different types of IUCD, the information reported to NCMH is coded and tabulated in terms of segments. A segment is defined as a period beginning with an insertion and *continuing* through the day of reporting (in this instance, February 29, 1964) or *terminated* by pregnancy, or by expulsion or removal of the device, or *lost to follow-up* without removal of the IUCD. The 10,324 cases contributed a total of 12,081 segments, including 8,114 continuing segments and 3,967 terminated segments.[15] The number of continuing segments equals the number of active cases; the excess of 1,757 terminated segments over the 2,210 closed cases corresponds to the number of reinsertions. A case is considered closed if the last reported segment is not followed by a reinsertion or if the case is lost to follow-up.

Each segment is identified by order of insertion (1st, 2nd, etc.); the number of first segments, 10,324, equals the total number of cases. The duration of each segment, i.e., the time between insertion and termination, or between insertion and February 29, 1964, is measured in terms of months. The dates of termination assigned to segments are: the estimated date of conception, the date of expulsion if known (with special rules for expulsions not noticed by the patient), or the date of

15. Some of the rates shown in this paper differ from those previously published in the Third Progress Report of the Cooperative Statistical Program for the Evaluation of Intra-Uterine Contraceptive Devices. This is due to the fact that the rates in this paper were computed on the basis of first segments while those previously published were based on cases. The differences are minor.

removal. Segments terminated as lost to follow-up end on the date of last contact with the patient.

For cases comprising a single (first) segment only, the duration of the case equals the duration of that segment. For cases with more than one segment, the assigned duration is the sum of the duration of all segments. In the computation of aggregate months of use, one half month is substituted for any period less than one month.

All closed cases and all terminated segments are classified by reported reason for closing or termination; one reason only is assigned in each instance. The reasons are grouped under three principal headings: relevant reasons, nonrelevant reasons, and lost to follow-up.

1. The category relevant reasons is intended to cover all reasons bearing upon the effectiveness and acceptability of intrauterine contraception and includes three subgroups: unintended pregnancies, expulsions of the IUCD, and relevant removals.

The term *unintended pregnancy* covers all conceptions occurring after insertion of the IUCD and prior to a removal or a noticed expulsion. *Expulsions* include complete expulsions into or from the vagina and partial expulsions requiring the removal of the device from the cervix. The reasons for relevant removals range from medical necessity to the personal preference of the couple. This subgroup excludes removals after partial expulsion (classified as expulsion) and removals after unintended pregnancy had occurred. Cases of pregnancy at insertion are included with relevant removals.

Unintended pregnancies, expulsions, and relevant removals are subdivided into first and later occurrences of each type of event. The number of first occurrences equals the number of patients who have experienced the particular event at least once.

2. The nonrelevant reasons include: cases of voluntary removal when pregnancy is desired, protection is no longer needed, or the patient departs from the locality of the study, and decisions of the investigator—usually involving the replacement of a less effective device by a more effective one. Since these reasons have no bearing on the acceptability of intrauter-

ine contraception, nonrelevant removals are not included in the computation of removal rates in the report.

3. Cases lost to follow-up are operationally defined as those women who on February 29 were at least three months overdue for a scheduled return visit, and from whom no information could be obtained by telephone, mail, or home visit. Also included were some women who moved away with the device *in situ*. It is not known whether these women are continuing and satisfied users or have discontinued for relevant or nonrelevant reasons.

Table 1 summarizes, for six major types of IUCD and a residual group comprising the remaining devices, the numbers of cases and the aggregate woman-months of use. The six types of IUCD shown separately are those represented by at least 400 cases each: Margulies Spirals 5 (large) and 5/J (small), Lippes Loops 1 (small) and 2 (large), the plastic bow of Birnberg, and the stainless steel ring of Hall and Stone.

TABLE 1

Number of Cases and Woman-Months of Use, by Type of Device

Type of device	Number of cases [a]	Woman-months of use
Spiral 5 (large)	3,090	23,799
Spiral 5/J (small)	737	6,376
Loop 1 (small)	901	9,812
Loop 2 (large)	2,374	15,842
Plastic bow	1,037	2,846
Steel ring	1,184	24,203
Other	1,001	6,427
Total	10,324	89,305

[a] By device at first insertion.

PREGNANCIES, EXPULSIONS, REMOVALS

Of the total 10,324 cases, 163 experienced at least one unintended pregnancy; 995, one or more expulsions; and 895, one or more removals for relevant reasons (Table 2). As stated previously, the number of patients experiencing each of these events equals the number of first occurrences of that event. Numbers of first pregnancies, first expulsions, and first remov-

TABLE 2

Numbers and Cumulative Rates of First Pregnancies, Expulsions, and Relevant Removals, by Type of Device

At last prior insertion	Number	Cumulative rates at 12 months after insertion [a]
First Pregnancies		
Spiral 5	19	1.1 ± 0.3
Spiral 5/J	14	2.6 ± 0.8
Loop 1	42	5.5 ± 1.0
Loop 2	23	1.3 ± 0.4
Plastic bow	12	4.0 ± 1.7 [b]
Steel ring	41	3.2 ± 0.6
Other	12	2.3 ± 0.9
Total	163	2.4 ± 0.2
First Expulsions		
Spiral 5	380	16.0 ± 0.9
Spiral 5/J	157	27.3 ± 1.9
Loop 1	163	20.0 ± 1.5
Loop 2	117	7.0 ± 0.7
Plastic bow	7	1.8 ± 0.8 [b]
Steel ring	84	7.6 ± 0.9
Other	87	11.6 ± 1.4
Total	995	13.3 ± 0.4
First Relevant Removals		
Spiral 5	335	14.4 ± 0.9
Spiral 5/J	79	14.3 ± 1.7
Loop 1	129	15.8 ± 1.5
Loop 2	184	11.6 ± 1.0
Plastic bow	20	4.6 ± 1.3 [b]
Steel ring	69	4.6 ± 0.7
Other	79	11.7 ± 1.9
Total	895	11.9 ± 0.5

[a] Rates computed per 100 first segments, but applicable per 100 cases (see text).
[b] Estimate based on rates at six months.

als are shown in Table 2 by type of device. The table also shows, for each type of event, *cumulative life table rates* at exactly 12 months after insertion. These rates, computed according to the procedure recently described for pregnancy rates by Robert G. Potter,[16] are based on experience during the first segment only. This procedure involves fewer tabulations and less expense than the alternative approaches of computing either on the basis of

16. R. G. Potter, "Additional Measures of Use-Effectiveness of Contraception," *Milbank Memorial Fund Quarterly*, XLI (Oct., 1963), pp. 400–418.

all segments relating type of device and duration of use to the last prior insertion, or on the basis of cases relating to the first insertion. Cumulative rates based on first segments differ only minimally from the corresponding rates of first events based on all segments or on cases. The cumulative rates shown in Table 2 may, therefore, be interpreted as the estimated percentages of patients who experienced at least one unintended pregnancy, expulsion, or relevant removal during the first year after the first insertion of an IUCD.

Of the 163 first unintended pregnancies, 84 occurred with the IUCD *in situ*. The remaining 79 pregnancies were classified as "device undetermined." In the case of the Margulies' spiral and the Lippes' loop, both of which have appendages, the presence of the device can ordinarily be established by inspection. For these types of IUCD, the great majority of pregnancies with device undetermined are almost certainly pregnancies after unnoticed expulsion. However, this is not true for the plastic bow and the stainless steel ring, which have no appendages and, therefore, cannot be seen or palpated. The presence of these devices can be determined only by probing the uterus or by X-ray.

Fig. 2 shows cumulative expulsion rates per 100 cases by type of device. For all devices combined, both spirals, Loop 1, the steel ring, and the residual group of "other" devices, these rates have been computed up to the end of the twenty-fourth month since first insertion, and for Loop 2 up to the end of the twelfth month. Adequate information on the plastic bow is not available beyond the sixth month. The cumulative expulsion rates rise steeply during the early months after insertion, but very gradually during later periods. With almost all devices, more than half of all expulsions during the first year occur in the first three months, the average being 55 per cent.

About one fifth of the first expulsions included in Table 2 were not noticed by the wearer. Numbers of unnoticed expulsions are shown in Table 3 with percentages per 100 reported expulsions, noticed and unnoticed, and rates per 100 cases during the first year, derived in approximation by multiplying the figures in the second column of Table 3 by the cumulative rates shown in the last column of Table 2.

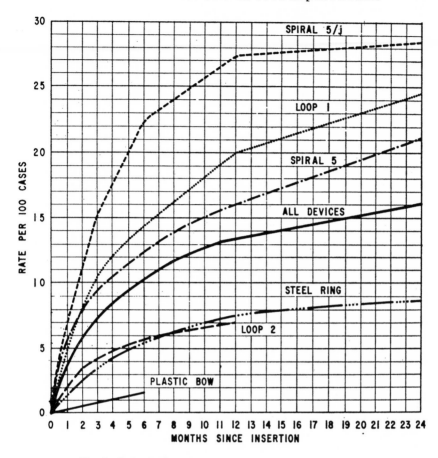

Fig. 2. Cumulative rates of expulsions by type of device.

The expulsion of an IUCD, if not noticed by the wearer, is usually soon followed by conception. Frequent pelvic examinations increase the chance of discovering the expulsion and, therefore, reduce the incidence of pregnancy after expulsion. To eliminate a possible bias introduced by variations in the frequency of follow-up visits, hypothetical pregnancy rates were computed based on the assumption that there are no routine examinations and that all first expulsions not noticed by the wearer are followed by conception in due time (Table 4).

The rates in the total column in Table 4 are the sum of (a) the cumulative pregnancy rates actually observed (taken from the

TABLE 3

Incidence of Unnoticed First Expulsions

| Type of device | Unnoticed First Expulsion | | Estimated rates per 100 cases at 12 months |
	Number	Per 100 expulsions	
Spiral 5	45	11.8	1.9
Spiral 5/J	16	10.2	2.8
Loop 1	64	39.3	7.9
Loop 2	28	23.9	1.7
Plastic bow	1	14.3	0.3
Steel ring	25	29.8	2.3
Other	25	28.7	3.3
Total	204	20.5	2.7

last column of Table 2), and (b) the estimated rates of additional pregnancies following unnoticed explusion and occurring within one year after first insertion. These estimated rates, shown in column (b) of Table 4, were calculated as 85 per cent of the first year's unnoticed expulsion rate for the corresponding devices, given in the last column of Table 3.[17] Since the incidence of expulsions tends to decline with the passage of time, the

TABLE 4

Hypothetical Cumulative Pregnancy Rates at 12 Months after Insertion

Type of device	Observed pregnancy rate [a] (a)	Additional estimated after unnoticed expulsion (b)	Total
Spiral 5	1.1	1.6	2.7
Spiral 5/J	2.6	2.4	5.0
Loop 1	5.5	6.7	12.2
Loop 2	1.3	1.4	2.7
Plastic bow	4.0	0.2	4.2
Steel ring	3.2	1.9	5.1
Other	2.3	2.8	5.1
Total	2.4	2.3	4.7

[a] Device *in situ* or undetermined. All rates per 100 cases.

17. The mean time of occurrence of first expulsions was approximately three months. It was estimated that 85 per cent of women conceived in nine months of noncontraceptive exposure.

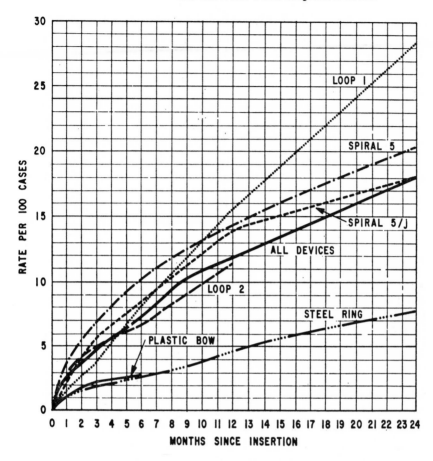

Fig. 3. Cumulative rates of relevant removals by type of device.

hypothetical pregnancy rates for the second and later years would be lower than those shown above for the first year.

Fig. 3 shows cumulative rates of relevant removals per 100 cases, by type of device. Compared with the expulsion rates shown in Fig. 2, these rates rise less steeply during the early months and more steeply during later months. For all devices combined, less than half of all removals during the first year occurred in the first three months, the average being about 40 per cent.

Among the relevant reasons for the removal of an IUCD, irregular bleeding (including spotting), pain (including cramps, backache, and other kinds of discomfort), or both were most frequently reported, accounting for about one half of all first removals included in Table 2. Numbers of such removal are shown in Table 5 with percentages per 100 first removals and approximate rates per 100 cases.

Of the 995 cases with first expulsions shown in Table 2, 219 were closed; in other words, no device was reinserted. In the remaining 776 cases, the first expulsion was followed by reinsertion of the same or another type of IUCD. Two expulsions each were reported for 186 patients, 57 had three each, 16 had four

TABLE 5

Incidence of First Removals for Bleeding, Pain or Both

Type of device	Number	Per 100 removals	Per 100 cases
Spiral 5	170	50.7	7.3
Spiral 5/J	34	43.0	6.1
Loop 1	67	51.9	8.2
Loop 2	125	67.9	7.9
Plastic bow	7	35.0	1.6
Steel ring	40	58.0	2.7
Other	43	54.4	6.4
Total	486	54.3	6.4

each, and nine had five or more expulsions apiece. The total number of expulsions reported for the 995 patients who experienced any was 1,394, or 1.4 per patient. Cumulative expulsion rates at 12 months after insertion of each type of device were much higher after reinsertion than after first insertion, as shown in Table 6.

In contrast to the experience following expulsion of a device, comparatively few (254) of the 895 first removals for relevant reasons were followed by reinsertion; the remaining 641 cases were closed. Only 33 patients experienced two relevant removals each, and only two patients, three relevant removals each. Of the unintended pregnancies, 20 were followed by reinsertion. One woman had two unintended pregnancies.

Since the participating investigators differ markedly in their policies regarding reinsertion, the reported numbers of closed cases and rates derived from these numbers do not permit objective comparisons between types of devices. To avoid this

TABLE 6

Number and Rate of Expulsions, by Order of Expulsion and Type of Device

Type of device	Number	Cumulative rate at 12 months after insertion [a]
	First Expulsion	
Spiral 5	380	16.0 ± 0.9
Spiral 5/J	157	27.3 ± 1.9
Loop 1	163	20.0 ± 1.5
Loop 2	117	7.0 ± 0.7
Plastic bow	7	1.8 ± 0.8 [b]
Steel ring	84	7.6 ± 0.9
Other	87	11.6 ± 1.4
Total	995	13.3 ± 0.4
	Later Expulsion	
Spiral 5	142	55.9 ± 3.8
Spiral 5/J	83	76.5 ± 4.3
Loop 1	41	66.2 ± 6.3
Loop 2	54	35.9 ± 4.3
Plastic bow	3	20.5 ± 13.3 [b]
Steel ring	16	27.2 ± 6.7
Other	61	61.3 ± 7.4
Total	400	53.9 ± 2.2

[a] Rate computed per 100 first segments, but applicable per 100 cases (see text)
[b] Estimate based on rates at six months.

bias, hypothetical rates of continuing use, 12 months after first insertion, have been computed and appear in Table 7.

These rates are based on the assumptions that (a) all noticed first expulsions are immediately followed by one reinsertion, and (b) no reinsertion is attempted after re-expulsion, pregnancy, or removal for relevant reason.

TABLE 7

Estimated Rates of Continuing Use

Type of device	Estimated per cent continuing use at one year
Spiral 5	78.3
Spiral 5/J	67.9
Loop 1	67.2
Loop 2	84.5
Plastic bow	91.5
Steel ring	89.4
Other	79.6
Total	79.8

Pelvic Inflammatory Disease

Pelvic inflammatory disease (PID), subsequent to the insertion of an IUCD, was reported in 105 cases. The distribution of these cases by type of device is shown in Table 8, together with cumulative rates per 100 cases at 12 months after first insertion.

It cannot yet be established to what extent the differences in reported incidence of PID reflect variations in socioeconomic status and in the sexual habits of patients, of diagnostic idiosyncrasies of investigators, or real differences between types and sizes of IUCD. Nor has it yet been possible to determine whether the overall incidence of PID is higher among wearers of IUCD than among other women in those segments of the population from which the patients were drawn.

In 50 cases of PID the device was removed, while in 48 cases the condition was treated successfully with the IUCD *in situ.* In the remaining seven cases, the PID followed an expulsion of the device or a removal for other reasons. About one third of the patients with PID were hospitalized; four women underwent surgery. A history of PID prior to insertion was obtained in more than half of the cases diagnosed as PID for which a complete report was submitted.

Among the 10,324 women using intrauterine contraception and reported to the NCMH, there were 138 who had the device

TABLE 8

Pelvic Inflammatory Disease

Type of device	Number	Cumulative rates per 100 cases at 12 months
Spiral 5	49	2.5 ± 0.3
Spiral 5/J	7	1.5 ± 0.6
Loop 1	11	1.4 ± 0.4
Loop 2	17	1.5 ± 0.5
Plastic bow	1	0.2 ± 0.2 [a]
Steel ring	1	0.1 ± 0.1 [b]
Other	19	4.2 ± 1.2
Total	105	1.7 ± 0.2

[a] Estimate based on rates at six months after insertion.
Based on clinic patients only: 0.4 ± 0.4.

removed because the couple wanted another child. Excluding women who changed their minds, those not traced by the investigators, and those with removals during the first two months of 1964, there remains a total of 68 removals for planning pregnancies. Of these women, 57 had conceived by February 29, 1964, and 11 had not. The monthly cumulative pregnancy rates reflect a normal level of fecundability. Almost two thirds of the women who wanted a child did conceive within six months and seven out of eight, within one year after removal of the IUCD.

CONCLUSION

The results of this study have led the Bio-Medical Division of the Population Council to conclude: ''The remarkable contraceptive effectiveness of intrauterine devices is now fully established. We consider the method as still experimental, however, until information relating to pelvic inflammatory disease and other possible medical sequelae is more complete than at present. Obviously, it is too early in the study of the device to anticipate long-term effects on reproductive function or carcinogenesis, but to date there is no reason to believe that the device is disadvantageous on either score. In our view, there is at present no medical reason to refrain from the use of the device in field trials that provide for adequate medical support.'' [18]

I heartily concur.

18. The Population Council, ''Report on Intra-Uterine Contraceptive Devices,'' *Studies in Family Planning*, III (April, 1964), pp. 11–12.

Louis Lasagna

THE QUANTIFICATION OF
DESIRED AND UNDESIRED EFFECTS
OF REPRODUCTIVE CONTROLS:
SOME PRINCIPLES AND PROBLEMS

It has been difficult to decide how best to approach my assignment in this Symposium. I know almost nothing of the
"bench" problems of experimentation in birth control; I am
supposed to know something about clinical trials. The plan of
presentation that I have evolved is simple and tripartite: (a) I
shall enumerate and discuss briefly the principles considered
crucial in health areas with which I am familiar; (b) I shall
examine the field of population control to see how clinical trials
resemble, or are dissimilar to, trials in other fields; and (c) I
shall draw some conclusions and make some recommendations.

PRINCIPLES OF CONTROLLED TRIALS

Comparison

The basic feature of modern clinical trials in medicine is their
comparative nature. The physician is not so much interested in
whether something does or does not happen after a given
treatment, as in whether that something happens more or less

frequently *than after no treatment, or after a standard treatment,* preferably the best available. Such a comparison usually involves both the primary desired effect and the "cost" of the treatment—"cost" here taken to include not just monetary considerations, but untoward side effects, long term hazards, etc.

One can find instances in the literature where the most dramatic kinds of "therapeutic effects" were observed, but where these were shown to occur just as frequently after a placebo. These "pseudo-effects" range from the disappearance of disease-producing microorganisms from the throat to the abolition of urinary and fecal incontinence in senile patients.[1]

Concurrency

A second principle is that the comparison of treatments be a concurrent one. It is generally considered unsatisfactory to use as a yardstick for comparison someone's memory of what "would happen" without treatment or after standard treatment, or so-called "historic" controls, i.e., a previously reported series. Fig. 1, for example, shows the amazing difference in prognosis of one untreated group of cirrhotic patients (the *X*'s) when compared with another, unselected group of untreated cirrhotics (the open circles).[2] In this case, the absence of a concurrent control group would have led to the erroneous conclusion that the performance of shunt surgery (the closed circles) increased by some 25 per cent the number of people alive two years after onset of esophageal varices [a serious complication of cirrhosis of the liver]. The authors in question wisely avoided such traps with their proper design. It is obvious that the very conditions of the experiment led to the selection of a group of cirrhotics with a better prognosis than the unselected cirrhotic.

For those who desire to visualize a similar hazard in the field covered by this Symposium, consider the following ill-advised

1. L. Lasagna, "Controlled Trials: Nuisance or Necessity?" *Methods of Information in Medicine,* I (1962), p. 79
2. A. J. Garceau, R. M. Donaldson, Jr., E. T. O'Hara, A. D. Callow, H. Muench, T. C. Chalmers, and the Boston Inter-Hospital Liver Group, "A Controlled Trial of Prophylactic Portocaval-Shunt Surgery," *New England Journal of Medicine,* CCLXX (1964), p. 496.

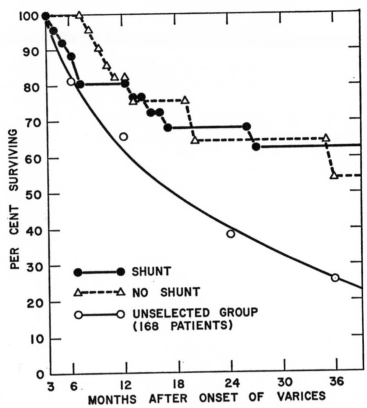

Fig. 1. Survival of the study groups compared with survival of 168 patients with varices known for three months. (Reproduced from *New England Journal of Medicine*, CCLXX [1964], p. 496.)

fictitious experiment: evaluation of a new contraceptive pill in Hiroshima the year after the nuclear explosion, using as a yardstick the performance of a diaphragm-and-jelly combination in a trial performed in 1944.

Randomized Allocation of Cases

Since a trial is concerned with the relative merits of treatments, one obviously does not want to confound treatment effects with other, temporarily irrelevant variables. One does not, therefore, compare the results of Treatment A in elderly, mentally inadequate patients with those of Treatment B in young intellectuals from a college community. Instead, one takes the total population available for study and allocates the group randomly to the two treatments. Otherwise, one will hopelessly confound treatment effects and population characteristics.

The substitution, for randomized groups, of groups selected in some other way is always unsatisfactory, no matter how closely the groups may appear to resemble each other in "relevant" characteristics. For one thing, one never knows for sure but that some variable which one does not suspect to be important is in fact *highly* relevant. For another, the statistical manipulations one will probably apply to the data, the calculation of error terms, etc., are predicated on randomization; to discard this fundamental assumption is to render one's statistical analyses inaccurate as well as pointless.

An important example of this sort is encountered in a certain study of the effectiveness of anticoagulant therapy in the management of patients with cardiac infarction [coronary thrombosis]. Patients in this trial were assigned to the drug or nondrug groups according to the day on which they were admitted to the hospital. Thus all patients admitted on odd days were allocated to the anticoagulant group, whereas those admitted on even days were given no anticoagulants. Since this plan is easily recognized by referring physicians, it becomes ridiculously simple to send in patients on the day when the type of therapy is such as the physician considers most appropriate for his patient. Thus, a physician who considers anticoagulants a dangerous and unnecessary measure could avoid sending this patient in on odd days, so long as their clinical situation did not demand immediate hospitalization. Another physician who might be "sold" on anticoagulants could adopt just the opposite procedure.

The potentialities for bias are obvious. In this particular study 589 patients were treated and 442 patients were not. Thus, patients were almost certainly *not* randomly selected since the excess of treated cases is greater than would be expected in a completely random selection of cases. One possibility is that physicians were in general eager to have their patients receive the "advantage" of anticoagulant treatment and tried to refer patients in on treatment days. Since a critically ill patient would probably be hospitalized as rapidly as possible, it is also conceivable that there may have been a higher percentage of sicker patients in the untreated group.

Diminishing Bias in Evaluation

Besides bias in allocation of cases, there can be bias in evaluating results. Such bias is usually diluted out by keeping the person responsible for evaluating treatment effects in the dark as to what treatment the patient is on. For example, if one wishes to enumerate thromboembolic deaths from an oral contraceptive, one should not scrutinize such deaths and discard all deaths "attributable to other causes" unless one is also to scrutinize in the same way similar data on a control group *not* on oral contraceptives, and make such decisions without knowing which patients were on drug. The same approach applies to inquiries as to whether patients adhered to instructions in taking their medication: if one wants to evaluate the possible role of casualness in following directions on success or failure of a treatment, one should question with equal vigor patients who have done well and those who have done poorly on treatment, and patients on the several treatments being compared—all without prior knowledge of which patients are which.

Statistical Evaluation

At the conclusion of an experiment, it is desirable that one evaluate the data from a statistical standpoint, so that one may know with what degree of confidence one can make statements and draw conclusions. Tests of significance depend on randomization, as mentioned above, but it makes no sense to perform such tests if the principles mentioned above have not been adhered to, since a "significant difference" is of little use if one is uncertain as to whether the difference is attributable to the primary treatments, devices, or procedures under consideration, or to a dozen other factors, such as different kinds of patients in the various treatment groups, biased collection of data, etc.

A special consideration in such mathematical handling is what to do with missing data. One cannot disregard missing data. In general, the only completely satisfactory way to handle missing data is to avoid having them. Since this is often impossible, one has to look searchingly at the results, and recalculate the data in a variety of ways. For example, one can contrast the results when missing data are assumed to be no different from the available data, with the results when one assumes that every patient lost from follow-up is a treatment failure, and with the results when one assumes that every patient so lost is a treatment success. In a concurrent comparison, one has the opportunity to contrast dropout rates from the several treatments under consideration. If one treatment is associated with many more dropouts than another, it may be impossible to draw firm conclusions about their comparative merits. The same may be true even when dropout rates are the same for different treatments, but the percentage of dropouts is very high, such as the 41 per cent reported in a recent trial.[3]

Cautious Generalization

Even in a perfectly designed and executed trial, the investigator needs to be cautious in his conclusions. He is really only entitled to say that ''in the patients of such-and-such an age group, parity, educational, and socioeconomic status for whom this preparation was prescribed, in such a way, and followed for such a period, the following seemed to occur.'' The results with one condom may not apply to other potentially inferior or superior brands.[4] The results with one dose level of an oral contraceptive cannot be extrapolated to higher or lower doses. The results in young Puerto Rican farm women cannot apply automatically to Cambridge matrons. The side effects seen with the taking of a drug for one year do not tell us about untoward effects when the drug is taken for five years. A drug ''prescribed'' to out-patients is not necessarily the same as a drug ''taken'' by in-patients, where one can be more certain that the medication was actually taken as intended.

A HARSH LOOK AT CURRENT PRACTICES

What is the situation in the field of conception control? Sadly, the answer is that almost none of the principles found essential

3. E. Mears and N. W. Please, ''Chemical Contraceptive Trial,'' *Journal of Reproduction and Fertility*, III (1962), p. 138.
4. Editorial, ''Which Contraceptive?,'' *British Medical Journal*, II (1963), p. 1284; Editorial, ''Birth Control,'' *Lancet*, II (1963), p. 1107.

for maintaining sanity in other fields are regularly observed in the literature on contraceptive devices.

This is not because no one has ever pointed out the traps. Tietze, for example, has written extensively on the importance of such variables as motivation,[5] socioeconomic status,[6] age,[7] months of use,[8] and clinic populations.[9] Gini [10] and Potter [11] have, quite rightly, attacked the clearly inadequate Pearl index,[12] which not only suffers from the disadvantage that it can be calculated in different ways, but blithely assumes that the rates for groups of women under observation for different periods are comparable and can be lumped together. (One is reminded of the play which included a minister, a prostitute, and a man paralyzed from the waist down so as to represent "a cross-section of humanity.") Despite clear warnings by distinguished experts in this field, much of the available data is uninterpretable because of a cavalier disregard of what should be well known.

Can I document this sweeping indictment? Let me try. Failure rates for foam tablets vary twofold, for diaphragm-and-jelly fourfold, for jelly alone fivefold,[13] for intrauterine rings ninefold.[14] Are foam tablets *inferior* to diaphragm and jelly? Certainly—look at the 49 pregnancy rate of Finkelstein with foam

5. C. Tietze, "The Use-Effectiveness of Contraceptive Methods," *Research in Family Planning,* ed. C. V. Kiser (Princeton: Princeton University Press, 1962).

6. C. Tietze, "The Clinical Effectiveness of Contraceptive Methods," *American Journal of Obstetrics and Gynecology,* LXXVIII (1959), p. 650.

7. C. Tietze, "Pregnancy Rates and Birth Rates," *Population Studies,* XVI (1962), p. 31.

8. C. Tietze and S. Lewit, "Recommended Procedures for the Study of Use-Effectiveness of Contraceptive Methods," *IPPF Medical Handbook,* Part I, Appendix 7.

9. C. Tietze, "The Clinical Effectiveness . . ." (see footnote 6).

10. C. Gini, "Sur la mesure de la fécondité naturelle de la femme mariée," *Revue de l' Institut International de Statistique,* IX (1941), p. 1.

11. R. G. Potter, "Additional Measures of Use-Effectiveness of Contraception," *Milbank Memorial Fund Quarterly,* XVI (1963), p. 400.

12. The index was calculated by Pearl himself in different ways. One version commonly used to estimate "contraceptive failure rates" is calculated as follows:

$$\frac{\text{Pregnancy rate per 100}}{\text{years of exposure}} = \frac{\text{Total number of conceptions} \times 1200}{\text{Total months of exposure}}$$

13. J. T. Dingle and C. Tietze, "Comparative Study of Three Contraceptive Methods: Vaginal Foam Tablets, Jelly Alone, and Diaphragm with Jelly or Cream," *American Journal of Obstetrics and Gynecology,* LXXXV (1963), p. 1012.

14. C. Tietze, "Intra-uterine Contraceptive Rings: History and Statistical Appraisal," *Intra-Uterine Contraceptive Devices,* ed. C. Tietze and S. Lewit (Amsterdam: Excerpta Medica International Congress, 1962) Series No. 54, p. 9.

against the nine of Stix with diaphragm.[15] Are foam tablets *superior* to diaphragm and jelly? Certainly—look at the 13 rate of Koya for foam against the 29 of Beebe and Belaval for diaphragm.[16] What is the pregnancy rate of a new contraceptive cream-jel in the hands of Finkelstein and Goldberg? Less than six if you believe the authors, 24 to 29 if you prefer Tietze's reworking of the same data.[17]

RECOMMENDATIONS

1. I believe a modified life table approach of the general kind proposed by Potter [18] is indicated in contraceptive trials. It is more informative than the Pearl index, involves fewer assumptions and allows the calculation of error terms.[19] It has the great advantage of getting away from the quaint notion that one woman followed for 20 years equals 240 women followed for one month.

2. The results of trials should be completely described, characterizing the population, the varying lengths of follow-up of different patients, the number of accidental pregnancies (here I would vote in favor of greater emphasis on total number of failures rather than on "unexplained" failures; I feel that an accidental pregnancy because a lady forgot to take a pill or was unaware that an intrauterine ring had been ejected [20] must be scored against the method, lest we end up with circular statements that *all* techniques, when "used properly," work 100 per cent of the time), the number of subjects who shifted to another technique and why (esthetics, convenience, side effects, etc.), the number of patients "lost" from the trial and why (moved, desired pregnancy, dead wife, dead husband, tubal ligation, illness, etc.).

3. There should be a greater emphasis on truly comparative

15. C. Tietze, ''The Clinical Effectiveness . . .'' (see footnote 6).

16. *Ibid.*

17. C. Tietze, ''Calculation of Pregnancy Rate,'' *American Journal of Obstetrics and Gynecology*, LXXIX (1960), p. 412.

18. R. G. Potter, *op. cit.*

19. There is, of course, little point in computing error terms for comparing differences between contraceptive methods if the groups subjected to the various methods have not been randomly created, for reasons discussed above.

20. N. J. Eastman, ''Intrauterine Devices for Contraceptive Purposes,'' *Obstetrical and Gynecological Survey*, XVIII (1963), p. 597.

trials. I see no compelling reason why proper clinical experiments cannot be performed in this field. Little would be lost, and possibly a great gained, from such an approach. Indeed, with a new type of oral contraceptive pill, for example, it would be most unethical to do otherwise.

Let us suppose that one has a new hormonal combination which, on the basis of animal experiments, looks as effective as an older drug and less likely to produce unwanted effects. One would then approach a group of potential users, explain the situation, and indicate that everyone would get an active medication, but that roughly half the women would receive an established drug, and half the new drug. The incentive for a woman to participate would be a free supply of medication plus the possibility that one might receive a new preparation that was as good as the old in preventing conception, but less likely to produce nausea, breast tenderness, phlebitis, etc. The alternative to this kind of approach is to encourage the marketing of countless oral contraceptives without convincing evidence that one is any better than any other. The controlled trial method could also be used to compare repository "one-shot-a-month" preparations or even abortifacients against standard techniques, with appropriate change in experimental design.

4. There should be a more systematic approach to the enumeration of untoward effects, especially from the newer hormones and chemicals. The following facts have been painfully accepted by clinical pharmacologists: (a) No drug has just one (desired) effect, so that there is always a price to be paid as the chemical buckshot hits not only the target organ but an occasional innocent organ standing by. (b) It may take decades for even dramatic mischief for drugs to rise to the surface of our awareness. (It took half a century to realize that aspirin could cause serious gastrointestinal bleeding.) (c) The figures on true incidence of side effects are extremely difficult to compile without a formal plan. (Witness the colossal fiasco of the Expert Advisory Committee on Enovid,[21] which took incomplete data,

21. The Ad Hoc Committee for the Evaluation of a Possible Etiologic Relation with Thromboembolic Conditions, *Final Report on Enovid*, submitted to the Commissioner of the Food and Drug Administration of the Department of Health, Education, and Welfare (Sept. 12, 1963).

made certain assumptions that are untenable, and then had the poor judgment to draw conclusions.) In view of the intended long-term use of many of the new contraceptive drugs now popular, it seems imperative that we be set up to detect damage of any kind—from phlebitis to cancer, from "predictable" toxicity to the most "far-fetched" kind of toxicity.

CONCLUSIONS

The field of conception control is needlessly muddled because of widespread failure to utilize information and techniques readily available to investigators. A change in experimental habits seems indicated.

ADDENDUM

For those interested in reading further about the principles of controlled trials, examples and techniques are described in the references immodestly listed below:

L. Lasagna, "The Controlled Clinical Trial: Theory and Practice," *Journal of Chronic Diseases,* I (1955), p. 353.

L. Lasagna and P. Meier, "Experimental Design and Statistical Problems," *The Clinical Evaluation of New Drugs,* ed. S. O. Waife and A. P. Shapiro (New York: Paul Hoeber, 1959).

L. Lasagna, "Controlled Trials: Nuisance or Necessity?," *Methods of Information in Medicine,* I (1962), p. 79.

L. Lasagna, "On Evaluating Drug Therapy: The Nature of the Evidence," *Drugs in Our Society,* ed. P. Talalay (Baltimore: The Johns Hopkins Press, 1964), pp. 91–104.

PART V

Methods of Controlling Reproduction

INTRODUCTION

This Part of the volume reports on the panel discussion on Methods of Controlling Reproduction. Dr. Lasagna served as chairman, with Drs. Nelson, Rock, Satterthwaite, Tietze, and Tyler as panel members. At the panel, summaries were presented of the papers by Dr. Lasagna and by Dr. Tietze (on Intrauterine Contraceptive Devices) printed in Part IV. In addition, the short papers by Drs. Tyler, Satterthwaite, and Nelson printed below were presented. A report of selected additional material covered in the panel discussion is given in this section following these papers.

Edward T. Tyler

CLINICAL USE OF ORAL CONTRACEPTION

At present, clinical use of oral contraceptives involves the woman's taking one pill a day for 20 days, starting on the fifth day of the menstrual cycle (the first day being considered the first day of menstruation). After the twenty-day course of pills is taken, bleeding will usually occur within two or three days and another course of pills is begun again on the fifth day, and so on. There may be some modification in the dosage schedule by the time this appears in print.

After eight years of clinical study, it is safe to say that oral contraception with progestational agents such as norethynodrel, norethindrone and similar compounds (combined with an estrogen) is extremely effective. Some believe that this form of contraception is 100 per cent effective when used properly. Many studies would support this conclusion but it is dangerous to ascribe 100 per cent effectiveness to anything in medicine, and for this reason "close to 100 per cent effective" would be more accurate. During these years it has been shown that there are certain medical problems associated with the use of the oral contraceptives. Some problems are very minor, whereas others have the potential of being serious. In the former class are the relatively minor problems of gastrointestinal disturbances, breakthrough bleeding, headaches, breast soreness, weight changes, and a variety of other complaints which, in the majority of cases, are not significant enough to warrant discontinuing the use of the contraceptive. In the class of serious problems is the present unanswered question of a possible relationship between oral contraception and abnormal blood clotting, which will be discussed in some detail later in this report.

From the beginning of the use of these agents, some of the most annoying side effects have been the occurrence of nausea, occasional vomiting, and other gastrointestinal disturbances. The incidence of these problems seems to vary somewhat with different preparations and dosage combinations (and there are now several preparations currently marketed in the United States, and many additional ones in various other countries), as well as with the population group involved and with the investigator. It is undoubtedly fair to say in summary at this time, that in the vast majority of patients these particular side effects will subside if the patient continues to take the medication. She will acquire a tolerance and ultimately will not be bothered with the complaints. It is generally agreed that the gastrointestinal disturbances are primarily attributable to the estrogenic hormone content of the pills.

Another well-recognized finding in studies of oral contraception is that a fair percentage of patients will have "breakthrough bleeding" (bleeding at times other than during the menstrual period) at some time during the administration of these pills, often for several days in a given cycle or perhaps just for a single day with only slight spotting. The exact reason for breakthrough bleeding is somewhat obscure but it may very well be related to irregularity in absorption of the hormone so that there is, in effect, a temporary withdrawal of hormone for a given time which permits the uterine lining to start to desquamate. This is most likely to occur when a few pills are omitted. While the problem of breakthrough bleeding is a nuisance, it is generally agreed that it is not serious enough to warrant limiting the use of this type of oral contraception. With proper instruction and education, if these can be made available, women can be reassured adequately enough to continue using the pills. In a similar category is the problem of amenorrhea. Some patients may not bleed after they have taken the last tablet in a cycle and this, of course, produces the added concern of a possible pregnancy. In our own studies, some women have used as many as seven cycles of pills with no bleeding between cycles. This also has been the experience of several other investigators. In many clinics, patients are now given instructions to resume medication seven or eight days following the last pill whether bleeding has occurred or not.

One of the serious recent questions, as mentioned previously, relates to whether this type of oral contraception can produce spontaneous clotting in blood vessels. A number of cases of thrombophlebitis among oral contraceptive users have been reported, as well as the more serious incidents of pulmonary embolism or cerebral embolism. It has been extemely important to determine whether there is a relationship between the medication and the occurrence of embolism. Unfortunately, it is almost an impossible task to determine whether there is a relationship. The mechanism of blood coagulation is so complicated that even elaborate series of tests cannot definitely indicate whether abnormal results, even if found, suggest increased or decreased tendency for the blood to clot spontaneously.[1] After obtaining results that were interpreted differently by six hematologists we discarded this type of study. Since it is well known that thrombophlebitis and pulmonary embolism can occur spontaneously, it had become important to know the incidence of spontaneously occurring clotting problems among oral contraceptive users compared with the general female population in the same age groups. These statistics are extemely difficult to obtain, but efforts are currently being made in this direction. The data in Table 1 from the National Disease and Therapeutic Index refer to this problem. According to figures available, some statisti-

---

1. Some of the factors that we have studied in several dozen patients are: Recalcified Clotting Time, Prothrombin: Quick and Owren, Thromboplastin Generation, Platelets, Euglobulin, Cryoglobulin, Plasminogen-Plasmin, Serum Mucopolysaccharides, 24 hour urine Mucopolysaccharides, and Serum Beta Lipoprotein.

cians claim that the total number of cases of thrombotic disorders thus far among pill users is actually about 50 per cent of what might have been expected, considering the total number of women now using oral contraception.

The possibility of a relationship between the use of synthetic progestational compounds as oral contraceptives and the occurrence of intravascular clotting was first suspected late in 1961, when fatal pulmonary embolism occurred in two young Los Angeles women who had been using oral contraceptives. Since then several additional cases have been recorded. From 1961 to the present time, 347 instances of thrombophlebitis (or phlebothrombosis) among women using a norethynodrel-estrogen combination, norethynodrel with mestranol (Enovid), for contraception have been reported to the manufacturer. In the same period, fatal pulmonary embolism has occurred in 35 cases, but in many there were other likely etiological factors, and at least nine were due to other causes.

When the initial cases of pulmonary embolism came to light, the United States Food and Drug Administration (FDA) investigators looked into the specific cases but were unable to conclude that there was a definite cause-and-effect relationship.[2] Undoubtedly because of the suspicion cast and, presumably, the nonvital nature of oral contraception as a drug indication, the FDA required the manufacturer to send a warning letter to all physicians, suggesting that norethynodrel with mestranol not be used for oral contraception in women with a tendency toward thrombophlebitis. (It should be noted, though, that while most cases of thrombophlebitis occurred in women with a related past history, many were found among women who gave no history of previous vascular disorders.)

Therefore, there is still no definite evidence linking thrombophlebitis with oral contraception, but at the time of this writing the matter is not completely resolved.[3] There is undoubt-

2. The Ad Hoc Committee for the Evaluation of a Possible Etiologic Relation with Thromboembolic Conditions, Final Report on *Enovid*, submitted to the Commissioner of the Food and Drug Administration of the Department of Health, Education and Welfare (Sept. 12, 1963).

3. E. T. Tyler, "Oral Contraception and Venous Thrombosis" (an editorial), *Journal of the American Medical Association*, CLXXXV (July 13, 1963), pp. 131–132.

TABLE 1

Estimated Number of Patient-Visits in Continental United States for Thrombophlebitis
and Pulmonary Embolism (Females 15–45 Years of Age)

Year	Thrombophlebitis lower extremities	Thrombophlebitis other sites	Pulmonary embolism and infarction	Total
1961 – 1st visits	70,000	36,000	5,000	111,000
All visits	318,000	214,000	65,000	597,000
1962 (6 mo.) – 1st visits	12,000	10,000	—	22,000
All visits	93,000	117,000	49,000	259,000

Source: National Disease and Therapeutic Index, Lee Associates, Ambler, Pennsylvania

edly still a question of rare individual patient idiocyncrasy to the drugs involved, with resultant increased coagulation tendencies.

RESULTS OF STUDIES

Since the initial use of progestagen-estrogen contraception, a substantial number of combinations of such agents have been studied and are under study at our clinic. The first preparation to be used on a large scale was the combination of norethynodrel 10 mg. with 0.15 mg. of 3-methylether of ethinylestradiol (mestranol). This combination was first studied by Pincus and his collaborators in Puerto Rico beginning in 1956. Shortly afterward we began a study of a combination of norethindrone 10 mg. with mestranol .06 mg. and a little later we also began studying the same 10 mg. norethynodrel tablet that was being used in Puerto Rico. After the 10 mg. norethynodrel tablet had been in use for a few years an attempt was made to find a practical lower dosage preparation. Therefore, a tablet was evaluated which contained 5 mg. norethynodrel with 0.075 mg. mestranol. This particular combination seemed equally effective as the 10 mg. preparation, and there were fewer side effects, notably those that related to the gastrointestinal tract. Once the 5 mg. dosage had been approved, further attempts were initiated to reduce the dosage. This resulted in the development of tablets containing 2½ mg. norethynodrel with .1 mg. mestranol and also tablets containing 2 mg. norethindrone with .1 mg. mestranol. At the time of preparation of this report both the 2 mg. norethindrone and the 2½ mg. norethynodrel tablets are on the market in the United States, as well as a 2½ mg. norethindrone acetate combination. A number of additional compounds have been tested and will probably reach marketing some time within the next few years depending on the adequacy of the data for the United States Food and Drug Administration approval. Among these are medroxy-progesterone-ethinylestradiol preparations, chlormadinone and mestranol and megastrol with ethinylestradiol. The lowest progestin dose tablet in large-scale study is one containing only 1 mg. of ethynodiol diacetate. At the time of preparation of this report there are three groups of preparations commercially available in the United States. These are the norethindrone-mestranol, norethindrone acetate-ethinylestradiol, and norethynodrel-mestranol combinations. We have tabulated our experience with these preparations and the summaries are given in Tables 2, 3, and 4.

In various journals from time to time we have reported our experiences with these preparations. Others have reported extensive experience with similar compounds. The reader is referred to the reports of Pincus and Rock, Celso Ramon Garcia, Edris Rice-Wray, Adeline Satterthwaite, Joseph Goldzieher, Eleanor Mears, and others. Several references to these reports are given at the end of this paper.

TABLE 2

Age Distribution of Women on First Admission, by Treatment

| Age in years | Norethynodrel | | Ethynodiol Diacetate | |
	Number	Per cent of known age	Number	Per cent of known age
15–19	14	4	11	7
20–24	124	30	49	30
25–29	141	34	54	33
30–34	92	22	29	17
35–39	38	9	22	13
40–44	6	1	0	0
Unknown	15	—	10	—
Total	430	100	175	100

Sequential Therapy

Following the demonstration of satisfactory results with the type of progestagen-estrogen contraception described above, and while recognizing that these preparations can be utilized in relatively low dosages, additional measures have been taken in the direction of lowering the overall hormone content of the contraceptive pills. A major step in this direction was the development of so-called "sequential" contraception. With this method, estrogen alone is used for the first 15 days and then the combination of progestagen and estrogen is used for the last five days of treatment. The usefulness of this method is based on the well-known fact that estrogens alone can inhibit ovulation. Hence, when adequate amounts of estrogen are given during the first portion of the cycle, ovulation can be prevented and the combination of progestagen and estrogen late in the cycle allows for adequate development of the endometrium so that the usual withdrawal bleeding is obtained. This form of contraception has now been in trial for about two years and seems to be working quite well. It has certain advantages, namely, that the total amount of hormone administered is less than that with the usual dosage of the combined tablet. Secondly, the progestagen is the more expensive component of the oral contraceptive tablets and, with this method, the combined tablet is used only five days instead of 20. Hence, it is possible that these pills will be less costly. On the other hand, the cost of packaging the sequential

TABLE 3

Distribution of Number of Cycles of Progestagen Intake Per Admission to Treatment

	Agent				
	Norethynodrel				
Number of cycles	*10 mg.*	*5 mg.*	*2.5 mg.*	*Any one of the levels* [a]	*Ethynodiol diacetate*
1–5	8	37	3	37	53
6–10	10	28	16	42	13
11–15	23	22	18	40	10
16–20	23	17	5	21	26
21–25	30	14	3	14	65
26–30	10	17	8	25	9
31–35	0	14	36	45	
36–40	1	15	20	29	
41–45	0	22	5	17	
46–50	0	20	0	20	
51–55	0	23		17	
56–60	0	69		19	
61–65	0	22		29	
66–70	0	8		25	
71–75	0	0		12	
76–80	0	0		19	
>80	0	0		22	
Total admissions	105	333 [b]	114	433 [b]	176 [c]
Total cycles	1,846	11,857	2,855	16,288	2,520
Women years	142	891	220	1,253	194

[a] In this column, cycles of progestagen intake for any woman, regardless of dosage level, are added together.

[b] Three women were readmitted to this treatment.

[c] One woman was readmitted to this treatment.

tablets may prohibit lowering the cost beyond a certain level. Furthermore, it must be emphasized that these pills must be taken in the proper sequence and this may produce a teaching problem in underdeveloped areas. From the physiologic standpoint, it should be noted that the usual contraceptives of the combined tablet type are dependent upon three factors for preventing conception. These are, as previously indicated, ovu-

TABLE 4

Incidence of Side Effects and Complaints During the Last Six Cycles for Each of 379 Patients on Norethynodrel-Mestranol Therapy and for Each of 124 Patients on Ethynodiol Diacetate Therapy [a]

Side effects or complaints	Norethynodrel-Mestranol Therapy		Ethynodiol Diacetate Therapy	
	No. of cycles	Rate per 100 cycles	No. of cycles	Rate per 100 cycles
Dysmenorrhea	225	9.9	75	10.1
Breakthrough bleeding or spotting	141	6.2	35	4.7
No withdrawal bleeding	51	2.2	5	0.7
Depression or nervousness	45	2.0	6	0.8
Headache or nausea	32	1.4	1	0.1
Other physical complaints [b]	31	1.3	8	1.1

[a] Only patients who had completed at least six cycles were included.

[b] Includes such complaints as leg cramps, sore breasts, backache, dizziness, etc.

lation inhibition, alteration in cervical mucous, and distortion of the endometrium. When the sequential approach is used, contraception is dependent entirely on inhibition of ovulation inasmuch as the other safeguards are not obtained with this method. Despite this, our preliminary studies are very encouraging.

Since it is possible that these contraceptive pills will be used for many years by some women in the next few decades, it is important that studies continue relative to possible long term toxicity. In this connection, our clinic in Los Angeles is proceeding with detailed metabolic and blood chemistry studies on a relatively large scale which are intended to provide data on possible alterations in the function of the liver, adrenals, thyroid, pituitary, and other vital structures. We are also performing endometrial biopsies and Papanicolaou vaginal smears at relatively frequent intervals on all patients to help provide statistics on possible tumor-promoting effects of these agents. These data are being reported from time to time as they are tabulated.

SUMMARY

Oral contraception, after eight years of use, has been shown to be a very effective method of voluntarily preventing pregnancy. It is very acceptable by patients, has aesthetic advantages over various methods of vaginal contraception, and is extremely effective. While there are still some questions as to the significance of certain side effects and the question of the relationship of more serious conditions to the use of the contraceptives, no evidence has appeared which would definitely incriminate these preparations as causative agents. It seems likely that the future will see expanding use of these preparations in the efforts at population control, but meanwhile, carefully controlled investigations must continue to probe into possible undiscovered deleterious effects.

REFERENCES

H. H. Cook, C. J. Gamble, and A. P. Satterthwaite, "Oral Contraception by Nonethynodrel," *American Journal of Obstetrics and Gynecology,* LXXXII (1961), pp. 437–445.

P. Eckstein *et al.,* "Birmingham Oral Contraceptive Trial," *British Medical Journal,* $\overline{V}$CCLXI (Nov. 4, 1961), pp. 1172–1183.

J. W. Goldzieher, L. E. Moses, and L. T. Ellis, "Study of Norethindrone in Contraception," *Journal of the American Medical Association,* CLXXX (1962), pp. 359–361.

G. Pincus *et al.,* "Effectiveness of Oral Contraceptive: Effects of Progestin-Estrogen Combination Upon Fertility, Menstrual Phenomena, and Health," *Science,* CXXX (July 10, 1959), pp. 81–83.

G. Pincus, "Field Trials with Norethynodrel as an Oral Contraceptive" (Worcester Foundation publication).

E. Rice-Wray, M. Schulz-Contreras, I. Guerra, and A. Aranda-Rosell, "Long-term Administration of Norethindrone in Fertility Control," *Journal of the American Medical Association,* CLXXX (1962), pp. 355–358.

J. Rock, C. R. Garcia, and G. Pincus, ''Use of Some Progestational 19-nor Steroids in Gynecology,'' *American Journal of Obstetrics and Gynecology*, LXXIX (1960), pp. 758–767.

E. T. Tyler and H. J. Olson, ''Fertility Promoting and Inhibiting Effects of New Steroid Hormonal Substances,'' *Journal of the American Medical Association*, CLXIX (1959), pp. 1843–1854.

E. T. Tyler *et al.*, ''An Oral Contraceptive: 4-Year Study of Norethindrone,'' *Obstetrics and Gynecology*, XVIII (1961), pp. 363–367.

Adaline P. Satterthwaite

EXPERIENCE WITH ORAL AND INTRAUTERINE CONTRACEPTION IN RURAL PUERTO RICO

At an eighty-five bed mission hospital in Humacao, a municipality of 30,000 in the southeastern part of Puerto Rico about thirty-five miles from San Juan, between 1951 and 1961 we attended approximately 4,800 deliveries and performed 2,000 female sterilizations, most of them postpartum. It was a surprise to me when I first arrived in Puerto Rico to find that most of the women who came for prenatal care for the second or third child wanted postpartum sterilization. Since 1937 when sterilization was made legal for socioeconomic as well as medical reasons, the "operation" was generally known and accepted as the means of family limitation. It seems to me that from 1937 to 1948 it was precisely this abuse and exploitation of female sterilization, both privately and in government hospitals, that resulted in the widespread effort of a revitalized Catholic clergy to apply pressure on obstetricians and leaders in the health professions responsible for influencing women at their most vulnerable and susceptible epoch during the prenatal and postpartum period. This phenomenon, which produced guilt feelings on the part of physician and patient alike, was responsible for the evolution of a so-called poststerilization syndrome by the newly founded Puerto Rico Medical School.

The performance of sterilization was so widespread that in one survey, one out of every five females in the reproductive years attending public dispensaries was found to be sterilized.[1] This occurred when the contraceptive methods available were the traditional chemical and mechanical methods that required a high degree of motivation and discipline and the tacit acceptance of both sexual partners. It seems quite obvious that the drop in the birth rate from 41 in 1950 to 31 in 1961 has indeed been due to sterilizations and out-migration rather than to the use of conventional contraceptives.

With this background it is obvious that both oral progestagens and the intrauterine devices provide a breakthrough. In fact, it has become virtually impossible to get sterilization performed even for medical reasons in the public hospitals. It is natural, then, that women will flock to clinics offering new effective methods. The government industrialization program which has created more job opportunities for women has been an important, though apparently unrecognized, factor in reducing family size. Because of the cost of maternity benefits, many of the employers favor women who can present medical certificates of sterilization or participation in contraceptive programs.

In 1957 we started field testing with oral progestagens.[2] The first subjects were women recruited by home visiting; two months later the program was extended to our postpartum clinic patients in response to their request. Now that oral progestagens are available on prescription many additional patients are being followed in the regular postpartum clinics of the hospital.

In the two year period from November, 1961 to November, 1963, we offered concomitantly three low-dose oral progestagens and intrauterine devices. We were able to get cooperation of two pharmaceutical companies [3] which provided the three progesta-

1. R. Hill, J. M. Stycos, K. W. Back, *The Family and Population Control* (Chapel Hill: University of North Carolina Press, 1959), p. 166.

2. Norethynodrel and mestranol (Enovid 10 mg.).

3. C. D. Searle and Company provided norethynodrel 2.5 mg. with mestranol 0.1 mg. (Enovid-E) and ethynodiol diacetate 1.0 mg. with mestranol 0.1 mg. (Ovulen); Ortho Research Foundation provided norethindrone 2.0 mg. with mestranol 0.1 mg. (Orthonovum 2 mg.).

gens, which were offered alternately to women who came to the clinic requesting "pills." We made no educational campaign, except to visit the public health units and government welfare agencies in the surrounding towns and acquaint them with our program. Women came to the clinic requesting service referred from the hospital out-patient department or recommended by our satisfied clients. Most of them arrived at the clinic having already decided which method they wished, usually on the basis of the advice of a neighbor or friend who was already receiving service. Since we had been offering pills for four years, most of them knew about the pills and wanted them.

When we first initiated a program giving intrauterine contraceptive devices (IUCD's), we gave them to women who did not qualify for sterilization according to the hospital rules for age and parity and who wanted "one shot" protection, and also to women who could not qualify for pills because of menstrual irregularities, late menarche and age, or who had found the pills unacceptable because of side effects—especially chloasma.[4] Soon, however, women also came asking for the IUCD. Eventually we had to set up artificial rules to discourage the women from switching from one method to the other. These consisted of making mandatory the use of a vaginal method—usually aerosol foam [5]—for three months. Our area had been well covered by voluntary distribution of an aerosol vaginal foam by the Family Planning Association and most of the 40 per cent of our patients who had had previous contraceptive experience claimed to have tried it and failed.

During this two year period, November, 1961 to November, 1963, 600 women chose the oral progestagens. Of these, 555 started the study. During the same period 608 women were fitted with intrauterine devices—almost equally divided between the two sizes of Margulies spirals and Lippes loops. It is not surprising to note that those electing IUCD were older and had more children (Table 1).

In the course of the two years, 30 per cent of the IUCD wearers discontinued: 17 per cent for relevant reasons, i.e., 2.5

4. Eds. note—irregular brown pigmentation on the skin of the face or elsewhere (usually associated with pregnancy).
5. Emko (trade name).

per cent for unintended pregnancies, 7.8 per cent for expulsion, and 6.7 per cent for pain, bleeding, and infections.

Table 2 shows the three compounds tested in the comparative study of the low-dose oral progestagens. All three contain the same amount of the same estrogen, i.e., 0.1 mg. mestranol. The difference in the compounds was in the type of progestagen—

TABLE 1

A Comparison of Women by Contraceptive Method Chosen,
Humacao, 1961–63

	Method Chosen	
	Intrauterine device	Oral contraceptive
Per cent over 30 years of age	24	12
Per cent with 4 or more children	40	25
Number of women	608	600

norethynodrel 2.5 mg., norethindrone 2 mg., and ethynodiol diacetate 1 mg. It will be observed that there was a very high rate of discontinuance of the oral contraceptives—a total of 57 per cent for the series. The incidence of dropouts was significantly higher for norethynodrel than for the other two, norethindrone and ethynodiol diacetate.

In Table 3 we see some specific reasons for closing. If one includes those who change methods with those who discontinue for side effects, one probably has a fair index of the unacceptability of oral contraception. I would point out that these two reasons include 32.4 per cent of those using norethynodrel 2.5 mg.; 21 per cent of those using norethindrone 2 mg., and 15.8 per cent of those using ethynodiol diacetate 1 mg. Twenty-four per cent of the total discontinued for those reasons related to the method.

You will note that the other reasons for closing out, namely because of separation from the husband, moving away, propaganda factors, or planning pregnancy, have approximately the same frequency in all three groups of patients. In general, we may say that all three preparations are equally effective but that norethindrone and ethynodiol diacetate were more acceptable.

Dr. Tyler has remarked on the percentage of "dropouts" in our Puerto Rican series.[6] In this series, 57 per cent of those using orals discontinued, whereas 70 per cent of those using the IUCD were continuing contraception at the end of the two year period. Because of this known variation between study populations and investigators, it is obvious that valid comparisons can only be made in a single environment. The women started with great enthusiasm because obviously, swallowing a pill is less arduous than using a vaginal method. However, to remember to do this every day requires steadfastness and discipline. Although we can argue that the oral progestagens offer a higher degree of protection to the individual woman, aside from cost considerations, they lack the advantage of continued protection from a nonrepetitive action that is offered by intrauterine devices. The women with large families who especially need protection are the ones who often fail to return to the clinic within the 8–10 day interval after finishing the medication and may already be pregnant by the time they return for supplies. In contrast, the IUCD wearer has an 83 per cent probability of continued protection if only relevant terminations are considered. As the devices are improved, it may be possible to reduce the frequency of expulsions and of pregnancies occurring with the device in utero, thus further increasing the protection that follows a single action. Furthermore, I think there is some importance in the fact that the protection is provided by a third party to the sexual act—a doctor or a nurse. This idea of letting someone else do it and take the responsibility may be a factor in the wide acceptance of sterilization. The advantage of the IUCD over sterilization is of course its reversibility, which leaves the choice still open.

From a practical point of view, the physician-time involved in fitting a woman with an intrauterine device and in consultation with her, is largely the time of insertion which perhaps might be at a maximum, 10 minutes per patient. The follow-up is very simple. If she is satisfied she may never return until she wants the device removed. In contrast, with the oral patients, at least in our population, we have to continue to counsel them in order

6. See Sheps' "Report of Panel Discussion," this volume.

TABLE 2

Study of Low Dose Oral Contraceptive Compounds, Humacao, 1961-63

	Compounds			
	Norethynodrel 2.5 mg.[a] and mestranol 0.1 mg.	Norethindrone 2.0 mg.[b] and mestranol 0.1 mg.	Ethynodiol diacetate 1.0 mg.[c] and mestranol 0.1 mg.	Total
Number of women starting on compound	201	190	164	555
Number of treatment cycles	2,755	2,776	2,071	7,602
Woman years of use	212	213	159	584
Closed cases				
Number	137	101	79	317
Per cent of those starting	68	53	48	57

[a] Enovid-E, 2.5 mg. supplied by C. D. Searle & Company, Chicago, Illinois.
[b] Orthonovum 2.0 mg. supplied by Ortho Research Foundation, Raritan, New Jersey.
[c] Ovulen 1 mg. supplied by C. D. Searle & Company.

TABLE 3

Reasons Advanced by Women for Terminating Oral Contraception,
by Compound Used, Humacao, 1961–63

Reasons for terminating use	Norethynodrel 2.5 mg.		Norethindrone 2.0 mg.		Ethynodiol Diacetate 1.0 mg.	
	Number	Per cent of total users	Number	Per cent of total users	Number	Per cent of total users
Side effects	45	22.5	31	16.3	21	12.8
Change of method	20	9.9	9	4.7	5	3.0
Contraception not needed	21	10.4	18	9.4	15	9.2
Contraception abandoned	13	6.4	13	6.8	13	7.9
Moved	12	5.9	9	4.7	12	7.3
Propaganda	12	5.9	5	2.6	6	3.7
Planning pregnancy	14	6.9	16	8.4	7	4.3
Number of cases closed	137	68	101	53	79	48

to reassure them and keep them active. They need to return for supplies at least every month or two.

After two years in our series, in a population with relatively low motivation for carrying out repetitive action, we found that of the 555 women who started oral progestagens, 43 per cent were still active users and out of the 608 women fitted with an IUCD, 70 per cent were still using the devices. In summary, from our experience, I would be much more in favor of the intrauterine devices, from the point of view of public health population control.

Warren O. Nelson

CURRENT RESEARCH ON NEW
CONTRACEPTIVE METHODS

I should like to mention some of the procedures we may look forward to in the future. This presentation will by no means exhaust the possibilities, but it will give regard to areas that look most promising, either because of pure research interest or because of the interest of pharmaceutical companies.

First, I should like to consider possible improvement of the present oral contraceptives used by females.[1] Undoubtedly a lower dose can be achieved, and there we are rapidly reaching, I think, a point of diminishing returns. It may be desirable to have a lower estrogen content but I do not think that a lower content of the progestagens, which are the more costly component, can materially reduce the cost because there will always be the expense of preparation, packaging, and merchandising. I doubt that we are likely to achieve a very much lower price. I think we

1. J. W. Goldzieher, L. E. Moses, and L. T. Ellis, "A Field Trial with a Physiologic Method of Conception Control," *Research in Family Planning*, ed. C. V. Kiser (Princeton: Princeton University Press, 1962), pp. 351–356.

would, however, find acceptable a lower dose, particularly of estrogen, for the regular administration of this drug.

Compounds with fewer side effects are desirable. I think this could be secured and less breakthrough bleeding achieved. Most important, however, would be the development of compounds requiring less frequent administration. This will be difficult to achieve with oral preparations, but not completely unsolvable. With injectable preparations, a reduction in frequency of administration can be achieved and we can look forward, I think, to improvement in this form of contraception used by women.

Next, I would like to mention a group of substances that we might call antizygotic or anti-implantation compounds.[2] Here we have a growing number of new drugs, the best known of which is Clomiphene.[3] A number have been written about and a number under study have similar or related effects. These compounds are effective only after fertilization, and effective primarily during the time the egg is traversing the tube. This passage in all mammals, including human beings, occupies three and a half to four days from the time of fertilization until the zygote emerges in the uterus. During that time, the cleaving egg is vulnerable to the effects of compounds of the type under discussion. Some of these actually destroy the cleaving egg; others appear to rush the eggs through the tube into the uterus, putting the egg there before it should be and as a consequence creating difficulties for the egg to implant in an environment where it does not belong at that particular time. In this regard, I might call attention to the fact that some of the compounds may be interfering with fertility in much the same way as appears to be the case for the intrauterine devices.

I do not agree totally with Tietze,[4] since I think the mechanism of action of those devices is primarily interference with implantation. This may be due to rushing the eggs through the tubes more rapidly than they ordinarily would pass, but the end result is the same.

The advantage of the antizygotic compounds lies in that they

2. W. O. Nelson, O. Davidson, and K. Wada, ''Studies on Interference with Zygote Development and Implantation,'' *Delayed Implantation*, ed. A. C. Enders (Chicago: University of Chicago Press, 1963), pp. 183–196.

3. MRL 41.

4. See pp. 491–492, this volume.

may be taken after the fact, that is, after the sex act. If they are as effective in human beings as they are in laboratory animals, a single dose during one of three days after the connubial act, would dispose of any embryo that had started to develop. Obviously, there are some disadvantages, including objections on moral grounds, but I do not believe this should be a concern in a consideration of scientific possibilities.

There will also be concern, I am sure, as to the possible teratogenic effects of these drugs. That is, a dose less than one that is totally effective might partially interfere with the development of the embryo and produce a monster. We do know that there are agents that do this. These agents are known to kill the implanted embryo, but in less than effective doses they are likely to cause abnormalities. These substances are referred to as antimetabolites.[5]

I should make it clear that the type of compounds I am talking about here, the antizygotic compounds, do not act in the same way as the antimetabolites. They act, instead, before implantation and if they are given in the same doses after implantation, nothing happens and the embryo goes on to term. Nonetheless, it can be anticipated that there will be great concern among the regulatory agencies, and a request for definite proof that they are not teratogenic. Thus far, we have no reason to believe that they are dangerous. If the dose is less than sufficient to interfere with progression of the pregnancy, the embryos are perfectly normal; or if a dose is so small as to destroy all but two or three of the litter, those that do survive are perfectly normal.

Finally, the other area that I would like to mention here is that of male physiologic contraceptives. First, as you know very well, we can interfere with spermatogenesis with all of the steroid compounds that are so effective in inhibiting ovulation in females.[6] Unfortunately, in the male these compounds not only interfere with sperm production, but also with hormone production. This reduction of hormone production also occurs in the

5. J. B. Thiersch, ''Effect of 6 Diazo – 5-OXO – L – Norleucine (DON) on the Rat Litter *In Utero*,'' *Proceedings of the Society for Experimental Biology and Medicine*, XCIV (1957), pp. 33–35.

6. C. G. Heller, D. J. Moore, C. A. Paulsen, W. O. Nelson, and W. M. Laidlaw, ''Effects of Progesterone and Synthetic Progestins on the Reproductive Physiology of Normal Men,'' *Federation Proceedings*, XVIII (1959), pp. 1057–1064.

female, but it is of no consequence, because the female hormones are replaced by the action of the drugs themselves.

There is some evidence that the injectable steroid, Provera,[7] will interfere with spermatogenesis without interfering with hormone production. This study was carried out by Dr. John McLeod, in a prison population, but is as yet not well documented. Furthermore, certain laboratory studies do not bear out the fact that Provera will interfere selectively with sperm production and not with hormone production.[8] Indeed, on the contrary, we have found that hormone production in rats is interfered with markedly when we use doses high enough to interfere with sperm production. That is the history, indeed, of all the steroids; it is much easier to interfere with a man's hormone production than with his sperm production by tampering with the levels of gonadotrophin.

We may use testosterone, a male sex hormone, since it too will very effectively inhibit sperm production.[9] It will also inhibit the production of testicular hormones, but in this case the synthetic hormone, being androgenic, will replace the testicular hormone whose production is inhibited. We could use testosterone as a contraceptive in males, but the difficulty is it must be injected since as yet there are no really good oral androgens. There are some that might be effective, but they produce effects on the liver, and I am sure would not easily be accepted by the regulatory agencies. I am afraid also that there would be very definite concern about possible stimulation of cancer, just as we have had much concern about the stimulation of cervical and breast cancer with estrogens in the female. We would also have that same concern about testosterone stimulating prostatic cancer in men.

Finally, I would like to mention a group of compounds which act to inhibit spermatogenesis in another way than by inhibiting

---

7. Trade name (Upjohn Company).

8. W. O. Nelson, "Control of Fertility in the Male," *Proceedings Second International Congress of Endocrinology*, ed. S. Taylor (Amsterdam: Excerpta Medica Foundation, 1965), pp. 794–804.

9. C. G. Heller, W. O. Nelson, I. B. Hill, E. Henderson, W. O. Maddock, E. C. Jungck, C. A. Paulsen, and G. E. Mortimore, "Improvement in Spermatogenesis Following Depression of the Human Testis with Testosterone," *Fertility and Sterility*, I (1950), pp. 415–522.

the pituitary gonadotrophins. There are a number of compounds shown to have this effect. The first were the nitrofurans; [10] and then there were the group of compounds called diamines; [11] and finally, the dinitropyrroles.[12]

All of these compounds act directly upon a specific cell type in the testis, that is on the primary spermatocyte which is the cell that carries out a very long prophase in preparation for the reduction of chromosomes. We call that process meiosis. It is important to distinguish between meiosis and mitosis. All cells in the body undergo mitosis; this is ordinary cell division. Only the germ cells undergo meiosis. This process consequently is a very special type of cell division.

All of the compounds in this last group inhibit the germ cell process at the meiotic stage, and appear to do nothing else. They have no effect on the hormone-producing cells in the testis, nor on any other hormone-producing elements in the body. The effect is quite reversible; if treatment is stopped, spermatogenesis returns. The diamines had long clinical tests in two prisons, and were shown to be completely effective orally; however, when they were given to subjects that were not in cages, an unfortunate effect emerged, that is the so-called "antabuse effect." Men on the drugs who might take a drink of alcohol would go through a very disturbing kind of reaction—not a serious one—but a highly disturbing one. This led very rapidly to the shelving of this group of compounds. Obviously they are not likely to be accepted.

The dinitropyrroles are the most effective of all. I think presently the greatest hope for an application of oral contraception to human males comes from this type of compound. Some

10. W. O. Nelson and R. G. Bunge, ''The Effect of Therapeutic Doses of Nitrofurantoin (Furadantin) Upon Spermatogenesis in Man,'' *Journal of Urology*, LXXVII (1957), pp. 275–281.

11. W. O. Nelson and D. J. Patanelli, ''Inhibition of Spermatogenesis,'' *Federation Proceedings*, XX (1961), p. 418; H. P. Drobeck and F. Coulston, ''Inhibition and Recovery of Spermatogenesis in Rats, Monkeys and Dogs Medicated with Bis (Dichloroacetyl) Diamines,'' *Experimental and Molecular Pathology*, I (1962), pp. 251–274; C. G. Heller, B. Y. Flageolle, and L. J. Matson, ''Histopathology of the Human Testes as Affected by Bis (Dichloroacetyl) Diamines,'' *Experimental and Molecular Pathology*, II (Supplement, 1963), pp. 107–114.

12. D. J. Patanelli and W. O. Nelson, ''A Quantitative Study of Inhibition and Recovery of Spermatogenesis,'' *Recent Progress in Hormone Research*, XX (New York: Academic Press, 1964), pp. 491–543.

are being tested now and if they are as effective in human beings as they are in laboratory animals, we should be able to maintain a state of infertility indefinitely by the administration of monthly doses with complete reversibility to the fertile status.

In the rat it takes three to four weeks after the first dose for the subject to become infertile, because of the sperm that are already formed or are beyond the point of vulnerability in the meiotic process, and are thus able to mature. Consequently, the animal remains fertile for about three weeks, after which time fertility is inhibited indefinitely as long as monthly medications are continued.

Mindel C. Sheps

REPORT ON THE PANEL DISCUSSION

The Nature of the Evidence

The emphasis of this discussion was on problems of evaluating the effects, whether desired or undesired, of contraceptives in use, as distinct from questions regarding the acceptability of family planning or of specific methods. The discussion was concerned with the assessment primarily of the intrauterine contraceptive devices (IUCD's) and of drugs, namely the hormone-like preparations currently in use.

Many questions were raised regarding the advantages and disadvantages of different devices or preparations. Data were presented but it was clear, from both the prepared papers and the discussion, that in most cases the available data do not provide adequate answers to such questions. Thus Dr. Tietze, in addition to the statements in his written paper (on IUCD's) regarding the difficulty of determining whether observed differences in results are due to differences between patients, doctors, or the devices, said: "On the face of it, it seems that the tailed devices are associated with higher rates of pelvic inflammatory disease than are the tailless ones. However, the bulk of the

487

exposure with the tailless devices has been contributed by private patients where one would expect less pelvic inflammatory disease, and about 90 per cent of the experience with tailed devices has been with clinic patients, so the matter is by no means settled at this time.''

It was Dr. Lasagna's contention that such problems would always beset efforts to evaluate the effects of different agents unless trials were carried out in conformity with accepted principles of experimentation. If provision were made to ensure that the different devices were given to comparable patients, and that the various investigators used all the devices under similar rules, it would be easier to make the determination. At the meeting, there was, however, definite disagreement about the feasibility of such plans, as exemplified by the following exchanges:

FREEDMAN: ''It seems to me that there are two separate problems. One is that of measuring the effectiveness of contraceptives used as they are supposed to be used. In this kind of situation the controls used in many medical studies are, it seems to me, fairly easily applicable. If, however, we are talking about field effectiveness of a contraceptive, including its acceptability, we have a different kind of problem, into which self-selection enters. In that case, I don't think we should be surprised that investigators aren't doing this in a perfect way. I think it is extremely difficult to deal with that problem in the same way as the first.''

LASAGNA: ''I don't quite agree that things are as difficult as you make them out to be. For example, let's take the simplest case: a comparison of two or more kinds of contraceptive pills. I see not a shred of trouble there in making a field comparison, do you?''

FREEDMAN: ''Yes, there would be.''

TIETZE: ''One difficulty is the fact that manufacturers of contraceptive products are generally not willing to have these products subjected to rigorous comparison in a double-blind test.''

LASAGNA: ''Oh dear, I don't believe that at all. In my experience, investigators inform manufacturers what supplies are required. Manufacturers should not dictate how to set up experiments. I cannot believe the situation is so different in this field.''

FREEDMAN: ''Your paper indicated that you are going to get a group of women to agree to this procedure. Well, that already is a highly selected population. The interesting question is: How do you get people to take these pills? If they already have agreed to take the pills, you have ruled out one of the most important problems as far as field acceptability is concerned.''

LASAGNA: ''I don't see that at all. You obviously aren't interested at all in how pills work with people who won't take them, but, given a group of people who are willing to try this pill or that, I think you can set up a perfectly good experiment . . .

''My experience, in first suggesting controlled trials in areas where such trials have not been routine, such as cancer and psychiatry, has been that clinicians in the fields usually say, 'you folks don't understand what our problems are. Things are just completely different with us from what they are in treating hypertension or anything else.' But it usually turns out that things really aren't all that different in regard to the basic principles of experimentation.

''My second comment would be: if there are insuperable obstacles to setting up formal comparative trials, then there are insuperable obstacles. But let us not delude ourselves into making comparative statements about methods when, in fact, we have no basis for making such statements. If we can't handle some of these obstacles, we will have to be content with saying: 'I really don't know what I am talking about when I make a comparative statement about different contraceptives' . . .

''I would also like to take a mild whack at these contraceptive chemicals—I like to think of them as *chemicals*. We don't really avoid worry because the chemicals resemble natural hormones. We see cases of poisoning at our institution from the hormone hydrocortisone, for example, which *is* manufactured by the body. Everyone is convinced that that particular hormone, given exogenously, can cause trouble. Therefore, I don't think that the fact that these oral contraceptives resemble natural products of the body means that they are incapable of causing mischief . . .

"I don't think drugs do predictable things. Drugs don't worry very much about what seems rational to us. Drugs rarely have but one effect. They usually hit many cells, many organs, many enzymes. Maybe I worry more about this because I see the troubles drugs cause every day, and because I have come to know that the harmful effects of drugs are rarely appreciated until a very long time has elapsed since their introduction. The accurate incidence of toxicity is often unavailable for decades. Whether a drug can kill is not, I think you will agree, a very subtle effect, but it may go undetected for years. Therefore, I say that we ought to suspend final judgment in regard to the oral contraceptives.

"I agree that these pills can be highly effective, and that the risks seem low, but I would also submit that if we don't set up a purposeful program to measure their toxicity in regard to all kinds of effects, we will delay needlessly the true assessment of the safety of these powerful chemicals.

"I think we need some data and I believe we ought to *look for trouble of any kind*. After all, hormonal factors seem to be related to such diverse states as cancer of the lung and coronary artery disease."

TYLER: "What about the coagulation problem? When one factor alters, another usually compensates."

LASAGNA: "I find myself completely confused by the field of coagulation factors. I think one has to look at the clinical events, however. I am less concerned about what happens *in vitro* than about what happens *in vivo*, although obviously, if you had a dramatic *in vitro* effect, it would make you exceedingly apprehensive."

In summary, it can be said that, as of now, the great bulk of available evidence about the comparative action (desirable or undesirable) of various contraceptives is not based on controlled experiments; it is not based on observations among comparable groups of people, made by the same physicians under comparable circumstances. Some believe that the data will nevertheless eventually supply the needed answers. Those that do not agree with this feel that it is essential, as well as possible, to subject contraceptive agents to assessment according to the principles of modern clinical pharmacology.[1] This argument may well become increasingly cogent as the variety and number of available agents grow.

Criteria of Effects

Several other questions, related to the points just discussed, were raised repeatedly, though not fully explored: (1) When the desirability of a method for a mass program rather than for an individual is in question, should the standards of efficacy be modified? In other words, can one lower the degree of effectiveness required? (2) In judging the relative safety of a contraceptive agent, should one compare the observed incidence of complications with their incidence following pregnancy (or childbirth) or with their incidence in the use of some other contraceptive method? (3) How are dangers to some individuals in a population to be weighed against the hazards of uncontrolled population growth? Thus one speaker said: "In parts of the world where there is a desperate demographic emergency, I should say that considerable hazards in the controlling of population growth would be justified in the face of the worse hazards of not controlling it." Though this question has implications beyond scientific considerations, information is needed from science as a basis for judgement.

SPECIFIC AGENTS

Intrauterine Contraceptive Devices

The mechanism of action was briefly discussed by Dr. Tietze as follows: "We do not know how these devices work. We know they do not interfere with ovulation, and they do not interfere with sperm transport. Sperm does get up into the tube; it has been found there in humans. The mode of action may be at least one of the following three: interference with any of the various components of fertilization, interference with egg transport through the tube into the uterus, or interference with implanta-

1. Similar controversies are, as Lasagna said, common in many branches of medicine. See M. C. Sheps, "Problems in the Clinical Evaluation of Drug Therapy," *Perspectives in Biology and Medicine*, V (Spring, 1962), pp. 308–323; M. C. Sheps and A. P. Shapiro, "The Physician's Responsibility in the Age of Therapeutic Plenty," *Circulation*, XXV (Feb., 1962), pp. 399–407.

tion. All of these are possible, and presently available laboratory and clinical data do not give support to any one of them.

"Personally, I feel very strongly that there must be a factor involved other than interference of the foreign body with implantation in the uterus. My reason for this position is that the frequency of ectopic pregnancies is much lower than would be expected if the ova were fertilized at the normal rate and were caught in the tube at the normal rate. I believe, therefore, that one of the two other factors, interference with fertilization or interference with egg transport, or both, must also be involved." [2]

In relation to other effects of these devices, it was observed that in some cases insertion of a device might aggravate pre-existing, unrecognized infection. This might be a desirable result, since it would lead to the treatment of otherwise undetected disease. Another side benefit cited was that, when insertion has been accompanied by appropriate examinations, early carcinoma has been detected in a number of cases.

Since it is sometimes difficult to be sure whether a device is still in position, Dr. Cole suggested a possible method that would not involve resort to X-ray. If some metal were incorporated in the device, a simple, inexpensive, radio frequency oscillator would detect its presence.

Progestagens

Dr. Tyler presented some analyses of the action and acceptability of the oral agents that are not included in his paper. Although he believes there is no evidence that they are carcinogenic in humans, it must be recognized that competent people have reservations.

Regarding "dropouts," i.e., women who discontinue the use of the agents, he said: "Depending on where studies were done and on the investigators, the per cent of dropouts is extremely different. For example, in India in a small study in Madras, reported in Singapore at the meeting of the International Planned Parenthood Federation last year, there was a very high

2. See C. Tietze, "Intrauterine Contraceptive Rings—History and Statistical Appraisal," *Intrauterine Contraceptive Devices*, ed. C. Tietze and S. Lewit (New York: Excerpta Medica Foundation, 1962), pp. 14–15.

percentage of dropouts, and my impression is that Dr. K. Menon felt that this was due to the fact that there was very poor motivation, any kind of side effect being sufficient to cause dropout; whereas, across in Ceylon, in Dr. Chennatamby's study, the dropout rate was much lower and the use of the preparation was much more successful.

"I can't understand the relatively high dropout rate in England, of about 20 per cent, much higher than in Australia or the United States. The lowest rate, which happens to be in Goldzieher's group in Texas, is, I think, somewhere about 0.8 per cent.

"Dr. Satterthwaite's dropout rate was a little higher than Goldzieher's, and that may have some relationship to the particular population group involved. In our series, we range between 5 and 10 per cent for the various preparations we are using. The dropout rate is probably related to the way in which the pills are given, the confidence of the physician or the clinic, and word-of-mouth discussion, in the general area where the patient is. I think confidence, in itself, makes a great deal of difference to these patients.

"After the initial year or two of our experience, we found that patients were not dropping out at the same rate as before. At the beginning, many women didn't want to take the pills or their husbands didn't want them to take them. This was simply a lack of confidence in the new method, or a fear of it."

In other discussions, several participants agreed that progestational agents are unlikely to postpone the menopause, since the onset of menopause is probably unrelated to the number of ova that have been released.

A possible relation between dosage and effectiveness was suggested. Thus, it was stated that pharmacologists would be shocked if there were no distribution of responses to a given dose of any chemical. Unless massive doses were used, it is to be expected that an occasional person might follow the directions very carefully, and still become pregnant.

In reply, it was claimed that, at the 10 milligram level, few failures were reported following conscientious and proper use. This dose, with the accompanying estrogen, would be expected to prevent ovulation in all women. At a dosage of one milligram, however, there would likely be failures of ovulation suppression, but a safety factor exists in the other mechanisms by which the agent interferes with pregnancy: namely, throwing the endometrial pattern out of gear with the ovum, and also change in certain other vital structures. The possibility of an occasional failure with continued lowering of the dosage to reduce price or side effects could not, however, be completely ruled out.

MEASURING THE RATE OF CONCEIVING

A discussion of appropriate methods of measuring contraceptive effectiveness included the following:

LASAGNA: "I was struck by the rather quaint notion that one woman followed for 20 years is the same as 240 women followed for one month. I would like to put as a proposition for Dr. Tietze to knock down, if he so desires, that the Pearl index should be gently laid to rest for all time.

"Dr. Tietze, would you like to rise to that bait?"

TIETZE: "I shall be very glad to do so, particularly since my friend, Bob Potter, is not now in the audience. He has done more in recent years to lay this ghost than anyone else; he really should have the honor of administering the *coup de grâce* on a solemn occasion of this type.

"Basically, the Pearl formula, which has been used now for about 30 years, is predicated on the assumption that the chance of conception per cycle or per month of exposure is uniform. We know now that this premise is incorrect, because couples differ greatly in their ability to achieve pregnancy. In a population not using contraception, conception occurs sooner among more fecund couples, and they thereby eliminate themselves from the group. The less fecund couples remain and, as time goes on, the pregnancy rate per month declines rather rapidly. In a group of couples using contraception, the same process takes place. The less skillful and less motivated couples as well as the more fecund couples are soon eliminated by pregnancy. The remaining couples are those who find the method congenial, who are in earnest about their desire to avoid pregnancy, and are perhaps less fecund than the average. Therefore, the rate of conception declines with time, and a pregnancy rate based on a group with a long average observation period is lower than the rate would have been if the observations had been made over a short time only.

"Therefore it is desirable to use, as a measure of contraceptive effectiveness, the percentage of couples who experience a pregnancy during the first year of use, computed by means of a life table procedure. Dr. Potter has worked out this rate and I have called it the cumulative pregnancy rate. I have proposed this term to him, and he has accepted it. We are now trying to gain more general acceptance for this measure."

SHEPS: "I think the problem Dr. Tietze pointed out, that the group is not homogeneous, is only one of the difficulties. Another circumstance that we don't really want to avoid, but want to measure, is the fact that individuals really change over time. For convenience in mathematical models, it is often helpful to assume a constant probability of conception over time, but we know that isn't true. Generally, there are changes with age and parity; in a contraceptive trial, there may be change in motivation, and change with learning. Therefore, it seems to me that we want to measure differences over time.

"We thus have a situation where three factors are mixed up in the Pearl index. They are: the bias in the index even for homogeneous groups, the fact that real populations are heterogeneous, and the fact that people change. For these reasons I find it impossible to interpret. I agree that life table indices are preferable. From a life table we may derive a curve that shows month by month the proportion that have not yet conceived. Such measures as the median or percentiles would be much more informative, as well as less confusing, than the pregnancy rate."

TIETZE: "This is exactly what Potter has done, and to pick a twelve-month point is just a matter of convenience."

Written Comment by R. G. Potter

As Drs. Sheps and Tietze have noted, couples vary with respect to their monthly risks of conception and as a consequence of this heterogeneity the Pearl pregnancy rate is influenced by the duration of observation or follow-up. Moreover an investigator rarely if ever has complete control over this aspect. Often couples are enrolling or becoming eligible over a period of many months, but the study, and therefore all observation, ends at a fixed calendar date. Even if a standard period of follow-up is prescribed for each clinic patient, some women are going to be lost from observation for reasons other than pregnancy—reasons such as shifting to another method, interrupting contraception to plan another baby, or moving away. There is also the problem, raised by Dr. Sheps, that the Pearl pregnancy rate is not readily interpreted and one would prefer more intuitive indices such as the proportion remaining protected for specified periods or the duration of exposure before half or some pre-designated percentage of the couples becomes pregnant.

Thus it is desirable to have a technique that provides such readily interpreted indices in a manner insuring independence from the extraneous factor of length of observation. A life table approach would appear to provide such measures since the proportions protected for specified durations of exposure, which are derived from it, are simply the product of, and therefore exclusively dependent on, the proportions surviving without pregnancy each successive month of exposure. The schedule of couple dropout for reasons other than pregnancy does not figure directly at all, although it must be noted that if this dropout is selective with respect to pregnancy proneness, it will affect the rates of pregnancy.

The technique is readily adapted to answering questions about the acceptability of a contraceptive method or about the rate of patient loss jointly from accidental pregnancy and dropout for 'relevant' reasons such as side effects or shifts to other methods. In the last case, for example, one computes a cumulative product of proportions surviving to the end of each successive month of exposure as active users of the prescribed method, having first excluded from the record of exposure those months in which patients drop out for such 'irrelevant' reasons as moving away or discontinuing contraception in order to plan another pregnancy. The versatility of the methodology along these lines is nicely illustrated by Dr. Tietze's paper in this volume relating to intrauterine contraceptive devices.

LIVE BIRTH PREGNANCY RATE

Related to the above discussion of the Pearl index was the discussion that followed the presentation of Chandrasekaran's and Freymann's paper.[3] This discussion centered upon the merits of the rate proposed by them for evaluating family planning and is summarized below.

One participant stated: ". . . The particular rate is essentially the Pearl pregnancy rate but includes only pregnancies that end in live births, accompanied by a quite strict definition of exposure, and is subject to the usual limitations of a Pearl pregnancy rate. Perhaps this index could be strengthened if it were adapted to a life table approach. For example, in comparing two groups—those who claim that during the past year they made some use of contraception as opposed to those who reported that they did not—one might find that the two groups were quite different in the initial three or four months. Suppose that in the next seven or eight months, however, the two sets of experiences come closer together. Thus, a life table analysis might show that out of those that start contraception, only a minority adhere to it. This finding might be missed with the index proposed.

"An aspect of the proposed index that I very much liked was the insistence on serious efforts to try to distinguish which couples were in a susceptible, fecundable state. Particularly in settings such as rural India, where so much of a marriage relation before secondary sterility is spent in either gestation or amenorrhea, it makes a great difference whether you are strict or not in finding and excluding amenorrhea, as well as gestation, for the exposure time.

"When it comes to whether you should restrict the numerator to live births, or try to include all pregnancies, this might depend on the situation. One might be comparing two groups, one of which has made especially energetic family planning efforts. As part of this, one might have closer relationships with these people, the records are better, and show more fetal losses. Under these circumstances, it would be very easy to load up the numerator with these fetal losses and end up with a relatively high pregnancy rate. In the group where one doesn't have this information about pregnancy interruptions, however, the index would be relatively low. In contexts like this, the reporting of fetal losses is either very weak or of an uneven quality, and I think the emphasis on live births only has merit.

3. See paper by Chandrasekaran and Freymann, this volume.

"On the other hand, when one is in a position to follow couples from month to month, and therefore to do a pretty good job of ascertaining the rate of fetal losses, it would be a shame to throw out that information."

Another participant said: "Three factors built into this situation tend to make any index insensitive. The first is the periods of pregnancy and of postpartum amenorrhea, just discussed. . . . The second factor is the great contribution that women with secondary sterility can make to total exposure time. This effect could be removed by a life table method.

"A third factor is pregnancies and live births which are wanted, and even planned. Since most desired pregnancies are of lower order, the most convenient way to deal with this would be to arrange the computation of the index in terms of parity order."

The desirability of restricting the index to live births was argued by another participant as follows: ". . . I can see that, when you are concerned with a method which is an attempt to inhibit conception, there is some kind of compelling logic about a measurement of the extent to which, despite your efforts, conception does occur. On the other hand, it seems to me that there is a clear-cut logic to using live births despite this. I would say this for two reasons. First, reproductive ends are phrased not in terms of conception, but in terms of births. Second, as to the success of any contraceptive procedure, you profit from other aspects of the situation than the ones you are attempting to manipulate. In other words, an undefinable part of your success results from factors you have not interfered with at all. Thus we can claim only that the particular method may have contributed to the success observed. It seems to me that a person who has succeeded because a conception led to a fetal death, is in essentially the same position as a person who has succeeded because she was lucky enough not to have intercourse at the right time of the month. So, I would suggest that there is rather good reason for evaluating successes in terms of the occurrence or nonoccurrence of a live birth. . . ."

PART VI

Report on the Symposium

Mindel C. Sheps and Jeanne Clare Ridley

EMERGING RESEARCH ISSUES

In addition to the discussions already reported, a number of themes clearly emerged from the prepared papers and the discussion. We shall attempt to outline some of these themes, drawing on the papers, the transcript of the discussion, and the excellent summaries of the discussions prepared by the rapporteurs.[1] Many interesting ideas in the papers were not fully explored in the discussions. The presentation here will be primarily of themes that were discussed and that can be considered challenging research issues, grouped as follows: (a) demographic change and its determinants, (b) population policy and programs, (c) methods of research and evaluation.

DEMOGRAPHIC CHANGE AND ITS DETERMINANTS

Considerable discussion throughout the conference centered around the questions: (1) how the "demographic revolution" was achieved in the Western world, and (2) whether the

---

1. We are particularly indebted to the rapporteurs: Margaret Bright, Donald P. Doolittle, Paul Geisel, Mary L. New, and Edward B. Perrin.

experience of the West is a useful model for understanding the likely population movements in the presently underdeveloped countries.[2]

Despite some disagreement as to probable historical developments in the West and the relative importance of likely determinants of past and present trends in mortality and natality, there was essentially a consensus that the historical facts are not well known and that a satisfactory theoretical framework is lacking. The relevance of past Western experience to current problems was debated more sharply. Related research issues, explicit and implicit, that came out under this particular heading will be treated under the topics of: (1) general aspects of the demographic transition in the West, (2) factors affecting patterns of natality in particular, and (3) questions relating especially to developing countries. In a fourth section we shall attempt to explore further the implications of this discussion, by choosing a relevant example—the incidence of first marriage in women, by age.

The Demographic Transition in the West

Historical levels of mortality and natality rates, the timing and rapidity of changes in these rates, and the reasons for these changes were felt to need study and critical analysis. Inadequacies of transition theory for the explanation of known facts were emphasized. Examples of specific questions raised were: What exactly is known about historical changes in vital rates and their interrelationships in different countries? What were the similarities and what were the differences in these changes? How did changes in mortality affect marriage patterns and childbearing patterns? How would our knowledge be deepened if we applied to the data more sensitive indicators of trends in mortality and natality, such as are now being used for current data?

The contributions of cohort analysis of natality patterns have been widely recognized but this method has not been exploited greatly in analyses of historical data.[3] Furthermore, the study

2. This discussion referred especially to issues raised in the papers by Glass, McKeown, and Blake. Additional relevant material may be found in the papers of Part II.

3. For an example of current applications of this method see the paper by Goldberg; the desirability of this approach is also discussed in Ryder's paper, this volume.

of cohort trends in mortality from specified causes was shown some time ago to yield major insights as compared with those from period data.[4] Yet, the analysis of mortality changes in successive historical cohorts has scarcely been employed, despite the reasonable expectation that it might be equally illuminating.

Other questions raised were: What were the specific conditions that contributed to the demographic transition? For example, what was the role of literacy, of a predominance of rationality of behavior, of urbanization? Specification of such terms as well as of the the traditional concept of industrialization, by efforts to define and identify their relevant components, should lead to a more sophisticated and fruitful approach. Thus, one of the components of modernization in the West may have been an increasing concern of people with what they thought were medically effective measures to improve health. In this way there arose, prior to a marked increase in population growth, a pattern of rational decision-making for oneself, which may have been an important precedent for making decisions about the number of children desired, at a subsequent stage of history.

Factors Affecting Natality Patterns

Special interest was focused on the need to identify specific variables that might explain natality changes. For instance, it was proposed that conflicts between levels of living and aspirations might be crucial in reducing birth rates, and on the other hand, that the effects of available feminine alternatives to reproduction and familial satisfactions in a society should be explored.[5]

Employment of women in nondomestic tasks outside of the home has been shown to affect natality in the United States. In Japan, such employment of urban women was related to lower natality; on the other hand there was no relation between natality and family-centered employment or premarital factory work. In Taiwan also, women employed in nonfamilial settings

4. See, for example, W. H. Frost, ''The Age Selection of Mortality from Tuberculosis in Successive Decades,'' *American Journal of Hygiene*, XXX (Nov., 1939), pp. 91–96.

5. See, for example, papers by Glass, Blake, and Smith, this volume.

had lower natality and were more interested in family planning than those employed in family handicraft enterprises. Such findings have implications for national policies as well as for research in depth, such as investigations of the meaning of work to these women.

In the United States, recent analyses indicated that socio-economic factors thought to be firmly established as major influences on natality act differentially within different subgroups classified by either religion or place of residence. The reasons are not understood, nor are the reasons why since the last war, the United States has witnessed a revolution in marriage patterns and in the spacing of births.[6]

Deficiencies in analyses of marriage patterns and of their relation to natality rates were repeatedly made evident. The relative neglect of this important subject by American demographers is explained in part by inadequacies of the system of marriage registration. In addition, however, special surveys in the United States and elsewhere usually concentrate on women currently married. They thus eliminate from their scope an adequate study of marriage patterns as well as ignoring the important contributions to reproduction made by women not currently married.

Discussion of the effects of changing age and sex structure of populations upon marriage potential brought out the complexity of appropriate analyses. The exposure to the possibility of marriage is a joint one involving the two sexes; the moment of entry into the marriage market is not clearly defined; the characteristics sought in a spouse may change if individuals remain at risk for a long time. Furthermore, the age differential between spouses is likely to be flexible in response to changing age-sex ratios in a population.

Prevalence of unstable marital unions is obviously relevant to natality levels. The exact role of such instability needs to be documented, and the possible effects of increased stability studied in detail.

Other questions regarding determinants of natality levels will be raised below. One further point will be made here. Studies of

6. See the paper by Goldberg, this volume.

natality trends and their correlates in the United States have probably been more ambitious and searching than those in any other country. Nevertheless, little claim can be made for an ability to understand these correlates or to predict future change. It therefore seems undeniable to us that even greater caution must be exercised in conclusions about other countries; even greater ignorance must be confessed. As emphasized in several papers, conviction that action is necessary should not lead to the neglect of a search for facts and of more probing investigation of hypotheses.

Developing Countries

Although little explicit mention was made of research in mortality trends in the developing countries (a fact probably related to the omission of prepared papers on this topic), it is known that their mortality levels vary considerably, as do the nature and rapidity of the declines in these rates. The causes that are operating to produce these changes have not been clearly identified in the different countries. Thus there exists a need for elucidating mortality trends in areas of moderate to high mortality levels. Again, the desirability of cohort analysis is apparent.

More attention was paid to the great variation that exists in natality levels and in the changes that are occurring in these levels. Deficiencies in our knowledge of these facts and in our understanding of the reasons for the variation were evident. The increase in crude birth rates observed in some developing countries may be produced by reduced mortality: marriages are lasting longer since the incidence of widowhood is reduced; a decrease in infant mortality may result in fewer births being unrecorded.

In view of the great gaps in our understanding of what occurred in the West and of what is now going on in the developing countries, the question of the usefulness of the Western model as a predictor of trends in the developing countries could be approached with little more than opinions. Two opposing views were expressed. One held that a thorough knowledge of Western experience, bolstered by a credible theoretical framework, would be invaluable in understanding events in the developing countries. Furthermore, our ignorance regarding historical change in the developed countries should stimulate intensified efforts at studying current change in developing areas and at evaluating the effects of population policies.

Others held that the experience of developed countries is irrelevant to the current situation in the less developed countries. The following reasons were put forth. The social and family structures are radically different. Recent declines in death rates have been much more rapid than those that occurred in the West. Accordingly, the number of surviving children per family has increased. A completely new technology of preventing births has been developed, which requires a different kind of motivation than was needed for older techniques. Finally, in contrast to what occurred in the West, governments and social leaders in many of the developing countries are strongly supporting programs to decrease the birth rate.

The cogency of these contentions can be established only by thorough investigation. Many of the hypotheses, such as the role of the family structure and of changes in this structure in natality rates, are clearly amenable to research. It was pointed out also that Western peoples had spontaneously lowered their birth rates when the growth of their populations was not nearly as rapid as the growth now being experienced in many developing countries. Accordingly, the questions of what causes human beings to do so remained relevant to the study of any population.

Applications to Changing Age at Marriage

Both the effects of increased age at marriage and the determinants of such a trend were discussed in considerable detail on several occasions. Formal demographic analysis based on simplifying assumptions that *all other factors are constant* has shown that increased age of women at marriage or at first birth may have a profound deflationary effect on birth rates by increasing the average interval between generations.[7] In fact, however, all other factors may not remain constant and, it was

7. In this volume, such analyses are exemplified in the papers by L. C. Cole and A. Coale in particular.

brought out, the relationship may be more complicated. Thus the rise that has occurred in India over a 30 year period, of two years in the average age at marriage, has been estimated, by a population model, to have produced a seven per cent decline in the birth rate. It was, however, suggested that such a shift might result in increased birth rates and the existence of some evidence to this effect was cited. Since those women in a population who marry later are different in many respects from those who marry young, it is difficult to predict the effect of changes in age at marriage on birth rates. Increasing age at marriage may be associated with higher levels of educational attainment, with a higher proportion of women in the labor force, and with changes in attitudes toward childbirth. To determine this effect on the basis of stable population models is one thing; to determine its actual influence in practice may be another.

Many populations have experienced changes in the frequency and age distribution of first marriages. The actual facts, when studied at all, have frequently been summarized as changes in the mean or median age at marriage in period data. More detailed analysis, especially on a birth cohort basis, is needed, not only of available historical data, but of improved data on current marriages.

What produces such changes in marriage patterns? How are they related to economic change, to family structure, to educational opportunities for women, to employment opportunities? What associated changes are produced, by the same variables, in patterns of childbearing within marriage? For example, it was suggested that increased age at marriage may be a reflection of increasingly responsible and rational attitudes that will carry over into marriage and into family planning.

There is evidence[8] based primarily on data from industrialized countries, that, all else being equal, both perinatal death rates and maternal risks rise with increased maternal age. What is the case in countries with high infant and maternal mortality? What is the interaction between intrinsic biologic factors and the social and economic concomitants of a higher age at mar-

8. Cf. Baird's paper, this volume.

riage? Thus, improved nutrition and better education might well counteract the effects of age *per se* and result in reduced mortality.

Consequently, the effects on both mortality and natality of increased age at marriage are likely to be complex and not predictable without very detailed study.

POPULATION POLICY AND PROGRAMS

Objectives

At present the primary objective of population policy in most countries is of course to reduce the rate of population growth through reduction of birth rates. Furthermore, it was generally felt that in many developing countries it is necessary that this deceleration be attained in as short a time as possible.

In this connection, it became clear that it is essential to delineate a number of relevant concepts which are often not clearly distinguished. The popular, though unattractive and inappropriate, term *population control* presumably implies simply a *deceleration of population growth* or reduction in the annual rate of natural increase. In the absence of migration, it may be produced by rising mortality, by falling natality, or by changes in the relations between these vital rates. *Reduced natality* may be achieved by various combinations of increased spinsterhood, increasing age at marriage, postponement of childbearing, longer intervals between births, fewer children per family, more childless couples, etc.

Family planning involved the deliberate decision by a couple about how many children they want and approximately at what intervals. If many couples want relatively few children and if they are successful in their efforts, a reduction in birth rates may follow. *Family limitation* implies only limitation to some maximum number of children. Successful limitation does not necessarily imply previous family planning or limitation to a number of children consistent with a low birth rate.[9]

In the opinion of some, there has been an unfortunate tendency to equate efforts to reduce natality with the promotion of

9. For a discussion of choice among possible procedures and techniques for family planning or limitation see Wishik's paper, this volume.

family planning. This identification has been not only a matter of terminology in which "family planning" is an euphemism for the desired goal, but it has been symptomatic of a relative disregard of other approaches toward attaining the actual objective, namely reduced natality rates. Furthermore, it has militated against the desirable distinction between the contributions of a family planning program: (1) to improved individual and family welfare and, (2) to a deceleration of the growth of a specified population, and in particular to rapid deceleration. A program that has great welfare implications and is associated with universal family planning may very possibly have only slight effects on birth rates.[10]

Types of Population Policy

The choice of policies that would be most effective in the short term and in the long term raises many unanswered questions. Population policies discussed at the meeting may be differentiated according to the avenues followed in approaching the overall objective of reduced natality.

Policies aimed at stimulating economic and social development not only for their direct benefits but for their expected effects on natality rates. The discussion relating to this avenue has been partly covered in the foregoing consideration of the factors involved in the Western demographic revolution; other facets are considered in the published papers in Parts I and II of this volume.

Policies aimed at changing the patterns of marriage and of childbearing. Throughout the conference there was recurrent convergence from different directions on the relations between the ultimate rate of population growth and the average number of children desired by couples and the timing of their births. In the highly developed United States, most couples are said currently to want from two to four children. An average of two children per couple would eventually imply a declining population; an average of four implies relatively rapid growth. In the developing countries, many couples evidently desire more than

---

10. This statement is true on a purely logical, theoretical basis; evidence for its pertinence is discussed in the next section. See also papers by Glass, Blake, and L. C. Cole, this volume.

four children, and start their families early. The adoption of completely effective practices of family planning would thus not necessarily produce an acceptable rate of population growth unless coupled with a desire for relatively small numbers of children, and preferably postponement of their births.

The desirability of exploring what would produce attractive alternatives to early marriages and to moderate or large numbers of children is therefore clear. Some considerations have been mentioned in the foregoing section on natality; others are put forward in prepared papers.[11] In addition, a discussant proposed that the existence of a world revolution in this regard should be recognized and the revolution promoted. It involves a number of changes that "pull the family apart;" the relationship between the husband and the wife is being changed, so that the wife achieves an identity that is not merely that of her husband. These changes tend to pull the parent and grandparent apart, so that the extended kinship system loses some of its grasp on the society. ". . . The participation of women in the labor force gets very close to a number of important concerns. We have to give a woman a way of finding some kind of dignity other than bearing one child after another. This can occur before she gets married, or after she gets married. Some other interests, some relationship to the society that is other than merely being a procreator, are needed: perhaps opportunities for a little education, a little experience, and a little attention to goals other than the familial ones before she gets married." Repeated suggestions were made that efforts of developing countries to increase economic production should, as regards population objectives, be aimed not at family handicraft but at enterprises located outside the house.

When suitable policies are defined, other dimensions for investigation arise, such as how to make the policies acceptable, how to implement them, and how to evaluate their effects.

Policies aimed at increased adoption of family planning and limitation. Current governmental population policies in developing countries consist almost entirely of programs promoting family planning. Many conference participants felt that the

---

11. Cf. papers by Blake and Smith.

major strategy now available was to capitalize on existing motivations for family planning, weak though they might be, and to take advantage of the newly available contraceptive methods that require little sustained motivation.[12]

One participant suggested also that ". . . finding effective ways quickly for the minority that does want to limit family size will help to induce the desire for a smaller family among the rest of the population. There is evidence that such populations need successful models to give social support and legitimacy to the whole enterprise."

Emphasis was given to the need for improved understanding of the interest and motivation of both men and women in these countries, of their actual reproductive behavior, and of the latitude or flexibility inherent in the attitudes.[13] Such understanding might determine the direction and nature of efforts to change motivation and behavior, as well as suggesting more suitable auspices for these efforts.

There is evidence, also, that the response to programs of this type varies considerably from one population to another; that in Taiwan where birth rates were dropping before any program was instituted, the response is appreciably different from that in Pakistan. It may be that a very important strategic consideration for programs of this type is the choice of when and where to introduce them. For example, a participant expressed the view that to provide successful models it is better to concentrate efforts in specific areas rather than spread them thin over a larger population.

The acceptability and effectiveness of contraceptives in different social groups will vary in different settings and will depend on the approach used. Accordingly there are many unsettled strategic issues with respect to the available target groups for such programs.

As yet, there is little evidence on which to assess the possible relation between family planning programs and the desired effect on population growth. A number of opinions on this question were expressed, but much more information and quan-

---

12. Relevant applied research is discussed in this volume in the papers by Smith, Freedman and Takeshita, Wishik, and Chandrasekaran and Freymann.

13. Cf. Mauldin's paper, this volume.

titative analysis were felt to be needed before such opinions could be validated.

In many cases, it was suggested, there may exist a considerable discrepancy between a program as it is laid out on paper in some central bureau and what actually goes on in the field. This may account for some of the apparent failures. It was urged that evaluation of the actual activities carried out in relation to their effectiveness should be an integral part of any program.

Policies regarding induced abortion. Family planning programs as such limit their activities to the promotion of methods that prevent conception. It was recognized, however, that in many countries induced abortion, whether legal or illegal, plays a primary role in the reduction of births.[14] The role of induced abortion in different societies and its relation to contraception and to population growth were discussed on a number of occasions. It was emphasized that women who resort to abortion, in countries where it is legalized as well as elsewhere, generally do so out of determination to limit the number of births they have. Thus it was stated that, though they do not like it, they find abortion "tolerable" as an alternative to having an unwanted child.

An article describing the history of the law legalizing abortion in Japan was cited. The primary reason for this legislation, it was stated, was the recognition that many women were undergoing illegal abortions, which were being performed under undesirable and dangerous circumstances. The legislation was intended to provide better care for these women under legal auspices. Although national leaders did feel that the country was overpopulated, action by individuals to limit births (primarily through abortion) had preceded any official policy.

Evidence that illegal induced abortion is common in Latin America was referred to. In the United States and in Britain, abortion is undoubtedly performed more frequently than is nominally allowed by law. Although no data were cited, there was an impression that the incidence of abortion performed by physicians is probably greater among women in higher socioeconomic groups than among those in the lower strata. It was

14. See C. Tietze, "Induced Abortion and Sterilization as Methods of Fertility Control," this volume.

suggested that it would be desirable to reconsider the legislation in Western countries. Reference was also made to signs of a change in attitude toward legislation on abortion in India and perhaps in other countries.

The need for studies of the frequency of abortions in various countries, of its effects, and of the differential rate of resort to this procedure by various subgroups of a population was recognized.

METHODS OF RESEARCH AND EVALUATION[15]

References have already been made, in the foregoing, to methodologic issues raised in the discussion. At every session, considerations of how to obtain appropriate data and of improved analytic methods arose. The following were among the topics discussed.

Improvement of Official Data

Apart from the obvious desirability of increasing the completeness and accuracy of existing national systems, more types of information were felt to be necessary, with special emphasis on data for cohort analyses of marital, natality, and mortality patterns.

Surveys

Reliance on special surveys for information in both developed and developing countries is likely to continue and, perhaps, grow. Suggestions for new emphases in such investigations included: broadening samples to include women not currently married, and include men particularly in developing countries, broadening the scope of studies to give more emphasis to behavior rather than concentrating on attitudes to family planning, and to such topics as the incidence of abortion, and directing studies as well as programs more generally toward social changes that might influence reproductive patterns. Another subject of study suggested as having relevance to population growth was change in the size of family, defined to consist of parents and dependent children. This variable is determined

15. The discussion that follows is related largely, though not at all exclusively, to the papers in Part III.

by natality, by child mortality, and by the social factors determining the age when a child is no longer dependent.

Increasing Specificity of Measurement

Recurringly, the need for increased specificity was emphasized: in defining components of social change, in defining objectives of population policy, and in defining the segments of a population that might be affected by given policies or programs. The desirability was strongly emphasized, in the analysis of data on mortality, reproduction, marriage patterns, or any other component of population change, of focusing sharply on the most relevant measurements of the phenomenon as evinced by the most sensitive subgroup of the population.[16] Many examples appear in the published papers; some will be discussed below.

Evaluation of Programs (General)

The value of analyzing the components of any policy or program and of planning for its evaluation at the time it is formulated was stressed. The question of how to separate out changes due to a program from changes that would have occurred without a program was raised. Eliminating the untenable assumption that no change can occur without a program, one may compare change in a population that has a program with change occurring in a population that does not. It was suggested that ". . . this is an implicit effort to establish a pseudo-control. It is not an experimental situation, but the reasoning amounts to assuming that the populations are comparable and that the second will provide a kind of yardstick that indicates what would have happened in the absence of a program.

"Rather than doing this *post facto* would it not be desirable to try in advance to delineate the comparisons or yardsticks we will use and to incorporate in the evaluation a method of judging how much change should really be ascribed to the program, and how much would have occurred anyway?"

Special problems of methodology were raised with respect to

16. See papers by Freedman and Takeshita, by Wishik, by Chandrasekaran and Freymann, and by Ryder, this volume.

evaluating family planning programs, for example: How should one define the group of women who are eligible for participation in a family planning program? How does one count those who are already using a contraceptive method and who come to a clinic for a change of method? What are suitable criteria for the ultimate effects of a program?

The Time of Occurrence of Specified Events

The importance of the time dimension has been stressed in foregoing discussions of recent United States natality data and of the role of changing age at marriage. It made an appearance also in the panel discussion of the Pearl pregnancy rate [17] and in recurrent emphases on the use of life table methods,[18] as well as in methodological emphasis on the analysis of intervals between events. A consideration not previously mentioned was advanced by one participant as follows: ". . . I think we have focused entirely too much on the prevention of birth. We regard the occurrence of the birth as being a failure, and nonoccurrence as a success. It is a little more subtle than this with regard to what we are, at least, in part, interested in. If we are interested in lowering the crude birth rate, we should pay much more attention to the time pattern of the activities we are looking at, as well as to their volume or amount.

"What I am trying to say here specifically is with regard to the idea of seeing how many pregnancies have occurred during a 12 month period. It certainly makes no difference—perhaps a negative difference—from the standpoint of a couple if they have a birth at eight months rather than say four months, within the interval of one year. But from the standpoint of population control, and of lowering the birth rate, any month of delay is a success. It may be a very modest one, but it is helpful. Any time a birth is delayed just a little bit, you are contributing to the lowering of the crude birth rate."

Premarital Conceptions ✓

In a number of societies (including the United States) the sequence marriage, conception, birth, is not infrequently

17. See pp. 494–496, this volume.
18. See paper by Potter *et al.*, this volume.

changed to conception, marriage, birth, where marriage may or may not intervene. Increased use of efficient contraceptives may produce a higher age at marriage in those cases where marriage follows conception.

The analysis of changing trends in premarital conception is complicated by the difficulties involved in estimating exposure to the risk of this event, and of estimating the frequency with which such conceptions end in abortion. The only two elements of the pattern that can usually be measured are premarital births and prenuptial conceptions that end in early legitimate births. Yet this subject must not be neglected in the study of natality.

The Impact of Successful Deceleration of Population Growth

Preoccupation with current problems did not completely eliminate all interest in the possible effects of success in the efforts to reduce birth rates. Concern that the current crude birth rate of 17 or 18 per 1,000 in Japan is too low, and the presence of a shortage in the young labor force, particularly in agriculture and small scale industry were cited.

More generally, a speaker pointed out: ". . . We must bear in mind the alternative costs involved in any demographic choice. Having made the choice we will be forewarned, and being forewarned we will be geared to coping with the demographic problems potentially involved. This to my mind is one of the most practical applied assets of basic scientific inquiry. Now, indicated population change, especially reduction in natality, will involve a spectrum of demographic dilemmas no matter what course natality takes.

"For example, we know that a stabilized condition of low natality will make human populations considerably older proportionately than is anywhere at present the case. This would necessarily have an economic impact; there will be fewer youthful dependents in such a population, but other problems will emerge. Such proportionately aged populations will inevitably be different qualitatively from younger ones. From our present viewpoint, they may be different in ways we do not now find desirable. . . ."

Another problem, that of reducing the number of children

desired by couples in terms of their enjoyment of life, to numbers compatible with slow population growth, has great implications for society. "I think that the full magnitude of this problem is not realized because many double standards of family size and natality behavior still exist. Developed people think developing ones should be limiting their families, and rich people think poor ones should be doing so. Many social scientists might feel that a much more open system of stratification is desirable, both for those at the higher reaches to move down if necessary, and for those in the lower reaches to move up. In any event, I think it is only when we see the family limitation problem as being one that is not for *them*, but potentially for all families in situations just like our own, that we have a broad sense of the kind of motivational issues involved.

"Consequently, I think of any solution in the context of working out some sort of acceptable *modus vivendi* not as the most likely prescription for individual happiness, or necessarily for happiness at all. On the other hand, we must take into account some incentive for people to modify their goals in this way. We must consider that together with the objective of very small families, it is necessary to think in the context of a rejuvenated and subjectively meaningful way of life."

PART VII

*Public Health and
Population*

James A. Crabtree

PUBLIC HEALTH IMPLICATIONS
OF THE POPULATION PROBLEM*

Since I can lay no claim to special competence in either mathematics or statistics, it may seem strange that I would undertake the task of dealing with an equation, both sides of which contain many variables and on neither side of which is there a single constant.

Public health is one side of the equation. It almost defies definition by terms that would be acceptable in all respects to any two of us here this evening. It means different things to different people at any one point of time; it means different things to any one person at any two points of time.

The population problem is the other side of the equation. It, too, means different things to different peoples, in different settings, and with different orientations. Indeed, all authorities on population keep reminding us that there is no "population problem," but a series of problems, each one different from all the others.

* Address delivered at closing of Symposium, June 5, 1964.

We recognize the existence today of two contrasting worlds in respect to such characteristics as the stage of industrialization, the degree of urbanization, and the development and diversity of social institutions. An even sharper contrast exists between these two worlds with respect to the actual character of demographic trends and to the complexity and subtlety of their effects. Unfortunately, most people tend to identify the "population problem" with only one of these two worlds.

Only my lack of expertise, which will soon be in evidence, gives me the temerity to go against all authority and seek some common ground for generalization.

Public health does have one outstanding feature that is universally recognized. This is the ambitiousness of its purpose and the range of its commitments. These ambitions have led public health to seek to embrace all the sciences that bear on human health and to bring them into useful co-relationships, realizing that where this can be done, the several sciences themselves find mutual enrichment and this in turn adds to the ambitiousness of public health's purposes.

From its efforts to bring the several sciences into workable co-relationships, a great lesson in science has been learned, namely, the deeper the insight one gains into any single phenomenon of science, the more meaningless becomes the concept of independence.

This one lesson has convinced public health throughout the world that its approach to the health realities of the future must be ecological; that no human health problem henceforth can be viewed except as another chain of consequences of man's intrusion into one or more of nature's equilibria; that both cause and consequence of health and disease must be expressed in multiples; that community disease reflects maladjustment between groups of people and either their recent or existing environment or both; and that community health—the goal of public health—can be achieved only by securing ecologic harmony.

It is perhaps fair to say that man has violated more ecological laws during the past hundred years than during ten preceding centuries. One of the major difficulties in achieving the objectives of public health today in many parts of the world is due to man's own unheeding manipulation of his multifaceted environment and more especially to the rapidity with which changes are manipulated.

The great health hazards of the past derived largely from the savagery of man's physical and biological environment. As long as this environment was reasonably stable—not readily manipulatable—man's only resort was to face it as best he could, and he did so by placing as heavy a reliance as possible upon the process of adaptation—a time-consuming process.

As some of the more crucial factors in this savage environment became better understood, and thus more amenable to manipulation, man freed himself from many of the principal hazards to his life—often quite dramatically—only to find that, in this wake of his great lifesaving successes, he had set into motion other forces arrayed against him and his health that he had been either unable or unwilling to foresee.

All these things have come about during an era in which the sciences that could be focused on man's lifesaving needs were essentially analytic; that is, where they addressed themselves to breaking down broader problems into more and more minute details. As a consequence, the particulars of man's physical and biological environment amenable to manipulation have greatly multiplied and with such rapidity that time is no longer vouchsafed man to enable him to place further reliance upon the processes of adaptation. Thus he is caught within a web of circumstances where most of his health problems, being man-made, appear to have solutions only through resort to further environmental manipulation.

In alluding to the environmental factors most readily amenable to manipulation and with greatest relevance for man's health, I have referred primarily to factors in man's physical and biological environment and have implied that relevance for man's health meant relevance for the issues of mortality and longevity.

But the problem to which you have addressed yourselves during the past three days introduces new and disturbing dimensions to the concept of man in his relationships to his environment as the principal determinant of human health. The population problem first of all forces public health to expand the concept of its own responsibilities to embrace issues that go beyond those of mortality and longevity; and secondly, it introduces an entirely new set of factors in man's own environment that must be taken into account because of their relevance for these broader issues. Here factors in man's cultural environment, including the determinants of his behavior, take on equal if not greater importance than those of his physical and biological environment, to which the more limited issues of mortality are so sensitive.

I stated earlier that the population problem means different things to different people. To some it means too many in total in some circumscribed area; to others it means too many of the wrong kind and too few of the right kind; to some it means people that are too mobile; to others it means those that are too fertile; and there have been times within my own lifetime when to a great many it has meant those that were too sterile!

Some prefer to view the problem at long range; others in the short run. Those of us who appear to be the more pessimistic have been accused of having our eyes on the long run, but generally our minds on the present state of things.

Those most vocal today about the problem tend to define it mainly in terms of "pressures of numbers" on our natural resources, and of the tragic social, political, and economic consequences of these pressures when in excess of tolerance limits. Note that I have not said health consequences!

It is from these circles that we hear warnings of our precious top soil washing down the hillsides into the sea, our forest resources running low, and our coal and petroleum deposits approaching exhaustion while mankind spawns and multiplies, heedless of the future and oblivious to the approach of disaster. Disaster here takes on different shades of meaning depending on whether one's orientation is social, economic, or political.

Others admit that this concern, in a sense, is justified, but insist that it should be qualified. They point out that the record of man's progress thus far is one of increasing ingenuity in controlling his environment and in husbanding his resources. They suggest that resourcefulness, while not a complete substitute for resources, is in fact, a partial one; and that what constitutes a resource in the modern world is subject always to startling changes.

There are those indeed who hold the view that the rapid growth of world population is a unique, unprecedented, and unrepeatable phenomenon of limited duration. They remind us that it had a beginning in the not too distant past and suggest that it will have an end in the not too distant future. They are convinced that the slowing down and levelling off of growth is unavoidable, but they of course beg the question of when and at what level.

As informed citizens, we in public health must have views on these issues, but not authoritative ones in a professional sense. A more rational professional view would be for us not to assume that the dynamics of population growth are immutable and eternal, or that those of resource development are approaching stalemate.

This is not the place to argue the relative merits of "economic development" vs. "population control" other than to suggest that if we look upon both, not as ends in themselves, but as means towards the higher goal of human fulfillment, then, in many parts of the world, neither holds much promise of success unless both are pursued in concert.

Public health is entitled to the view that where high fertility is not cancelled by high mortality, the gains reflected in the lower mortality will be negated if human capacities are not fully utilized. It would certainly seem not only socially sensible but professionally indicated to divert energy from childbearing to economic development wherever poverty and malnutrition are prevalent and where the difference from year to year between death and survival is largely a matter of luck and of the capriciousness of crops and weather.

Public health has been accused of being aloof from the population question. The charge is made that since it is responsible for the problem, it should assume greater responsibility for its solution. Even when the problem is reduced to one bare essential—i.e., the widening of the gap between natality and mortality—nothing could be more deceptive than to assert that public health must take the sole or even the main responsibility for it. To do so would be to ignore the fact that the marked upswing in population growth antedates the modern public health movement by more than a century.

Public health has always derived its frame of reference from the societies it has served. Thus far, this frame of reference has been to identify the factors that have greatest relevance for life extension and to devise means whereby that end could be achieved, keeping always clear that the extent to which that end is to be pursued is at all times a question for a higher and broader authority to resolve.

In no single area of the world today has public health, within this frame of reference, failed to live up to its part of the bargain. For every corner of the globe, public health has devised means, which societies could adopt if they chose to, that would make still further inroads upon the forces of mortality and add immeasurably to the extension of human life.

The criticism that can be made of public health with every justification is that in the headiness of its victorious battles with one after another of the forces of mortality, it seldom, if ever, paused to consider some of the potential consequences (health or other) of a successful total war.

It has been either unwilling or unable to foresee that the time might come when its frame of reference would be changed; when it would be asked to identify, with the clarity characteristic of its past record of performance, the factors that have relevance for human fertility and natality and to devise means that could be applied to narrowing the gap between natality and mortality, even if the need were to be based on no other grounds than those of securing ecologic harmony—a *sine qua non* for community health.

Now that the time has arrived when its frame of reference is being changed, when it is being exhorted to help "pull the chestnuts" of an insecure society "out of the fire," public health is found wanting. It is weak in several important respects.

(1) It cannot identify clearly, and certainly cannot evaluate, the factors that affect reproductive behavior of large aggregates of people. In the "long term" this is the deficiency in most urgent need of correction. It was to this need that this Symposium was dedicated.

(2) It has no easily sanctioned means to suggest which can be

applied with confidence and with reasonable dispatch towards narrowing the gap between natality and mortality, especially in those parts of the world where some believe the need is greatest. I stress "applied with confidence." Public health here shows lack of faith in its own traditional methodology by its seeming reluctance to address itself in any particular locale to two conventional questions: What and where are the most significant reservoirs of population? Where does innovation or manipulation have the greatest potential? It also lacks confidence in its innovative processes because it lacks sophistication in identifying the aspirations, the fundamental values, and the major cultural premises that give full validity to the lives of the people in question.

(3) It finds itself quite frustrated in its efforts to accomodate itself to new strategies now needed to deal with the myriad of health problems that have origins in a new complex, a totality from which no single fact of contemporary demography can be dissociated. In "short term" this weakness is in most serious need of correction.

I have used here the words "long term" and "short term." The goal of bringing natality and mortality into a balance that has greatest relevance for public health is, of necessity, long term, for the following reasons.

First, many of the demographic characteristics of the world's population that have great relevance for public health are already determined for the year 1980, and indeed, some of the most important are already determined for the remainder of this century. Persons already born have fixed the childbearing potential for 1980 as well as the upper limits of the numbers of those who, past the fertile age, will constitute our "senior citizens" at the end of the century.

Second, only relatively few countries in the world, up to now, have evolved clearly expressed population policies. In none of them has its public health system been effective in implementing these policies. The rest of the world, including most of the more highly developed countries, has had up to now no comprehensive and fully sustained policy. As a consequence, there is no country, whatever its stage of development, in which there is a reservoir of experience in implementing population policy, which within the "short run" can, with confidence, be transferred to any other.

My own amateurish review of some of the literature has led me to conclude that birth rates are unpredictable and that *post facto* explanations generally are not persuasive.

In the area of the world that I know best (United States), my epidemiological sense or self rebels at any attempt to rationalize our birth rate, which was at about the replacement level in the 1930's, abruptly spiralling to its postwar "explosion," on grounds that our people generally had become less responsible, had less concern for the future, were less well educated, or had suddenly forgotten all that was known about the practice of contraception. I find it equally difficult to accept a reversal of these same factors as accounting for the beginning of a decline in our birth rate which appears to have occurred a few years ago.

My public health bias leads me to say that, where everything else is equal, the likelihood of success of any public policy aimed at reducing natality will correlate positively with the survival rate of those born.

Thus, within this context, public health must have a "short term" goal also, which is to accommodate itself to a framework of demographic circumstances that over the short term it is powerless to alter substantially.

I can think of no public health problem of great consequence anywhere in the world that has not been given new dimensions by recent changes in population, either qualitative, quantitative, or both. Moreover, I am convinced that public health is in no position today to place major immediate reliance upon counter changes in demography to narrow these dimensions and to thus help solve most of its own immediate problems.

I am sure that each of you is more knowledgeable than I about the details of these demographic changes, the extent to which they differ in different areas of the world, and the effects they are exerting on the scientific, social, economic, and political milieus in which public health must operate.

Our generation is being bombarded with warnings that public health must find new and bold approaches to contemporary health problems that have been transformed in character by the dynamics of population growth and behavior.

The plea is universal for more knowledge to provide greater specificity of approach. Lacking such specificity, public health in more and more of its problems finds itself fumbling with inadequate tools.

Traditional epidemiology which served public health so successfully in the past by focusing its concern on statistical aggregates and single variables is today insecure. It has inadequate theories and thus is not clear on the appropriate questions to ask. It has a strong feeling of incompatibility with the widely held notion that in a large bulk of human disease and disability, and of human behavior with respect thereto, every case is unique. As long as we rationalize our ignorance by giving credence to that concept, this time-tested tool will have limited utility.

Some of the most fundamental impacts of our rapidly shrinking world on public health are at the same time the most subtle and elusive. This is especially the case in the three areas of (a) planning, (b) policy determination, and (c) administration.

The professional public health planner in the past has tended to operate within the orbit of his own guild and has been reluctant to move in as an active participant and cast his lot with those concerned with community planning in its broader dimensions. As society is forced to face more realistically and more urgently the facts of contemporary demography and the organizational complexities they pose, broad dimensional planning is acquiring not only more sophistication but far greater acceptance and prestige than ever before.

Yet it is important to note that it is not as easy today for the public health planner to travel in this company as it once would have been. With broad dimensional planning acquiring greater sophistication and more sensitivity to the social, economic, and political consequences of public health's own achievements, the public health planner who formerly was sought out and welcomed is not quite so welcome today unless he can make a persuasive case for his point of view as being one compatible with the concept of balance, as employed in planning terms.

Earlier I stated that the deeper the insight one gains into any single phenomenon of science the more meaningless becomes the concept of independence. It follows that as this concept loses meaning, the more skeptical one becomes of the absolute.

Acceptance of the absolute has given public health policy of the recent past its highly authoritarian character. Today variant evidence is a feature of our life. The health sciences therefore, if they are to deal with this kind of evidence, must become integrative and synthetic and not solely experimental and analytic.

The time has already passed when for any nuisance to be in conflict with health policy, it must be labelled with its exact contribution to the death rate. Public health is no longer confined to black and white issues of death and life, but to quality as opposed to mere quantity of living.

Positive health, an elusive concept but one that looms large in today's health policy, when reduced to its essentials is in considerable measure, a matter of the amenities—the value of which is culturally determined.

With public health policy forced to rely more heavily upon that wonderful fusion of variant evidence—wisdom—public health action and practice will proceed with somewhat less scientific precision and be based somewhat more on professional judgments. As a consequence, most, if not all, contemporary action will involve calculated risk.

In seeking to minimize this risk, society is likely to question more vigorously than in the past the competence of the professions that pronounce these judgments.

We may recall that modern public health, as we know it, is somewhat less than a century old. It emerged, not under the leadership of medicine, but out of a philosophy that we would tend to associate today with social work, and it gained stature through its adeptness in employing the tools and techniques of engineering.

It was not until the great breakthroughs in the life sciences that biology and medicine moved into a position of leadership in matters of health policy. Through most of my lifetime, not only has medicine been the central core of public health, but society has had almost blind faith in it as the protector and promoter of human health and as the source of authoritative judgments on public health policy.

Whether medicine will continue to have "top billing" remains to be seen. There is evidence that a challenger for front position is on the horizon. This is a group of disciplines that go to make up the social and behavioral sciences. There is no question but that these have taken root and are showing signs of lusty growth. Once they mature, as surely they will, their unique orientation to the health issues ahead may well give them far more sophisticated judgments on matters of broad health policy than medicine will be able to supply. In this event they will "take over the reins" and move into the "driver's seat."

Even law, which in many parts of the world gives validity and stability to public health policy, has felt the impact of our changing world, especially of the increasing interdependencies involved in maintaining human existence. In the part of the world that I know best, one of the most significant phenomena within my lifetime has been the great expansion of "administrative law."

In order to deal with the increasingly complex and more rapidly emerging demographically inspired challenges of the times, our society is turning more and more to administrative law as the more flexible, effective, and efficient instrument of policy than the more cumbersome and less resilient processes of statutory law that formerly sufficed when needs were less exacting and more slowly emerging.

I can think of no single aspect of current population changes that does not pose for public health, or for any other field of public service, urgent problems of organization and administration.

Whether it is the sinister pressure of mere numbers, or the radical changes in kinds, or the unorthodox patterns of movement and cluster, or the expanding range of interdependencies, any one or combination of which gives uniqueness to the complexity in any particular area of the world, these, together with concomitant social and economic changes, are producing everywhere a high degree of social schizophrenia and the alienation of man from social relations with those organizational instruments that formerly gave him a sense of security and order.

As a consequence, these are bringing all societies—some by deeds alone, others by word and deed—into recognition of the same point, namely, that the social integration of these unique complexities has no effective vehicle except government. This is so, even though in isolated instances, government's role is no more than that of forcing general acceptance of the increasing relevance of moral and ethical values to all social institutions. The concept of government everywhere has changed from one focused on the maintenance of law and order to that of instigator of social progress.

There are very few countries in the "modern" world in which this concept has met greater resistance than in the United States. Our reluctance to embrace it in fuller spirit accounts for our almost chaotic pattern of organization of health services and the inordinate waste of our skilled manpower that, except for our affluence, could not be tolerated.

One may recall that public health has hardly more than three generations of professionals laying claim to a vocation scientifically based. The great bulk of public health's organizational and administrative experience has been derived from dealing with small segments of a broader problem. Here, administration was successful because the administrator himself had a clearly defined and limited objective, he was fully conversant with the scientific basis for his actions, and he had an almost encyclopedic knowledge of the details of his enterprise. He, therefore, had minimal needs for organizational and management theory to secure the results he sought.

Although the nature and extent of his responsibilities radically have changed, he continues his intuitive approach to his organizational problems as though the strangling competition for his share of resources would, in some magic way, disappear.

Gradually, perhaps in desperation, he is beginning to give credence to the notion that the very processes of organization itself exert power and influences, and thus a resource, previously ignored but today essential, is a valid body of administrative theory that can be applied to his broader dimensioned problems and issues.

Certainly it can be said that in no respect has public health been more rudely shaken by our population dilemma than in the area of organization and administration. It must, in its own interest, find a solution. But how much more exciting it is to indulge in the hope that whatever solution it does find may by some circumstance serve as a prototype for dealing with the organizational aspects of society's total needs.

LIST OF CONTRIBUTORS AND OTHER PARTICIPANTS*

Contributors

SIR DUGALD BAIRD, M.D., F.R.C.O.G., Regius Professor of Obstetrics and Gynaecology, University of Aberdeen, Scotland

JUDITH BLAKE, Ph.D., Assistant Professor of Demography, School of Public Health, University of California, Berkeley

C. CHANDRASEKARAN, Ph.D., Director, Demographic Training and Research Centre, Bombay, India

ANSLEY J. COALE, Ph.D., Professor of Economics and Director, Office of Population Research, Princeton University

LAMONT C. COLE, Ph.D., Professor and Chairman of Zoology, Cornell University

JAMES A. CRABTREE, M.D., Dr. P.H., Dean, Graduate School of Public Health, University of Pittsburgh

RONALD FREEDMAN, Ph.D., Professor of Sociology and Director, Population Studies Center, University of Michigan

MOYE W. FREYMANN, M.D., Dr. P.H., Chief Consultant in Health and Family Planning, Ford Foundation, India

D. V. GLASS, Ph.D., F.B.A., Martin White Professor of Sociology, The London School of Economics, University of London

DAVID GOLDBERG, Ph.D., Associate Professor of Sociology and Associate Director, Population Studies Center, University of Michigan

LOUIS HENRY, Institut national d'études démographiques, Paris

* Affiliations are listed as of the date of the Symposium.

534

JOHN E. GORDON, M.D., Professor Emeritus of Epidemiology, Harvard University School of Public Health

LOUIS LASAGNA, M.D., Associate Professor of Medicine and of Pharmacology and Experimental Therapeutics, The Johns Hopkins University School of Medicine

W. PARKER MAULDIN, M.S., Associate Demographic Director, The Population Council, Inc.

THOMAS McKEOWN, M.D., Ph.D., F.R.C.P., Professor of Social Medicine, University of Birmingham, England

WARREN O. NELSON,† M.D., Professor of Anatomy and Endocrinology, The Albany Medical College of Union University

MARY L. NEW, M.P.H., Research Associate, Harvard University School of Public Health

A. S. PARKES, C.B.E., F.R.S., Mary Marshall Professor of Physiology of Reproduction, Physiological Laboratory, University of Cambridge, England

ROBERT G. POTTER, Ph.D., Associate Professor of Sociology, Brown University

JEANNE CLARE RIDLEY, Ph.D., Associate Professor of Population Statistics, Graduate School of Public Health, and Associate Professor of Sociology, University of Pittsburgh

NORMAN B. RYDER, Ph.D., Director, Center for Demography and Ecology, University of Wisconsin

ADALINE P. SATTERTHWAITE, M.D., Director, Research Program and Family Planning Clinic, Ryder Memorial Hospital; Research Associate, University of Puerto Rico Medical School and Instructor, School of Nurse Midwifery

MINDEL C. SHEPS, M.D., M.P.H., Professor of Population Statistics, Graduate School of Public Health, University of Pittsburgh

M. BREWSTER SMITH, Ph.D., Professor of Psychology and Associate Director, Institute of Human Development, University of California, Berkeley

JOHN Y. TAKESHITA, Ph.D., Assistant Professor of Sociology and Research Associate, Population Studies Center, University of Michigan

CHRISTOPHER TIETZE, M.D., Director of Research, National Committee on Maternal Health, Inc.

† Deceased.

EDWARD T. TYLER, M.D., President, American Association of Planned Parenthood Physicians, and Associate Clinical Professor of Medicine, Obstetrics and Gynecology, School of Medicine, University of California, Los Angeles

SAMUEL M. WISHIK, M.D., Population Council Advisor to The National Research Institute of Family Planning, Family Planning Directorate, Government of Pakistan, and Professor of Maternal and Child Health, Graduate School of Public Health, University of Pittsburgh

JOHN B. WYON, M.B., Assistant Professor of Population Studies, Harvard University School of Public Health

Other Participants

MARSHALL C. BALFOUR, M.D., The Population Council, Inc.

MARGARET BRIGHT, Ph.D., School of Hygiene and Public Health, The Johns Hopkins University

ANTONIO CIOCCO, Sc.D., Graduate School of Public Health, University of Pittsburgh

LESLIE CORSA, JR., M.D., Bureau of Maternal and Child Health, California State Department of Health

DONALD P. DOOLITTLE, Ph.D., Graduate School of Public Health, University of Pittsburgh

JOHN D. DURAND, Ph.D., Bureau of Social Affairs, Population Branch, United Nations

NICHOLSON J. EASTMAN, M.D., Ford Foundation

JOHAN W. ELIOT, M.D., School of Public Health, University of Michigan

PAUL N. GEISEL, Ph.D., Graduate School of Public Health, University of Pittsburgh

OSCAR HARKAVY, Ph.D., Ford Foundation

A. BRUCE JESSUP, M.D., Agency for International Development, U.S. Department of State

DUDLEY KIRK, Ph.D., The Population Council, Inc.

CLYDE V. KISER, Ph.D., Milbank Memorial Fund

FORREST E. LINDER, Ph.D., National Center for Health Statistics, U.S. Public Health Service

FELIX E. MOORE, Ph.D., School of Public Health, University of Michigan

MINORU MURAMATSU, M.D., Institute of Public Health, Japan

FRANK W. NOTESTEIN, Ph.D., The Population Council, Inc.

EDWARD B. PERRIN, Ph.D., School of Medicine, University of Washington, Seattle

STEVEN POLGAR, Ph.D., Planned Parenthood/World Population

JOHN ROCK, M.D., Rock Reproductive Clinic, Inc.

MARCUS ROSENBLUM, Office of the Surgeon General, U.S. Public Health Service

OSWALD K. SAGEN, Ph.D., National Center for Health Statistics, U.S. Public Health Service

VICTOR A. SUTTER, M.D., Pan American Health Organization

IRENE B. TAEUBER, Ph.D., Office of Population Research, Princeton University

CARL E. TAYLOR, M.D., School of Hygiene and Public Health, The Johns Hopkins University

VINCENT H. WHITNEY, Ph.D., Department of Sociology, University of Pennsylvania

JAE MO YANG, M.D., Yonsei University Medical School, Seoul, Korea

GLOSSARY*

Abortifacient—producing abortion.

Amenorrhea—absence of menstruation.

Androgen—generic term for a substance capable of stimulating male secondary characteristics.

Anovular—Anovulatory—not related to ovulation. Anovular (menstrual) cycles in the human female—more or less regular uterine bleeding occurring in the absence of ovulation.

Antigen—a material or agent that stimulates an immune response by the body.

Antimeiotic—preventing or inhibiting meiosis.

Antizygotic—interfering with the development of the zygote (fertilized ovum).

Asymptote (*n.*)—Asymptotic (*adj.*)—a limiting value which is approached by a curve.

Atresia—used to denote the degeneration of the ovarian follicles that occurs with aging.

Blastocyst—an early stage in the development of the embryo.

Cohort—a group of persons who experience a certain event in a specified period of time. A birth cohort, e.g., generally refers to a group of persons born in a defined period; a marriage cohort is a group married in a specified period.

Cohort Rates—vital rates (mortality, natality, etc.) experienced by a birth cohort or marriage cohort.

Corpora Lutea (*pl.*)—Corpus Luteum (*sing.*)—a body formed at the site of the discharged ovum after ovulation which secretes progesterone. It is active during pregnancy or, if conception fails to occur, until the next menses.

Dysmenorrhea—difficult and painful menstruation.

* (*b*) denotes biological usage; (*d*) denotes demographic usage; and (*med.*) denotes medical usage.

DYSTOCIA—difficult childbirth.

-ECTOMY—suffix meaning removal of.

ENDOMETRIUM—the lining of the uterus.

EPIDIDYMIS—a convoluted part of the duct leading out from the testis.

ESTROGEN—a generic term for a substance that can reproduce the physiological concomitants of estrus; secreted by the ovary of humans as well as of other animals.

ESTRUS (*n.*)—ESTROUS (*adj.*)—the period of heat in animals, the only time the female accepts the male.

FECUNDABILITY—probability of conception per unit of time, i.e., per menstrual cycle.

FECUNDITY—(*b*) pronounced capacity for reproduction; (*d*) capacity to bear living children.

FERTILITY—(*b*) capacity to conceive and bear young; (*d*) the production of live born children.

FOLLICLE—used here to denote an ovarian (Graafian) follicle. Each ovary contains a large number of such follicles, each one of which can give rise to one ovum. This structure secretes estrogenic hormones.

FOLLICULAR PHASE—(of menstrual cycle) the first part of the menstrual cycle, before ovulation occurs, which is largely under the influence of the estrogen secreted by the Graafian follicle.

FSH—(FOLLICLE STIMULATING HORMONE) a gonadotrophic hormone produced by the pituitary. In the female it stimulates growth of the ovarian follicle and its production of estrogen; in the male it is essential to the production of spermatozoa.

GAMETE—any germ cell, whether ovum, spermatozoon, or pollen cell.

GONAD—sex gland, i.e., ovary or testis.

GONADOTROPHIN or GONADOTROPIN (*n.*)—GONADOTROPHIC(-PIC) (*adj.*)—a gonad-stimulating substance.

GROSS REPRODUCTION RATE—the average number of live-born daughters that would be born to a hypothetical female birth cohort, subjected to a defined schedule of age-specific fertility rates and with zero mortality before the end of the reproductive period.

GRAAFIAN FOLLICLE—see follicle.

HARMONIC MEAN—a measure of central tendency, used rather infrequently, which is never larger than the more usual arithmetic mean. It can be defined best by an example. Assume three values 0.05, 0.20, and 0.25. The harmonic mean is

$3 \div \left\{ \dfrac{1}{.05} + \dfrac{1}{.20} + \dfrac{1}{.25} \right\} = 0.103$, while the arithmetic mean is 0.167.

HOMOLOGY—correspondence in function, relation, or origin.

HYPOPHYSIS (*n.*)—HYPOPHYSIAL (*adj.*)—pituitary body, an endocrine gland at the base of the brain, which produces gonadotrophic hormones.

HYPOTHALAMUS—a part of the brain; influences the function of the hypophysis.

ICSH—(INTERSTITIAL CELL STIMULATING HORMONE) synonymous with LH.

IN SITU—in the usual position, e.g., in the body.

INTERSTITIAL CELLS—cells of the testis that secrete the male sex hormone testosterone.

IN VITRO—in glass, i.e., in a test tube.

IN VIVO—in life, i.e., in the body.

JOINT FAMILY—a group composed of two or more nuclear families that are linked through lineal, collateral, or both types of relationships.

LH—(LUTEINIZING HORMONE) a gonadotrophic hormone produced by the pituitary. In the female it induces ovulation and stimulates the formation of the corpus luteum; in the male it stimulates the activity of the interstitial cells.

LUTEAL PHASE—(of the menstrual cycle) the postovulatory part of the cycle which is largely under the influence of progesterone, secreted by the corpus luteum.

MEIOSIS or MIOSIS—special cell division that occurs during development of gametes, reducing the number of chromosomes in the cell.

MENORRHAGIA—excessively profuse or prolonged menstruation.

MITOSIS—the usual process of cell division which involves the division of chromosomes without reduction in their numbers.

MULTIPARA—(*med.*) a woman who has two or more pregnancies that resulted in viable offspring, whether or not the offspring were alive at birth.

Mutagenic—having the power to cause mutation, with particular reference to mutations or changes in genes.

Neonatal Death—the death of an infant that has not reached one month of age.

Nidation—embedding of fertilized ovum in the uterus.

Nullipara (*n.*)—Nulliparous (*adj.*)—a woman who has never borne children.

Oocyte—a cell which, by a series of divisions, gives rise to the definitive ovum.

Para—(*med.*) refers to the number of previous deliveries of viable infants. A para 4 woman has had four such deliveries.

Parity—(*d*) refers to the number of live-born children. A woman of parity 4 has had four live-born children.

Parturition—childbirth, labor.

Perinatal Mortality—stillbirths plus neonatal deaths.

Perineum—the part of the body between the thighs.

Period Rates—natality, mortality, or other rates computed for a specified period, such as a given calendar year.

Pituitary Body—hypophysis.

Placebo—an inert compound, identical in appearance with material being tested in experimental research, used to provide a comparison with the effect of the material being tested.

Precision Matching—a control procedure by which two samples are composed of matched individuals who have been paired according to selected factors.

Pre-eclampsia—early stage of eclampsia, a disease associated with pregnancy and characterized by high blood pressure and convulsions.

Primigravida—a woman who is pregnant for the first time.

Primipara—(*med.*) a woman who has delivered one viable child.

Pro-estrus (*n.*)—Pro-estrous (*adj.*)—in animals, the period in the estrus cycle immediately preceding estrus.

Progestagen (-ogen)—a generic term for the class of chemicals with effects similar to those of progesterone.

Progestational—stimulating the uterine changes essential for the implantation and growth of the fertilized ovum.

Progestational Phase—(of menstrual cycle) synonymous with luteal phase.

PROGESTERONE—the active principle produced by the corpus luteum; essential to the preparation of the uterus for reception of the fertilized egg, also necessary for the maintenance of pregnancy.

PROGESTIN—progestagen.

PROPHASE—a stage in cell division.

PUERPERIUM—the period (of about six weeks) after delivery, during which the uterus usually regains its normal size and when the probability of conception is low.

SALPINGECTOMY—removal of all or part of the fallopian tube; a method of female sterilization.

SEMINIFEROUS TUBULES—the tubules in the testis, the lining of which gives rise to spermatozoa.

SOUND (UTERINE)—an instrument used to discover the position of the uterus, by its insertion into the uterus.

SPECIFIC RATES—vital rates (morality, natality) calculated for defined subgroups of a population, such as marriage rates for spinsters aged 20–24.

SPERMATOCYTE—a cell which, by a series of divisions, gives rise to a definitive spermatozoon.

SPERMATOGENESIS—the production of spermatozoa.

SPERMICIDE—an agent that destroys spermatozoa.

STABLE POPULATION—a theoretical population model with a constant schedule of age-specific mortality rates, birth rates, and age composition. The rate of growth of a stable population is constant (i.e., it may be zero, negative, or positive), although its size is not necessarily constant.

STANDARDIZED RATES—an index for vital rates calculated so that comparisons can be made without their being affected by the age (or sex) composition of the populations.

STATIONARY POPULATION—a stable population with a rate of natural increase equal to zero (birth rate equals death rate).

STEM FAMILY—a group composed of two or more nuclear families that are linked through a lineal relationship.

STEROIDS—a class of chemicals to which the sex hormones belong.

STILBESTROL—a specific orally-active estrogenic agent.

TENACULUM FORCEPS—an instrument used for picking up tisssue.

TERATOGENESIS (*n.*)—TERATOGENIC (*adj.*)—the production of congenital abnormalities.

Testosterone—androgenic hormone secreted by interstitial cells of the testis.

Thermogenic—producing heat.

Variance—(statistical) a measure of the scatter of observations around their average or arithmetic mean.

Variolation—inoculation against smallpox, with the use of smallpox virus; in contrast, vaccination involves the use of cowpox virus.

Vasectomy—excision of a segment of the vas deferens in which the spermatozoa are conveyed; a method of male sterilization.

Viable Fetus—a fetus whose period of gestation has lasted sufficiently long to permit extrauterine life (about 28 weeks).

Zygote—the fertilized ovum.

INDEX

Abel-Smith, B., 24
Aberdeen, Scotland:
  family size, 355–356;
  mortality rates, 360–361, 364–365, 374;
  study of health and physique of women,
    357–375
Abortion, 301
  data:
    Europe, 402–404, 406–409;
    India, 382, 393, 395, 411, 513;
    Japan, 112, 404–406, 410, 512;
    Latin America, 95, 512;
    Taiwan, 177–179;
    United States, 400–402;
  policies regarding, 7, 16–17, 21–22, 95,
    395, 400–416, 512–513;
  see also Pregnancy wastage
Acceptability:
  of family limitation, 43–49, 75–80,
    108–109, 193–194, 200–201, 439, 478,
    480, 492–493
Action-research programs in family planning, *see* Family planning programs
Africa, 146–152, 371
Agarwala, S. N., 117, 159, 270, 274, 275
Age:
  at childbearing, 45, 256;
  at marriage, 122, 162, 506;
  at maturity, 224–225, 244;
  at menopause, 244
Age structure of population, 239–240
  and mortality, 259–261;
  effects on births, 152, 239–243, 249–
    259;
  on marriage, 124–126, 292, 504
Ahmed, N., 114
Albania, 409
Altman, P. L., 226

Amenorrhea, 159–160, 247, 349, 350, 356,
  379, 380, 382–395, 465
Anderson, C. A., 59
Antonov, A. M., 356
Aranda-Rosell, A., 472
Argentina:
  birth rates, 146–152;
  birth registration, 172;
  fertility study, 96;
  modernization, 158;
  marriage, 162–165
Arrow, K. J., 320
Asdell, S. A., 224
Ashton, T. S., 38
Attitudes:
  on family planning, 109–112, 202,
    214–215;
  toward family size, 45–59, 104–108,
    123, 131–132
Aubry, P., 16
Australia, 49–51
Austria, 50–51, 106, 245
Axelrod, M., 121
Azumi, K., 63

Back, K. W., 85, 104, 105, 116, 117, 414
Bacon, Francis, 47
Badenhorst, L. T., 117
Baird, D., 362, 507
Baker, J. R., 418
Bang, S., 23, 102, 117
Bangalore City, India, 111, 278
Banks, H. S., 35
Banks, J. A., 47
Basavarajappa, K. G., 159
Basu, D., 322
Basutoland, Africa, 173
Baumert, G., 50, 57, 64

545